McGraw-Hill Ryerson

Pre-Calculus 11

Student Workbook

AUTHORS

Scott Carlson
B.Ed., B.Sc.
Golden Hills School Division No. 75
Alberta

Barbara Gajdos
B.Ed.
Calgary Catholic School District
Alberta

Andrea Hook
B.Sc., B.Ed.
Ottawa-Carleton District School Board
Ontario

Emily Kalwarowsky
B.Ed., B.Sc.
Northland School Division
Alberta

Antonietta Lenjosek
B.Sc., B.Ed.
Ottawa Catholic School Board
Ontario

McGraw-Hill Ryerson

Toronto   Montréal   Boston   Burr Ridge, IL   Dubuque, IA   Madison, WI   New York
San Francisco   St. Louis   Bangkok   Bogotá   Caracas   Kuala Lumpur   Lisbon   London
Madrid   Mexico City   Milan   New Delhi   Santiago   Seoul   Singapore   Sydney   Taipei

COPIES OF THIS BOOK MAY BE OBTAINED BY CONTACTING:

McGraw-Hill Ryerson Ltd.

WEB SITE:
http://www.mcgrawhill.ca

E-MAIL:
orders@mcgrawhill.ca

TOLL-FREE FAX:
1-800-463-5885

TOLL-FREE CALL:
1-800-565-5758

OR BY MAILING YOUR ORDER TO:
McGraw-Hill Ryerson
Order Department
300 Water Street
Whitby, ON L1N 9B6

Please quote the ISBN and title when placing your order.

The McGraw-Hill Companies

McGraw-Hill Ryerson

McGraw-Hill Ryerson
Pre-Calculus 11 Student Workbook

ISBN-978-0-07-073882-9
ISBN-0-07-073882-3

http://www.mcgrawhill.ca

4 5 6 7 8 9 MP 1 9 8 7 6 5 4 3 2

Printed and bound in Canada

Care has been taken to trace ownership of copyright material contained in this text. The publishers will gladly accept any information that will enable them to rectify any reference or credit in subsequent printings.

TI-84™ and TI-Nspire™ are registered trademarks of Texas Instruments.

PUBLISHER: Jean Ford
PROJECT MANAGER: Janice Dyer
DEVELOPMENTAL EDITORS: Kelly Cochrane, Jackie Lacoursiere, Susan Lishman, Paul McNulty
MANAGER, EDITORIAL SERVICES: Crystal Shortt
SUPERVISING EDITOR: Janie Deneau
COPY EDITOR: Linda Jenkins
ANSWER CHECKERS: Antonietta Lenjosek, Damian Marek
EDITORIAL ASSISTANT: Erin Hartley
MANAGER, PRODUCTION SERVICES: Yolanda Pigden
PRODUCTION COORDINATOR: Scott Morrison
COVER DESIGN: Michelle Losier
ELECTRONIC PAGE MAKE-UP: APTARA
COVER IMAGE: Courtesy of Ocean/Corbis

Acknowledgements

The publishers, authors, and editors of *McGraw-Hill Ryerson Pre-Calculus 11 Student Workbook* wish to extend their sincere thanks to the reviewers who contributed their time, energy, and expertise to the creation of this workbook. We are grateful for their thoughtful comments and suggestions.

Kristi Allen
Wetaskiwin Regional Public Schools
Alberta

Karen Bedard
School District No. 22 (Vernon)
British Columbia

Yvonne Chow
Strathcona-Tweedsmuir School (Independent)
Alberta

Lindsay Collins
South East Cornerstone School Division No. 209
Saskatchewan

Julie Cordova
St. James-Assiniboia School Division
Manitoba

Ashley Dupont
St. Maurice School (Independent)
Manitoba

Janet Ferdorvich
Alexis Nakota Sioux Nation School (Independent)
Alberta

Carol Funk
School District No. 68 (Nanaimo/Ladysmith)
British Columbia

Jessika Girard
Conseil Scolaire Francophone No. 93
British Columbia

Pauline Gleimius
B.C. Christian Academy (Private)
British Columbia

Marge Hallonquist
Elk Island Catholic Schools
Alberta

Jeni Halowski
Lethbridge School District No. 51
Alberta

Jason Harbor
North East School Division No. 200
Saskatchewan

Dale Hawken
St. Albert Protestant School District No. 6
Alberta

Murray Henry
Prince Albert Catholic School Division No. 6
Saskatchewan

Barbara Holzer
Prairie South School Division
Saskatchewan

Andrew Jones
St. George's School (Private)
British Columbia

Candace Ketsa
Greater St. Albert Catholic Regional Division No. 29
Alberta

Jenny Kim
Concordia High School (Private)
Alberta

Ana Lahnert
School District No. 36 (Surrey)
British Columbia

Debbie Loo
School District No. 41 (Burnaby)
British Columbia

Gloria Lowe
School District No. 6 (Rocky Mountain)
British Columbia

Teréza Malmstrom
Calgary Board of Education
Alberta

Khushminder Mann
School District No. 36 (Surrey)
British Columbia

Rodney Marseille
School District No. 62 (Sooke)
British Columbia

Dick McDougall
Calgary Catholic School District
Alberta

Georgina Mercer
School District No. 81 (Fort Nelson)
British Columbia

Vince Ogrodnick
Kelsey School Division
Manitoba

Crystal Ozment
Nipisihkopahk Education Authority
Alberta

Solange Pahud
Edmonton Catholic School District
Alberta

Oreste Rimaldi
School District No. 34 (Abbotsford)
British Columbia

James Schmidt
Pembina Trails School Division
Manitoba

Dixie Sillito
Prairie Rose School Division
Alberta

Holly Stanger
Prairieland Regional Division No. 25
Alberta

Clint Surry
School District 63 (Saanich)
British Columbia

Contents

Overview

This McGraw-Hill Ryerson Pre-Calculus 11 Student Workbook is designed to complement the student resource.

Student Workbook Features for Students

- Each section begins with Key Ideas that summarize the concepts needed to complete the exercises.
- The sections continue with working examples that guide you through the skills needed to complete the exercises.
- The working examples often include references to the *Pre-Calculus 11* student resource. These references suggest that you compare the methods used to solve the examples, or review similar examples to help consolidate your understanding of the concepts.
- Exercises are organized into three sections: Practise, Apply, and Connect.
- A selection of questions in the exercise sections include references to similar questions in the *Pre-Calculus 11* student resource.
- A review of all sections is included at the end of each chapter.
- Each chapter includes at least one Skills Organizer that assists you in summarizing the important information in that chapter.
- Answers to all questions are provided at the back of the book.
- To access Study Checks for each chapter, which will help you identify what skills and concepts you need to reinforce, go to www.mhrprecalc11.ca and follow the links to the Student Workbook.

Student Workbook Features for Teachers

- For SMART Board™ lessons related to each topic, go to www.mhrprecalc11.ca and follow the links to the Student Workbook.

Chapter 1 Sequences and Series

1.1 Arithmetic Sequences

KEY IDEAS

Concept	Definition	Examples
Sequence	• an ordered list of elements that follows a pattern or rule	$-3, -1, 1, 3, 5, 7, \ldots$ Pattern: increase by 2
Terms of a sequence	• the elements in a sequence • the first term of a sequence is t_1, the second term is t_2, the third is t_3, and so on	$t_1 = -3$, $t_2 = -1$, $t_3 = 1$, $t_4 = 3$, $t_5 = 5$, $t_6 = 7$
Common difference in an arithmetic sequence	• to form each successive term, add a *constant* called the *common difference* • to determine the common difference, d, take any two consecutive terms in the sequence and subtract the first term from the second term: $d = t_2 - t_1 = t_3 - t_2 = t_n - t_{n-1}$ • if there is a common difference, the sequence is an *arithmetic sequence*	For the above sequence, $t_2 - t_1 = d$ $-3 - (-1) = 2$ So, $d = 2$. This relationship is the same for any two consecutive terms. So, this is an arithmetic sequence.
Terms of a general arithmetic sequence	$t_1 = t_1$ $t_2 = t_1 + d$ $t_3 = t_1 + 2d$ $t_4 = t_1 + 3d$ . . . $t_n = t_1 + (n-1)d$	$t_1 = -3$ and $d = 2$ $t_2 = -3 + 1(2) = -1$ $t_3 = -3 + 2(2) = 1$ $t_4 = -3 + 3(2) = 3$ . . . $t_n = -3 + (n-1)(2)$

General term of an arithmetic sequence	• t_n is the *general term*
	• to find the value of any term in the sequence, use the formula for the general term
	• the formula for the general term is $t_n = t_1 + (n-1)d$, where
	    t_1 is the first term of the sequence
	    n is the number of terms ($n \in N$)
	    d is the common difference
	    t_n is the general term or nth term
		To find the 126th term in the above sequence, substitute known values into the formula for the general term:
		$t_1 = -3$, $d = 2$, $n = 126$
		$t_n = t_1 + (n-1)d$
		$t_{126} = -3 + (126 - 1)(2)$
		$t_{126} = 247$

Working Example 1: Determine a Particular Term

A construction company hires a plumber to install pipes in new homes. The plumber will be paid $65 for the first hour of work, $110 for two hours of work, $155 for three hours of work, and so on.

a) State the first three terms of the sequence. Use these terms to determine the common difference, d. Then, use this information to state the next three terms of the sequence.

b) Write the general term that you could use to determine the pay for any number of hours worked.

c) What will the plumber get paid for 10 h of work?

Solution

a) The first three terms of the sequence for this problem are given: $t_1 = 65$, $t_2 = 110$, $t_3 = 155$.

> How do you know that this is an arithmetic sequence?
> How many terms do you need before you know that a sequence is arithmetic?

Determine the common difference by subtracting the first term from the second term:

$$d = t_2 - \underline{\hspace{1.5cm}}$$

$$= 110 - \underline{\hspace{1.5cm}}$$

> What other terms can be subtracted to find the common difference?
> Does the order of subtraction matter?

$$= \underline{\hspace{1cm}}$$

The next three terms are

$$t_4 = t_3 + d = \underline{\hspace{1.5cm}} + \underline{\hspace{1.5cm}} = \underline{\hspace{1.5cm}}$$

$$t_5 = t_3 + \underline{\hspace{1cm}}(45) = 155 + \underline{\hspace{1.5cm}} = \underline{\hspace{1.5cm}}$$

$$t_6 = \underline{\hspace{1.5cm}} + 3(\underline{\hspace{1cm}}) = \underline{\hspace{1.5cm}} + 135 = \underline{\hspace{1.5cm}}$$

b) Substitute t_1 and d into the formula for the general term of an arithmetic sequence:

$$t_1 = 65 \text{ and } d = \underline{\hspace{1.5cm}}.$$

$$t_n = t_1 + (n - 1)d$$

$$t_n = \underline{\hspace{1.5cm}} + (n - 1)\underline{\hspace{1.5cm}}$$

$$t_n = 65 + \underline{\hspace{1.5cm}}n - 45$$

> What is the expanded form of $(n - 1)45$?

$$t_n = 45n + \underline{\hspace{1.5cm}}$$

The general term of the sequence

is $t_n = \underline{\hspace{3cm}}.$

> What is your interpretation of "20" in this scenario? Why might a tradesperson charge an additional amount for the first hour of work?

c) For 10 h of work, the amount the plumber gets paid is the _____ term in the sequence. Determine t_{10} by using the general term found in part b).

$t_n = 45n + 20$

$t_{10} = 45(\rule{1cm}{0.4pt}) + 20$ Substitute $n = \rule{1.5cm}{0.4pt}$.

$t_{10} = \rule{1.5cm}{0.4pt} + 20$

$t_{10} = \rule{1.5cm}{0.4pt}$

The value of the tenth term is _____. Therefore, for 10 h of work, the plumber will be paid $470.

📖 Compare this method with those on pages 10–11 of *Pre-Calculus 11*.

Working Example 2: Determine the Number of Terms

A farmer decides to plant an apple orchard. She plants 24 apple trees in the first year and 15 apple trees in each subsequent year. How many years will it take to have 204 apple trees in the orchard?

Solution

This sequence is arithmetic because the terms in this sequence have a common difference of _____. Begin by listing the values you know.

common difference: $d = \rule{1.5cm}{0.4pt}$

first term: $t_1 = \rule{1.5cm}{0.4pt}$

nth term: $t_n = 204$

Solve for n by substituting the known values into the formula for the general term.

> Why are you solving for n?

$t_n = t_1 + (n - 1)d$

$\rule{1.5cm}{0.4pt} = \rule{1.5cm}{0.4pt} + (n - 1)(\rule{1cm}{0.4pt})$

$\rule{1.5cm}{0.4pt} = 24 + \rule{1cm}{0.4pt}n - 15$

$204 = \rule{1.5cm}{0.4pt} + 15n$

$195 = 15n$

$\rule{1.5cm}{0.4pt} = n$

There are _____ terms in the sequence. Therefore, it will take 13 years to have 204 trees in the orchard.

Working Example 3: Determine t_1, t_n, and n

An amphitheatre has 25 seats in the second row and 65 seats in the seventh row. The last row has 209 seats. The numbers of seats in the rows produce an arithmetic sequence.

a) How many seats are in the first row?

b) Determine the general term, t_n, for the sequence.

c) How many rows of seats are in the amphitheatre?

Solution

a) The number of seats in the first row is equivalent to finding the _____ term of this arithmetic sequence. To find the number of seats in the first row, subtract the common difference from t_2.

Find the common difference, d, to solve for the number of seats in any row.

Method 1: Use Logical Reasoning

Information you know: $t_2 =$ _____ and $t_7 =$ _____.

If you think about this sequence on a number line, it might help determine the number of common differences between terms.

There are 5 common differences between the second and seventh term.

So, $25 + d + d + d + d + d = 65$, or $25 +$ _____ $d = 65$.

$25 +$ _____ $d = 65$

_____ $d = 65 -$ _____

$d = \dfrac{\square}{5}$

$d =$ _____

Method 2: Use a System of Equations

Create a system of equations. Use the formula for the general term to write an equation for t_2 and t_7.

For $n = 2$

$$t_n = t_1 + (n - 1)d$$
$$t_2 = t_1 + (\text{_____} - 1)d$$
$$\text{_____} = t_1 - d \quad ①$$

For $n = 7$

$$t_n = t_1 + (n - 1)d$$
$$\text{_____} = t_1 + (\text{_____} - 1)d$$
$$65 = t_1 - \text{_____} d \quad ②$$

Solve the system of equations by subtracting the two equations: $① - ②$.

$$25 = t_1 - d \quad ①$$
$$65 = t_1 - 6d \quad ②$$
$$\text{_____} = \text{_____} d \quad ① - ②$$
$$\text{_____} = d$$

> Why does subtracting the equations help you solve for d?
> Does the order of subtraction make a difference to the value of d?

Once you know d, the common difference, you can determine the number of seats in the first row.

$$t_2 = t_1 + d$$
$$\underline{} = t_1 + \underline{}$$
$$\underline{} = t_1$$

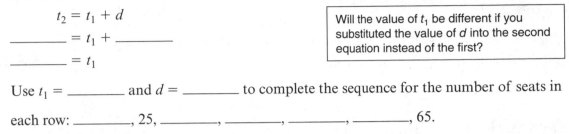

Will the value of t_1 be different if you substituted the value of d into the second equation instead of the first?

Use $t_1 = $ _____ and $d = $ _____ to complete the sequence for the number of seats in

each row: _____ , 25, _____ , _____ , _____ , _____ , 65.

b) To find the general term of the sequence, substitute the known values, $t_1 = $ _____ and $d = 8$, in the formula for the general term.

$$t_n = t_1 + (\underline{} - 1)\underline{}$$
$$t_n = \underline{} + (n-1)\mathbf{8}$$
$$t_n = \mathbf{17} + 8n - \underline{}$$
$$t_n = \underline{} + 8n$$

The general term is $t_n = 9 + 8n$.

c) The last row has 209 seats. Use the general term and solve for n to find the number of rows.

$$t_n = 9 + 8n$$
$$\underline{} = 9 + 8n$$
$$200 = 8n$$
$$\underline{} = n$$

There are 25 rows of seats in the amphitheatre.

📖 See a similar example on pages 13–14 of *Pre-Calculus 11*.

Check Your Understanding

Practise

1. State whether each sequence is arithmetic. If it is, state the common difference and the next three terms.

   a) 9, 14, 19, 24, …

   14 – _____ = _____ and _____ – 14 = 5

   There is a common difference of _____, so this _____ an arithmetic sequence.
   $\qquad\qquad\qquad\qquad\qquad\qquad\qquad\qquad$ (*is* or *is not*)

   The next three terms:

   t_5: 24 + **5** = _____

   t_6: _____ + 5 = _____

   t_7: _____ + _____ = _____

   b) 1, 1, 2, 3, 5, …

   1 – _____ = 0 and 2 – _____ = _____

   There _____ a common difference, so this _____ an arithmetic sequence.
   $\quad$ (*is* or *is not*) $\qquad\qquad\qquad\qquad\qquad$ (*is* or *is not*)

   c) 11, 7, 3, −1, …

   d) 2, 4, 8, 16, 32, …

   e) −8, −5, −2, 1, 4, …

   f) 35, 22, 9, −4, −17, …

2. Given the first term and common difference, use mental math to write the first four terms. Then, write the general term for each sequence in simplified form.

a) $t_1 = 5, d = 6$

The first four terms of the sequence are 5, _____, _____, _____.

To determine the general term, substitute the given values into $t_n = t_1 + (n-1)d$.

$t_n = $ _____ $ + (n-1)$ _____

$ = $ _____ $ + 6n - $ _____

$ = $ _____ $ + 6n$

The general term is $t_n = $ _____.

b) $t_1 = 50, d = -9$

c) $t_1 = 4.5, d = -1.5$

d) $t_1 = \frac{1}{5}, d = \frac{2}{5}$

3. The general term of an arithmetic sequence is given. Find the indicated term.

a) $t_n = 7n - 3$, t_1

Substitute $n = 1$ in $t_n = 7n - 3$.

> Why do you substitute $n = 1$ in this case?

b) $t_n = -2n + 5$, t_8

Substitute $n = $ _____ in $t_n = -2n + 5$.

c) $t_n = 6n - 9.5$, t_{15}

d) $t_n = -\frac{1}{7}n + \frac{2}{7}$, t_{20}

4. For each of the following arithmetic sequences, determine the values of d and t_1. Then, fill in the missing terms of the sequence.

a) _____, _____, _____, 27, 39

$d = 39 - $ _____

$= $ _____

$t_3 = $ _____ $- 12$

$= $ _____

b) _____, _____, 6, -2, _____

$d = -2 - $ _____

$= $ _____

$t_5 = t_4 + d = $ _____

$= -10$

$t_2 = t_3 - d = $ _____

$= $ _____

c) _____, 19.4, _____, _____, 29

$19.4 + $ _____ $d = $ _____

$3d = 29 - $ _____

$d = $ _____

> How many differences are there between 19.4 and 29? Explain.

d) _____, $-\frac{1}{2}$, _____, _____, $\frac{5}{2}$

5. For each sequence, determine the position, n, of the given value.

a) $-3, -8, -13, \cdots, -58$

$t_1 = $ _____ and $d = $ _____

Substitute the known values in
$t_n = t_1 + (n-1)d$. Solve for n.

b) $-19, -13, -7, \cdots, 119$

$t_1 = $ _____ and $d = $ _____

$119 = -25 + $ _____

$n = $ _____

c) $1.8, 2.2, 2.6, \cdots, 8.6$

d) $5, 4\frac{7}{8}, 4\frac{6}{8}, \cdots, \frac{3}{8}$

Apply

6. State whether the term 89 is part of each arithmetic sequence. Justify your answers.

a) $t_n = 9 + (n-1)5$

$89 = 9 + $ _____ $n - 5$

b) $t_1 = -8, d = 23$

$t_n = $ _____ $ + (n-1)$ _____

n is a whole number, so _____.

c) $t_n = 107 - 3n$

d) $-9, 0.8, 10.6, \ldots$

7. Determine the common difference, first term, and general term for each arithmetic sequence.

a) $t_8 = 33$ and $t_{14} = 57$

    Subtract the two equations and solve for d. Then, determine t_1.

    $33 = t_1 + (8 - 1)d$ ①

    $57 =$ _____ ②

b) $t_{10} = 50$ and $t_{27} = 152$

c) $t_5 = -20$ and $t_{18} = -59$

d) $t_7 = 3 + 5x$ and $t_{11} = 3 + 23x$

📖 For a similar example to #7, see pages 13 and 14 of *Pre-calculus 11*.

8. At the end of the second week after opening, a new fitness club has 870 members. At the end of the seventh week, there are 1110 members. If the increase in membership is arithmetic, how many members were there in the first week?

9. Five fence posts are equally spaced between two corner posts that are 42 m apart. How far apart are the five fence posts?

10. The terms x, $0.5x + 7$, and $3x - 1$ are consecutive terms of an arithmetic sequence. Determine the value of x and state the three terms.

> Explain why, for an arithmetic sequence, $t_3 - t_2 = t_2 - t_1$. How might this knowledge help you solve for x in this case?

📖 The concepts in #10 are similar to those used in #11 on page 17 of *Pre-Calculus 11*.

11. An engineer's salary is $90 000. The company has guaranteed a raise of $5230 every year with satisfactory performance. Assuming satisfactory performance in each year, when will the engineer's salary be $168 450?

12. The sum of the first two terms of an arithmetic sequence is 15, and the sum of the next two terms is 43. Write the first four terms of the sequence.

Create and solve a series of equations to find d.

$$\underline{\hspace{1cm}} + (t_1 + \underline{\hspace{1cm}}) = 15 \ ①$$

$$(t_1 + \underline{\hspace{1cm}} d) + (t_1 + \underline{\hspace{1cm}} d) = 43 \ ②$$

> Once you determine d, what will substituting this value in the equation give you?

13. Consider the calendar month shown.

MONTH						
M	T	W	T	F	S	S
1	2	3	4	5	6	7
8	9	10	11	12	13	14
15	16	17	18	19	20	21
22	23	24	25	26	27	28
29	30	31				

a) What type of sequence do the numbers in each row form? Justify your answer. Write the general term for the sequence.

b) What type of sequence do the numbers in each column form? Justify your answer. Write the general term for the third column.

c) Choose numbers in any diagonal sloping downward to the right. Do these numbers form a sequence? Justify your answer. If they do form a sequence, write the general term for the diagonal with $t_1 = 2$.

Connect

14. Consider the graph.

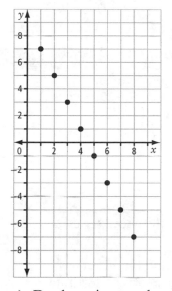

> How are the terms in a sequence related to the points (1, 7), (2, _____), (3, _____), …? Why does it make sense that an arithmetic sequence would be in a straight line (linear)?

a) Do the points on the graph represent a sequence? Justify your answer, stating the sequence represented.

b) Describe how you can find the general term for this sequence. Then, use your answer to find the general term.

> What is the formula for the general term of an arithmetic sequence?

c) What is t_{60}? t_{300}?

d) Describe the relationship between the slope of the graph and your formula from part b).

e) Describe the relationship between the y-intercept and your formula in part b).

	KEY IDEAS	

Concept	Definition	Examples
Series	• the sum when you add the terms of a sequence together • for any sequence with terms $t_1, t_2, t_3, t_4, \ldots, t_n$, the associated series is $S_n = t_1 + t_2 + t_3 + t_4 + \cdots + t_n$	For the sequence $-1, 1, 3, 5, 7$, the series is $(-1) + 1 + 3 + 5 + 7$
Arithmetic series	• the sum when you add the terms of an arithmetic sequence together • write the general arithmetic series as $S_n = t_1 + (t_1 + d) + (t_1 + 2d) + (t_1 + 3d) + \cdots + [t_1 + (n-1)d]$ or $S_n = t_1 + (t_1 + d) + (t_1 + 2d) + (t_1 + 3d) + \cdots + (t_n - d) + t_n.$ • You can find the value of any term in a series by substituting known values into the formula for the general term.	For the above series, $d = 2$. To find the 126th term in the above series, substitute $d = 2$ and $n = 126$ into the general term. $t_{126} = -1 + (126 - 1)(2)$ $t_{126} = 249$

Sum of an arithmetic series	• to determine the sum of an arithmetic series, use one of these formulas, depending on what is known
	
	– if you know n, t_1, and d, use
	
	$S_n = \frac{n}{2}[2t_1 + (n-1)d]$, where
	
	    t_1 is the first term
	    n is the number of terms
	    d is the common difference
	    S_n is the sum of the first n terms
	
	– if you know n, t_1, and t_n, use
	
	$S_n = \frac{n}{2}(t_1 + t_n)$, where
	
	    t_1 is the first term
	    n is the number of terms
	    t_n is the nth term
	    S_n is the sum of the first n terms
		For the above series, if you know d,
		$S_{126} = \frac{126}{2}[2(-1) + (126 - 1)2]$
		$S_{126} = 63[248]$
		$S_{126} = 15\ 624$
		
		If you know $t_{126} = 249$,
		$S_{126} = \frac{126}{2}(-1 + 249)$
		$S_{126} = 63(248)$
		$S_{126} = 15\ 624$

Working Example 1: Determine the Sum of an Arithmetic Series

A toy car is rolling down an inclined track, picking up speed as it goes. The car travels 4 cm in the 1st second, 8 cm in the 2nd second, 12 cm in the 3rd second, and so on.

a) How far does the toy car travel in the 50th second?

b) Determine the total distance travelled by the car in 50 s.

> What assumptions are you making about the acceleration of the car in this scenario?

Solution

a) For this arithmetic sequence, $t_1 = $ _____, $d = $ _____, and $n = $ _____.

Substitute these values into the formula for the general term.

$t_n = t_1 + (n - 1)d$

$t_{50} = $ _____ $+ ($ _____ $- 1)$ _____

$t_{50} = 4 + ($ _____ $) 4$

$t_{50} = $ _____

> Considering the car increases its speed by 4 cm each second, how could you use logical reasoning to arrive at this solution?

The toy car travels _____ cm in the 50th second.

b) You can use two methods to find the total distance travelled in 50 s.

Method 1: Use the Formula $S_n = \frac{n}{2}(t_1 + t_n)$

S_{50} represents the total distance travelled by the car in 50 s.

> What information do you need to use this formula?

Substitute $n = $ _____, $t_1 = $ _____, and $t_{50} = $ _____.

$S_{50} = $ _____ $($ _____ $+ $ _____ $)$

$S_{50} = 25($ _____ $)$

$S_{50} = $ _____

Method 2: Use the Formula $S_n = \frac{n}{2}[2t_1 + (n - 1)d]$

> What information do you need to use this formula?

Substitute $t_1 = $ _____, $d = $ _____, and $n = $ _____.

$S_{50} = \dfrac{\boxed{}}{2}[2(4) + ($ _____ $- 1)$ _____ $]$

$S_{50} = 25[8 + ($ _____ $)4]$

$S_{50} = 25[8 + $ _____ $]$

$S_{50} = 25($ _____ $)$

$S_{50} = $ _____

> Which formula is most efficient in this case? Why?

The toy car travels _____ cm in 50 s.

📖 Compare these methods with the methods shown on page 25 of *Pre-Calculus 11*.

Working Example 2: Determine the Terms of an Arithmetic Series

The sum of the first six terms of an arithmetic series is 297. The sum of the first eight terms is 500.

a) Determine the first ten terms of the series.

b) Use two different methods to find the sum to ten terms.

Solution

a) For this series, there is information provided to create two equations:

① $n = 6$, $S_6 =$ _____   ② $n =$ _____, $S_8 =$ _____

Substitute the given information into the formula $S_n = \frac{n}{2}[2t_1 + (n-1)d]$.

① $S_n = \frac{n}{2}[2t_1 + (n-1)d]$

$297 =$ _____ $[2t_1 + ($ _____ $- 1)d]$

$297 = 3[2t_1 +$ _____ $d]$

_____ $= 2t_1 + 5d$

> Why do you divide each side by 3?

② $S_n = \frac{n}{2}[2t_1 + (n-1)d]$

$S_8 =$ _____ $[2t_1 + ($ _____ $- 1)d]$

_____ $= 4[2t_1 +$ _____ $d]$

_____ $= 2t_1 + 7d$

Solve the system of two equations.

$99 = 2t_1 + 5d$ ①

$\underline{125 = 2t_1 + 7d}$ ②

_____ $=$ _____ d

_____ $= d$

> Why do you subtract the two equations?

Substitute d into one of the equations to solve for t_1.

$99 = 2t_1 + 5($ _____ $)$

$99 = 2t_1 +$ _____

$34 = 2t_1$

_____ $= t_1$

Since $t_1 =$ _____ and $d = 13$, the first ten terms of the series are _____ $+ 30 +$

_____ $+$ _____ $+ 69 +$ _____ $+$ _____ $+ 108 +$ _____ $+ 134$.

b) Find the sum of the first ten terms.

Method 1: Use the Formula $S_n = \frac{n}{2}[2t_1 + (n-1)d]$

When is it better to use this formula to find the sum of the series?

Substitute $n =$ _____, $t_1 =$ _____, and $d =$ _____.

$S_{10} = \frac{10}{2}[2(\underline{\qquad}) + (\underline{\qquad} - 1)\underline{\qquad}]$

$S_{10} = 5[\underline{\qquad} + \underline{\qquad}]$

$S_{10} = 5(\underline{\qquad})$

$S_{10} = 755$

Method 2: Use the Formula $S_n = \frac{n}{2}(t_1 + t_n)$

When is it better to use this formula to find the sum of the series?

Substitute $n =$ _____, $t_1 =$ _____, and $t_{10} = 128$.

$S_{10} = \frac{10}{2}(\underline{\qquad} + 134)$

$S_{10} = 5(\underline{\qquad})$

$S_{10} = 755$

Which formula do you prefer to use?

See page 26 of *Pre-Calculus 11* for similar examples.

Working Example 3: Determine an Unknown Value Given the Sum of an Arithmetic Series

Determine the indicated value given the characteristics of each arithmetic series.

a) Find t_1 given $d = 4$, $S_n = 1830$, and $n = 30$.

Substitute into the formula $S_n = \frac{n}{2}[2t_1 + (n-1)d]$.

$S_n = \frac{n}{2}[2t_1 + (n-1)d]$

$1830 = \underline{\qquad}[2t_1 + (\underline{\qquad} - 1)(4)]$

Why is this formula the best to find t_1 in this case?

$\underline{\qquad} = [2t_1 + \underline{\qquad}]$

$\underline{\qquad} = 2t_1$

$\underline{\qquad} = t_1$

b) Find n given $t_1 = 6$, $t_n = 69$, and $S_n = 375$.

Substitute into the formula $S_n = \frac{n}{2}(t_1 + t_n)$.

Why is this formula the best to find t_1 in this case?

$S_n = \frac{n}{2}(t_1 + t_n)$

$\underline{\qquad} = \frac{n}{2}(\underline{\qquad} + \underline{\qquad})$

$\underline{\qquad} = n(\underline{\qquad})$

Why do you multiply each side by 2?

$\underline{\qquad} = n$

Check Your Understanding

Practise

1. Determine the sum of each arithmetic series.

   a) $3 + 12 + 21 + 30 + 39 + 48$

   $S_n = \underline{\hspace{1cm}}(t_1 + \underline{\hspace{1cm}})$

   b) $19 + 31 + 43 + 55 + 67 + 79 + 91$

   c) $t_1 = 25, t_n = 73, n = 9$

   d) $t_1 = -20, t_n = -2, n = 10$

2. For each arithmetic series, determine S_{30}.

   a) $5 + 5.3 + 5.6 + 5.9 + \cdots$

   $t_1 = \underline{\hspace{1cm}}, d = \underline{\hspace{1cm}},$ and $n = \underline{\hspace{1cm}}$

   Substitute in the formula $S_n = \frac{n}{2}[2t_1 + (\underline{\hspace{1cm}})d]$.

   $S_{30} = \underline{\hspace{1cm}}[2(\underline{\hspace{1cm}}) + (30 - 1)\underline{\hspace{1cm}}]$

   $S_{30} = 15[\underline{\hspace{1cm}}]$

   $S_{30} = \underline{\hspace{1cm}}$

   b) $-21 - 15.5 - 10 - 4.5 - \cdots$

   c) $\frac{1}{9} + \frac{4}{9} + \frac{7}{9} + \frac{10}{9} + \cdots$

3. Determine the sum of each arithmetic series.

    a) $t_1 = 42$, $d = -5$, and $n = 18$
        b) $t_1 = -11.2$, $d = 7.8$, and $n = 23$

4. Determine the value of the first term, t_1, for each arithmetic series.

    a) $d = 6$, $S_n = -256$, $n = 32$
        b) $d = -2$, $S_n = -350$, $n = 25$

    c) $d = 5$, $S_n = 1250$, $n = 20$
        d) $d = -4$, $S_n = -345$, $n = 15$

5. For the arithmetic series, determine the value of n.

    a) $t_1 = -42$, $t_n = 75$, $S_n = 330$
        b) $t_1 = 4$, $t_n = 213$, $S_n = 2170$

    c) $t_1 = 5$, $t_n = -190$, $S_n = -1480$
        d) $t_1 = \frac{5}{3}$, $t_n = \frac{53}{3}$, $S_n = 87$

Apply

6. In a grocery store, cans of soup are stacked in a triangular display. There are 4 cans in the top row and 20 cans in the bottom row. How many cans are in the display if there are 17 rows?

7. The sum of the first nine terms of an arithmetic series is 162, and the sum of the first 12 terms is 288. Determine the first five terms of the series.

📖 See page 26 of *Pre-Calculus 11* for similar examples.

8. Find the first five terms of the arithmetic series with $t_{12} = 35$ and $S_{20} = 610$.

$t_n = t_1 + (n - 1)d$

$\mathbf{35} = t_1 + \underline{\hspace{1cm}} d$

$t_1 = \underline{\hspace{2cm}}$

Substitute t_1 into $S_n = \frac{n}{2}[2t_1 + (n - 1)d]$. Then, solve for d.

$\mathbf{610} = \underline{\hspace{1cm}}[2(35 - 11d) + (\underline{\hspace{1cm}} - 1)d]$

9. Determine an expression for the sum of the terms of an arithmetic series with general term $t_n = 3n - 2$.

Connect

10. Describe a method to determine the sum of all the multiples of 5 between 1 and 999. Use your method to find the sum.

> What key pieces of information do you need to answer this question? What formula can you use to find the sum?

11. A student has the choice between two summer jobs that will last 12 weeks (3 months).

- **Job A** pays $1350 per month with a monthly raise of $100.
- **Job B** pays $360 per week with a weekly raise of $5.

Assuming that the student wants to make the most money possible, which job should the student accept? Explain.

KEY IDEAS		

Concept	Definition	Examples
Geometric sequence	• a sequence in which the ratio between consecutive terms is constant • multiply the same value or variable with each term to create the next term	1, 3, 9, 27, 81, 243, … In this sequence, each term is 3 times the previous one. The next term in this sequence is 243(3) = 729.
Common ratio of a geometric sequence (r)	• the constant by which each term is multiplied • to determine r, take any two consecutive terms and divide the second term by the first term: $r = \dfrac{t_n}{t_{n-1}}$ that is, $r = \dfrac{t_2}{t_1} = \dfrac{t_3}{t_2} = \dfrac{t_n}{t_{n-1}}$ • can be negative or positive, but cannot be zero	For the above sequence, $r = \dfrac{t_2}{t_1} = \dfrac{3}{1} = 3$. This is true for any two consecutive terms in the sequence. For example, $\dfrac{t_6}{t_5} = \dfrac{243}{81} = 3$.
Terms of a general geometric sequence	$t_1 = t_1$ $t_2 = t_1 r$ $t_3 = t_1 r^2$ $t_4 = t_1 r^3$ . . . $t_n = t_1 r^{n-1}$	For the above sequence, $t_1 = 1$ $t_2 = 1(3) = 3$ $t_3 = 1(3)^2 = 9$ $t_4 = 1(3)^3 = 27$ . . . $t_n = 1(3)^{n-1}$

General term of a geometric sequence	• when n is a positive integer, $t_n = t_1 r^{n-1}$, where t_1 is the first term of the sequence
	    n is the number of terms
	    r is the common ratio
	    t_n is the general term or nth term
	
	• use the general term to find the value of any term in the sequence
		The 15th term in the above sequence is
		$t_{15} = 1(3)^{15-1}$
		$t_{15} = 3^{14}$
		$t_{15} = 4\,782\,969$

Working Example 1: Determine t_1, r, and t_n

Andrew and David organize a tree planting challenge. They have people plant a tree and then sign up three more people to join the challenge. Andrew and David are the first to join the challenge, each planting one tree and each signing up three more people.

a) State the values for t_1 and r for the geometric sequence that represents this situation. Then, state the geometric sequence.

b) Determine the general term that relates the number of trees planted to the number of people who sign up for the challenge.

Solution

a) The initial planters are Andrew and David, so $t_1 = 2$. Since they each sign up three other people, $t_2 = $ _____.

Determine the common ratio, r, by dividing the second term by the first term.

$$r = \frac{t_2}{t_1}$$

$$r = \text{_____}$$

$t_1 = 2$, $t_2 = $ _____, $t_3 = $ _____, $t_4 = $ _____, $t_5 = 162$, ...

b) Substitute $t_1 = 2$ and $r = $ _____ into the formula for the general term.

$$t_n = t_1 r^{n-1}$$

$$t_n = (2)(\text{_____})^{n-1}$$

> Why is it incorrect to write the general term as 6^{n-1}?

The general term of the sequence is $t_n = $ _____.

> 📖 See page 34 of *Pre-Calculus 11* for a similar example.

Working Example 2: Determine a Particular Term

A company stores 5 kg of a radioactive material. After one year, 92% of the radioactive material remains. How much radioactive material will be left after ten years? State your answer to nearest tenth of a kilogram.

Solution

$t_1 = 5$, $r = 0.92$, $n = 10$

> Why do you use 0.92 instead of 92% for the common ratio? Why is $n = 10$?

The general term is $t_n = ($ _____$)($ _____$)^{n-1}$.

Substitute $n = 10$ and solve.

$$t_{10} = 5(\text{_____})^{\square - 1}$$

$$t_{10} = 5(\text{_____})^{\square}$$

$$t_{10} \approx \text{_____}$$

After ten years, approximately _____ kg of radioactive material remains.

> 📖 See page 35 of *Pre-Calculus 11* for a similar example.

Working Example 3: Determine t_1 and r

In a geometric sequence, the fifth term is 1050 and the seventh term is 26 250.

a) Find the values of t_1 and r.

b) List the first four terms of the sequence.

Solution

a) $t_5 =$ _____, $t_7 =$ _____

Create an equation for each of the known terms using the general term, $t_n = t_1 r^{n-1}$.

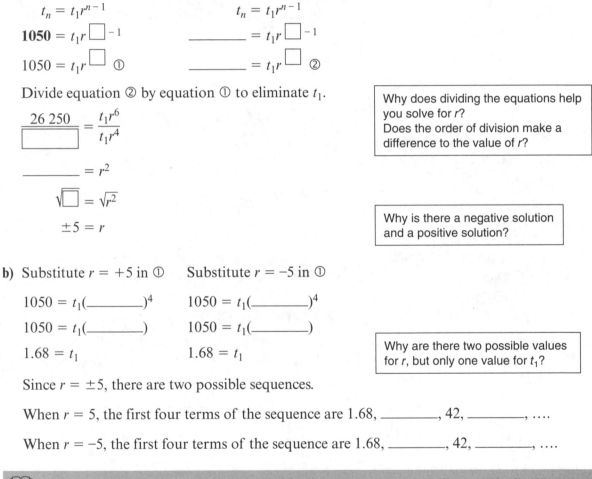

$t_n = t_1 r^{n-1}$

$1050 = t_1 r^{\boxed{}-1}$

$1050 = t_1 r^{\boxed{}}$ ①

$t_n = t_1 r^{n-1}$

_____ $= t_1 r^{\boxed{}-1}$

_____ $= t_1 r^{\boxed{}}$ ②

Divide equation ② by equation ① to eliminate t_1.

$\dfrac{26\ 250}{\boxed{}} = \dfrac{t_1 r^6}{t_1 r^4}$

_____ $= r^2$

$\sqrt{\boxed{}} = \sqrt{r^2}$

$\pm 5 = r$

> Why does dividing the equations help you solve for r?
> Does the order of division make a difference to the value of r?

> Why is there a negative solution and a positive solution?

b) Substitute $r = +5$ in ①   Substitute $r = -5$ in ①

$1050 = t_1(\underline{})^4$ $1050 = t_1(\underline{})^4$

$1050 = t_1(\underline{})$ $1050 = t_1(\underline{})$

$1.68 = t_1$ $1.68 = t_1$

> Why are there two possible values for r, but only one value for t_1?

Since $r = \pm 5$, there are two possible sequences.

When $r = 5$, the first four terms of the sequence are 1.68, _____, 42, _____, ….

When $r = -5$, the first four terms of the sequence are 1.68, _____, 42, _____, ….

📖 Compare this method with the methods shown on pages 36–37 of *Pre-Calculus 11*.

Working Example 4: Apply Geometric Sequences

Listeria monocytogenes are bacteria that are sometimes found in food. It takes about 7 h for the number of these organisms to double when the temperature is 10 °C. Suppose the bacteria count in a sample of food is 100.

a) Write the first five terms of the geometric sequence that models this situation.

b) How long will it take for the bacteria count to reach 1 638 400?

Solution

a) The food sample has 100 bacteria and they double in number every 7 h.

The first five terms of the geometric sequence that models this situation are

100, 200, _____, _____, _____.

b) The number of doubling periods is $n - 1$. This is the exponent of r in the general term, $t_n = t_1 r^{n-1}$.

Find the general term by substituting the known values into the general term.

$t_1 = $ _____ and $r = $ _____

$t_n = t_1 r^{n-1}$

$t_n = 100(\text{_____})^{n-1}$

Solve for $t_n = 1\ 638\ 400$.

_____ $= 100(2)^{n-1}$

$16\ 384 = (\text{_____})^{n-1}$

To find n, express 16 384 as a power with the same base as the right side.

$16\ 384 = 2^{n-1}$

$2^{\boxed{}} = 2^{n-1}$

_____ $= n - 1$

> The bases are equal, so for the two sides to be equivalent, the exponents must also be equal.

There are 14 doubling periods, and each is 7 h long.

$14(\text{_____}) = $ _____

It takes 98 h for the bacteria count to reach 1 638 400.

Check Your Understanding

Practise

1. State if the sequence is geometric. If it is, state the common ratio and the next three terms.

   a) 5, 10, 15, 20, ...

   b) 1, 3, 9, 27, ...

   c) 3, 0.3, 0.03, 0.003, ...

   d) 36, 30, 24, 18, ...

   e) $25, 5, 1, \frac{1}{5}, ...$

   f) $-8, 4, -2, 1, ...$

2. Given the first term and common ratio of each geometric sequence, write the general term.

   a) $t_1 = 3, r = 4$

   Substitute in $t_n =$ _____$^{n-1}$

   b) $t_1 = 36, r = -\frac{1}{3}$

   c) $t_1 = 4.5, r = -1.5$

   d) $t_1 = \frac{1}{5}, r = -\frac{2}{5}$

3. The general term of a geometric sequence is given. Determine the indicated term.

   a) $t_n = 2(-2)^{n-1}, t_{10}$

   Substitute $n =$ _____ into t_n.

   b) $t_n = 0.5(4)^{n-1}, t_9$

   c) $t_n = -1000(-0.1)^{n-1}, t_{11}$

   d) $t_n = -(-1)^{n-1}, t_{200}$

4. Match each geometric sequence to the correct corresponding general term.

a) $2, 10, 50, \ldots$ **A** $t_n = 4(-3)^{n-1}$

b) $3, -12, 48, \ldots$ **B** $t_n = 5(3)^{n-1}$

c) $4, -12, 36, \ldots$ **C** $t_n = 3(3)^{n-1}$

d) $5, 15, 45, \ldots$ **D** $t_n = 3(-4)^{n-1}$

e) $2, -4, 8, \ldots$ **E** $t_n = 2(5)^{n-1}$

f) $3, 9, 27, \ldots$ **F** $t_n = 2(-2)^{n-1}$

Apply

5. Given two terms of a geometric sequence, find the general term for the sequence.

a) $t_2 = 6$ and $t_3 = -12$

Substitute the known values into the formula for the general term, $t_n = t_1 r^{n-1}$.

For $n = 2$ For $n = 3$

$6 = t_1 r^{\boxed{} - 1}$ $\underline{} = t_1 r^{3-1}$

$6 = \underline{}$ $-12 = \underline{}$

Divide the two equations to solve for r. Then, solve for t_1. Write the general term.

b) $t_2 = 4$ and $t_4 = 64$ c) $t_4 = 64$ and $t_7 = 8$

To see a similar problem, see pages 36–37 of *Pre-Calculus 11*.

6. The diagrams show the side lengths of three 30°-60°-90° triangles. Find the side lengths of the next triangle in the sequence.

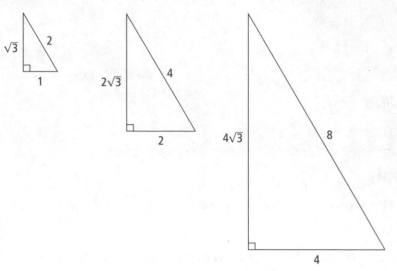

7. Find the number of terms, n, in each of the following geometric sequences.

a) 4, 12, 36, …, 2916

b) 2, −4, 8, …, −1024

c) 4374, 1458, 486, …, 2

d) $\dfrac{1}{25}, \dfrac{1}{5}, 1, …, 625$

8. Consider a geometric sequence with $t_3 = 18$ and $t_7 = 1458$.

    a) Are there one or two values for the common ratio? Explain how this affects the sequence.

    b) State the first five terms of the sequence(s).

9. Find the first four terms of a geometric sequence with $t_5 = 1536$ and $t_{10} = 48$.

10. Find the missing terms in each geometric sequence.

    a) 4, _____, 16, _____

    b) 2, _____, _____, 432

    c) 3, _____, 12, _____

11. The population of a city increases by 6.5% each year for ten years. If the initial population is 200 000, what is the population after ten years?

12. Determine the value of x that makes the sequence 4, 8, 16, $3x + 2$, ... geometric.

13. The value of a rare comic book is expected to follow a geometric sequence from year to year. It is presently worth $800 and is expected to be worth $1250 two years from now.

a) How much is the comic book expected to be worth one year from now?

b) How much is the comic book expected to be worth three years from now?

Connect

14. Consider the graph.

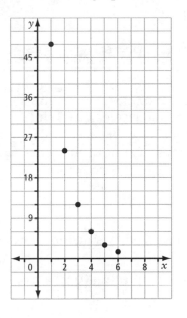

The points (1, 48) and (2, 24) correspond to the terms in the sequence $t_1 = 48$ and $t_2 = 24$.
How are the coordinate pairs related to the sequence?
How is the graph of a geometric sequence different from the graph of an arithmetic sequence?

a) Do the points on this graph represent a geometric sequence? If so, list the first five terms of the sequence.

b) Does a general term exist? Justify your answer. State the general term for this geometric sequence.

15. A balloon filled with helium has a volume of 20 000 cm^3. The balloon loses one tenth of its helium every 24 h.

a) What type of sequence does this situation represent? Justify your answer.

b) Describe how you can determine what volume of helium will be in the balloon at the start of the seventh day. What is the volume at this time?

⟪ **KEY IDEAS** ⟫

Concept	Definition	Examples
Geometric series	• the sum when the terms of a geometric sequence are added together • write the general geometric series as $S_n = t_1 + t_1 r + t_1 r^2 + t_1 r^3 + \cdots + t_1 r^{n-1}$, where t_1 is the first term n is the number of terms r is the common ratio S_n is the sum of the first n terms of the series	The sequence 1, 3, 9, 27, 81, 243, … has a common ratio, r, of 3. It is a geometric sequence. When you add the terms of this sequence together, it becomes a geometric series: $1 + 3 + 9 + 27 + 81 + 243 + \cdots$ The general geometric series for this series is $S_n = 1 + 1(3) + 1(3)^2 + 1(3)^3$ $+ \cdots + 1(3)^{n-1}$
Sum of a geometric series	• when you know t_1, r, and n, determine the sum of a geometric series using the formula $S_n = \dfrac{t_1(r^n - 1)}{r - 1}, r \neq 1$, where t_1 is the first term in the series n is the number of terms r is the common ratio S_n is the sum of the first n terms • when you know r, t_1, and t_n, use the formula $S_n = \dfrac{r t_n - t_1}{r - 1}, r \neq 1$, where t_1 is the first term n is the number of terms r is the common ratio t_n is the nth term S_n is the sum of the first n terms	$t_1 = 1, r = 3, n = 15,$ $S_{15} = \dfrac{1(3^{15} - 1)}{3 - 1}, r \neq 1$ $S_{15} = \dfrac{1(14\,348\,907 - 1)}{2}$ $S_{15} = 7\,174\,453$ $t_1 = 1, r = 3, t_{15} = 4\,782\,969$ $S_{15} = \dfrac{3(4\,782\,969) - 1}{3 - 1}$ $S_{15} = \dfrac{14\,348\,906}{2}$ $S_{15} = 7\,174\,453$

Working Example 1: Determine the Sum of a Geometric Series

Determine the sum of each geometric series.

a) $12 - 6 + 3 - 1.5 + \cdots \ (S_{11})$

b) $2 + 8 + 32 + \cdots \ (S_8)$

Solution

a) For this geometric series, $t_1 =$ _____, $r =$ _____, and $n =$ _____. Substitute these values into the formula to determine the sum of the series.

$$S_n = \frac{t_1(r^n - 1)}{r - 1}$$

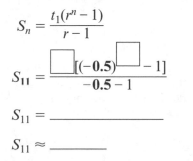

$$S_{11} = \frac{\boxed{}[(-0.5)^{\boxed{}} - 1]}{-0.5 - 1}$$

> What is the order of operations for evaluating the sum?

$S_{11} =$ _____

$S_{11} \approx$ _____

The sum of the first 11 terms of the geometric series is approximately _____.

b) For this geometric series, $t_1 =$ _____, $r =$ _____, and $n =$ _____. Substitute these values into the formula for finding the sum of a series.

$$S_n = \frac{t_1(r^n - 1)}{r - 1}$$

$$S_8 = \frac{2\left[\left(\boxed{}\right)^8 - 1\right]}{\boxed{} - 1}$$

$$S_8 = \frac{2^{\boxed{}}}{3}$$

$S_8 =$ _____

The sum of the first eight terms of the geometric series is _____.

Working Example 2: Determine the Sum of a Geometric Series for an Unspecified Number of Terms

Determine the sum of each geometric series.

a) $10 + 5 + \frac{5}{2} + \cdots + \frac{5}{64}$

b) $1 - 3 + 9 - \cdots - 243$

Solution

a) First determine the number of terms in the series by substituting the known values in the general term of a geometric sequence.

$$t_n = \underline{\hspace{2cm}}, \ t_1 = \underline{\hspace{2cm}}, \ r = \frac{1}{2}.$$

$$t_n = t_1 r^{n-1}$$

$$\frac{5}{64} = \underline{\hspace{1.5cm}} (\underline{\hspace{1cm}})^{n-1}$$

$$\frac{5}{640} = \left(\frac{1}{2}\right)^{n-1}$$

| Why do you divide both sides by 10? |

$$\frac{1}{128} = \left(\frac{1}{2}\right)^{n-1}$$

$$\left(\frac{1}{2}\right)^7 = \left(\frac{1}{2}\right)^{n-1} \quad \text{Express the left side as a power.}$$

| When the base is the same on each side of the equal sign, what does this tell you about exponents? |

$$\underline{\hspace{2cm}} = n - 1$$

$$\underline{\hspace{2cm}} = n$$

There are eight terms in the series.

Use the formula for the sum of a geometric series to find the sum of the series.

Substitute $n = \underline{\hspace{1.5cm}}, \ t_1 = \underline{\hspace{1.5cm}}, \ r = \frac{1}{2}.$

$$S_n = \frac{t_1(r^n - 1)}{r - 1}$$

$$S_8 = \frac{10\left[\left(\boxed{}\right)^{\boxed{}} - 1\right]}{\boxed{}}$$

$$S_8 = \frac{\boxed{}}{\boxed{}}$$

$$S_8 = \underline{\hspace{2cm}}$$

The sum of the geometric series is \underline{\hspace{2cm}}.

📖 Compare this method with the methods shown on pages 50–51 of *Pre-Calculus 11*.

b) Use the formula $S_n = \dfrac{rt_n - t_1}{r - 1}$.

$t_1 = 1, r = $ _____, $t_n = $ _____

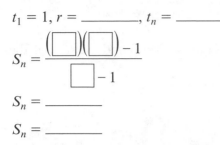

$S_n = \dfrac{(\boxed{})(\boxed{}) - 1}{\boxed{} - 1}$

$S_n = $ _____

$S_n = $ _____

The sum of the geometric series is _____.

> Compare the solutions in parts a) and b). Which formula do you prefer for the sum of a geometric series with an unspecified number of terms? Why?

Working Example 3: Apply Geometric Series

A tennis tournament has 128 players. When players win their match, they go on to play another match. If they lose their match, they are out of the tournament. What is the total number of matches that will be played in this tournament?

Solution

Since there are two players per match, the first term is _____ ÷ 2. So, $t_1 = $ _____.

After each round of matches, half the players are eliminated due to loss, so $r = $ _____.

At the end of the tournament a single match is played to decide the winner, so $t_n = $ _____.

Substitute the known values into the formula.

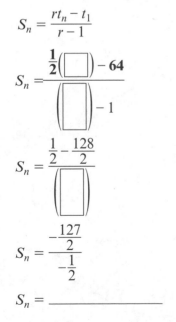

$S_n = \dfrac{rt_n - t_1}{r - 1}$

$S_n = \dfrac{\frac{1}{2}(\boxed{}) - 64}{(\boxed{}) - 1}$

$S_n = \dfrac{\frac{1}{2} - \frac{128}{2}}{(\boxed{})}$

$S_n = \dfrac{-\frac{127}{2}}{-\frac{1}{2}}$

$S_n = $ _____

There will be _____ matches in the tournament.

📖 Compare this working example with the example on page 52 of *Pre-Calculus 11*.

Check Your Understanding

Practise

1. State whether each series is geometric. If it is, state the common ratio and the sum of the first seven terms of the series.

   a) $6 + 18 + 54 + \cdots$

   b) $8 - 24 + 72 - \cdots$

   c) $3 - 9 + 18 - 54 + \cdots$

   d) $\frac{1}{3} + \frac{1}{6} + \frac{1}{12} + \cdots$

2. Determine the indicated sum for each geometric series.

   a) $2 + 6 + 18 + \cdots \ (S_8)$

   $t_1 = $ _____ and $r = $ _____

   b) $2.1 - 4.2 + 8.4 - \cdots \ (S_9)$

   c) $30 - 5 + \frac{5}{6} - \cdots \ (S_7)$

   d) $24 - 18 + \frac{27}{2} - \cdots \ (S_6)$

3. What is S_n for each geometric series?

   a) $t_1 = 2, r = -2, n = 12$

   b) $t_1 = 2700, r = 10, n = 8$

4. Calculate the sum of each geometric series.

   a) $1 + 6 + 36 + \cdots + 279\,936$

   b) $1200 + 120 + 12 + \cdots + 0.0012$

   c) $-6 + 24 - 96 + \cdots + 98\,304$

   d) $\dfrac{1}{3} + \dfrac{2}{9} + \dfrac{4}{27} + \cdots + \dfrac{128}{6571}$

5. Determine S_n for each geometric series with the given general term t_n.

   a) $t_n = 2(3)^{n-1}$

   $t_1 = $ _____ , $r = $ _____

   b) $t_n = 5(2)^{n-1}$

   c) $t_n = 3(4)^{n-1}$

   d) $t_n = 4(2)^{n-1}$

6. Determine the number of terms in each geometric series. Then, find the sum of the series.

a) $3 + 6 + 12 + \cdots + 3072$

$t_n =$ _____, $t_1 =$ _____, $r =$ _____

Substitute in $t_n = t_1 r^{n-1}$.

Then, substitute in $S_n = \dfrac{r t_n - t_1}{r - 1}$.

$S_{11} =$ _____

b) $3.4 - 7.14 + 14.994 + \cdots - 138.859\ 434$

Apply

7. A large company has a strategy for contacting employees in case of an emergency shutdown. When an emergency occurs, each of the five senior managers calls three employees. Then, each of these employees calls another three employees, and so on. This is sometimes referred to as a phone tree. If the tree consists of exactly seven levels, how many employees does the company have?

8. In a geometric series, $t_1 = 12$, $t_4 = 96$, and the sum of all of the terms of the series is 98 292. How many terms are in the series?

9. On the first swing, a pendulum swings through an arc of 40 cm. On each successive swing, the length of the arc is 0.98 times the previous length. In the first 20 swings, what is the total distance that the lower end of the pendulum swings, to the nearest hundredth of a centimetre?

10. A doctor prescribes 200 mg of medication on the first day of treatment. The dosage is reduced by one half on each successive day for one week. What is the total amount of medication prescribed, to the nearest milligram?

11. Every person has two parents, four grandparents, eight great-grandparents, and so on. Determine the number of ancestors a person has back through ten generations.

12. When you shut off a circular saw, it continues to turn. Each second after shut-off, the speed of the blade is $\frac{2}{3}$ of the speed in the previous second. After the first 8 s, the saw has turned 258 times. What was the speed of the saw before the motor was shut off, to the nearest tenth of a turn per second?

13. Dalla is rock climbing. She climbs 60 m up a cliff in the first hour. In each of the next four hours, she climbs 75% of the distance of the previous hour. What is the total distance Dalla climbs after five hours?

Connect

14. The second term of a geometric series is 15. The sum of the first three terms is 93. Describe how you would find the terms of the series. Use your method to determine the series.

15. The air in a hot-air balloon cools as the balloon rises. If the air is not reheated, the balloon rises more slowly every minute. Suppose that a hot-air balloon rises 50 m in the first minute. In each succeeding minute, the balloon rises 70% as far as it did in the previous minute.

   a) What type of series does this situation represent? Justify your answer.

   b) Describe a method to determine how far the balloon rises in n minutes. Use your method to determine how far the balloon rises in 7 minutes, to the nearest metre.

Concept	Definition	Examples
Infinite series	• a series with an unlimited, or infinite, number of terms	You can continue adding 2 to the last term of the sequence 2, 4, 6, 8, 10, 12, … forever.
	• ∞ is the symbol for infinity; something that is infinite has no ending—it goes on forever	Adding the terms of this sequence creates an infinite series: $2 + 4 + 6 + 8 + 10 + 12 + \cdots$
	• a *partial sum*, S_n, of an infinite series is the sum of the first n terms in the series	$S_1 = 2$, $S_2 = 6$, $S_3 = 12$, $S_4 = 20$
Infinite geometric series	• a geometric series that goes on forever	$4 + 2 + 1 + 0.5 + 0.25 + \cdots$
	• to converge on something means to approach it; an infinite series is *convergent* if the sequence of partial sums approaches a fixed value—a sum	Convergence test: $r = \dfrac{t_2}{t_1}$ $= \dfrac{2}{4}$ $= \dfrac{1}{2}$
	• if an infinite geometric series is convergent, the value of the common ratio is a proper fraction between -1 and 1 $(-1 < r < 1)$	Since r is between -1 and 1 the sequence is convergent.
	• to find the sum of an infinite geometric series, where $-1 < r < 1$, use the formula $S_\infty = \dfrac{t_1}{1 - r}$, where t_1 is the first term of the series r is the common difference S_∞ represents the sum of an infinite number of terms	$S_\infty = \dfrac{4}{1 - \dfrac{1}{2}}$ $= 8$ $4 + 8 + 16 + 32 + 64 + \cdots$ Convergence test: $r = \dfrac{t_2}{t_1}$ $= \dfrac{8}{4}$ $= 2$
	• an infinite series is *divergent* if the sequence of partial sums does not approach a fixed value	r is not between -1 and 1, so this series is divergent.

Working Example 1: Sum of an Infinite Geometric Series

Decide whether each infinite geometric series is convergent or divergent. State the sum of the series, if it exists.

a) $0.5 - 1 + 2 - 4 + \cdots$

b) $12 + 3 + \dfrac{3}{4} + \dfrac{3}{16} + \cdots$

Solution

a) $t_1 = $ _____, $r = $ _____

The series is _____ if the value of r is between -1 and 1;
      (*convergent* or *divergent*)

otherwise, it is _____.
      (*convergent* or *divergent*)

In this case, $r = $ _____.

This series is _____ and the sum _____ exist.
      (*convergent* or *divergent*)   (*does* or *does not*)

b) $t_1 = $ _____, $r = $ _____

The series is _____ because _____ $< r <$ _____.

To find the sum of the series, substitute the known values into the formula for the sum of an infinite geometric series.

$$S_\infty = \frac{t_1}{1 - r}$$

$$S_\infty = \underline{\quad\quad}$$

$$S_\infty = \frac{12}{\dfrac{3}{4}}$$

$$S_\infty = \underline{\quad\quad}$$

📖 Compare with Example 1 on page 61 of *Pre-Calculus 11*.

Working Example 2: Apply the Sum of an Infinite Geometric Series

In the first month, an oil well in Manitoba produced 36 000 barrels of crude oil. Every month after that, it produced 95% of the previous month's production.

a) Write the series of terms that represents this situation.

b) If this trend continues, what will be the lifetime production of this well?

c) What assumption are you making about the well and its production? Is your assumption reasonable?

Solution

a) The series is 36 000 + [_____(0.95)] + t_2(_____) + _____ ⋯.

So, the series is _____ + _____ + 32 490 + _____ + ⋯.

b) This is a geometric series where $t_1 =$ _____ and $r =$ _____.

The series is _____ because _____ $< r <$ _____.
        (*convergent* or *divergent*)

The lifetime production of the well is equal to the sum of the series. Substitute the known values into the formula for the sum of an infinite geometric series.

$$S_\infty = \frac{t_1}{1 - r}$$

$$S_\infty = \frac{\textbf{36 000}}{1 - \boxed{}}$$

$$S_\infty = \frac{36\ 000}{\boxed{}}$$

$$S_\infty = \underline{}$$

The lifetime production of the well is _____ barrels of crude.

c) This calculation assumes that the well will always produce 95% of the previous month, not more and not less, which is probably unrealistic. At some point the company will shut down operations because it will no longer make financial sense to continue operations.

📖 Compare with Example 2 on page 62 of *Pre-Calculus 11*.

Working Example 3: Apply the Sum of an Infinite Geometric Series to Express a Repeating Decimal as a Fraction

Apply the sum of an infinite geometric series to express the repeating decimal $2.1\overline{35}$ as a fraction.

Solution

This repeating decimal expands to $2.1\overline{35} = 2.135\ 353\ 535....$

Write the repeating decimal as an infinite series.

$$2.1\overline{35} = 2.1 + \frac{35}{1000} + \frac{35}{\boxed{}} + \frac{35}{\boxed{}} + \cdots$$

After the term 2.1, the series $\frac{35}{1000} + \frac{35}{100\ 000} + \frac{35}{10\ 000\ 000} + \cdots$ is geometric with

$t_1 = \underline{\hspace{1cm}}$ and $r = \frac{1}{100}$. The series is convergent because $\underline{\hspace{1cm}} < r < \underline{\hspace{1cm}}$.

To find the sum of the infinite geometric series, substitute the known values in $S_\infty = \frac{t_1}{1-r}$.

$$S_\infty = \frac{\boxed{}}{1 - \frac{1}{100}}$$

$$S_\infty = \underline{\hspace{1.5cm}}$$

$$S_\infty = \underline{\hspace{1.5cm}}$$

Add the sum of the series to 2.1.

$$2.1\overline{35} = 2.1 + S_\infty$$

$$2.1\overline{35} = \frac{\boxed{}}{10} + \frac{\boxed{}}{\boxed{}}$$

$$2.1\overline{35} = \frac{\boxed{}}{990} + \frac{35}{990}$$

$$2.1\overline{35} = \frac{\boxed{}}{990}$$

$$2.1\overline{35} = \underline{\hspace{1.5cm}}$$

Therefore, $2.1\overline{35}$ is equivalent to the fraction $\underline{\hspace{1.5cm}}$.

Working Example 4: Given the Sum and Common Ratio of an Infinite Geometric Series, Find the First Term

The sum of an infinite series is 92 and the common ratio is $\frac{1}{4}$.

a) What is the value of the first term?

b) Write the first three terms of the series.

Solution

a) To solve for t_1, substitute the known values $S_\infty = 92$ and $r = \frac{1}{4}$ into the formula

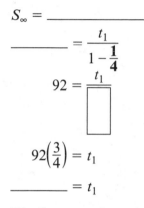

$$S_\infty = \underline{\hspace{3cm}}.$$

$$\underline{\hspace{2cm}} = \frac{t_1}{1 - \frac{1}{4}}$$

$$92 = \frac{t_1}{\boxed{}}$$

$$92\left(\frac{3}{4}\right) = t_1$$

$$\underline{\hspace{2.5cm}} = t_1$$

The first term is $\underline{\hspace{1.5cm}}$.

b) $t_1 = \underline{\hspace{1.5cm}}, r = \frac{1}{4}$

The first three terms of the series are $\underline{\hspace{1.5cm}} + \underline{\hspace{1.5cm}} + \underline{\hspace{1.5cm}}$.

Check Your Understanding

Practise

1. Decide whether each infinite geometric series is convergent or divergent. State the sum of the series, if it exists.

   a) $-81 + 27 - 9 + 3 - \cdots$

   $t_1 = \underline{\hspace{1cm}}, r = \underline{\hspace{1cm}}$

   b) $24 + 6 + \dfrac{3}{2} + \dfrac{3}{8} + \cdots$

   c) $\dfrac{1}{4} - \dfrac{5}{16} + \dfrac{25}{64} - \dfrac{125}{256} + \cdots$

   d) $0.1 + 0.05 + 0.025 + 0.0125 + \cdots$

   e) $\dfrac{2}{7} + 2 + 14 + 28 + \cdots$

   f) $-5 + 5 - 5 + 5 - \cdots$

2. Determine the sum of each infinite geometric series, if it exists.

   a) $t_1 = -1, r = \dfrac{3}{4}$

   b) $t_1 = -4, r = \dfrac{4}{3}$

   c) $t_1 = -36, r = \dfrac{2}{3}$

   d) $t_1 = 144, r = -\dfrac{7}{12}$

   e) $t_1 = 8, r = -\sqrt{2}$

   f) $t_1 = 8, r = -\dfrac{5}{\sqrt{6}}$

3. Express each of the following repeating decimals as a fraction.

a) $0.\overline{3}$

b) $0.\overline{25}$

c) $4.\overline{51}$

d) $1.1\overline{23}$

4. Does 3.9999... = 4? Support your answer.

$3.9999 = 3 +$ _____

$0.9999 = \dfrac{9}{10} +$ _____ $+$ _____ $+$ _____ $\cdots$

For this infinite series, $t_1 =$ _____ and $r =$ _____.

> What is the sum of this infinite series?

5. What is the sum of each infinite geometric series?

a) $2 + 2\left(\dfrac{3}{5}\right) + 2\left(\dfrac{3}{5}\right)^2 + 2\left(\dfrac{3}{5}\right)^3 + \cdots$

b) $3 + 3\left(-\dfrac{4}{7}\right) + 3\left(-\dfrac{4}{7}\right)^2 + 3\left(-\dfrac{4}{7}\right)^3 + \cdots$

Apply

6. Each of the following represents an infinite geometric series. For what values of x will each series be convergent?

   a) $1 + x + x^2 + x^3 + \cdots,\ x \neq 0, 1$

   b) $4 + 2x + x^2 + \dfrac{x^3}{2} + \cdots,\ x \neq 0, 1$

7. The length of an initial swing of a pendulum is 65 cm. Each successive swing is 0.75 times the length of the previous swing. If this process continues forever, how far will the pendulum swing?

   $t_1 =$ _____, $r =$ _____

   $S_\infty = \dfrac{65}{1 - \boxed{}}$

8. A rubber ball is dropped from a height of 32 m. Each time it bounces it rebounds to 60% of its previous height. If the ball bounces indefinitely, what is the total vertical distance it travels?

   $t_1 =$ _____, $r =$ _____

   $S_\infty = \dfrac{\boxed{}}{1 - 0.60}$

Connect

9. The sum of an infinite series is 105 and the common ratio is $-\frac{2}{3}$.

   a) Explain how you can use the given information to find the first term. Justify your answer.

   b) Write the first three terms of the series.

10. The first term of an infinite geometric series is -18, and its sum is -45.

    a) Explain how you can use the given information to find the common ratio. Justify your answer.

    b) Write the first four terms of the series.

Chapter 1 Review

1.1 Arithmetic Sequences, pages 1–13

1. Identify which of the following are arithmetic sequences. For each arithmetic sequence, state the common difference and find the general term.

   a) $1, 5, 10, 15, \ldots$

   b) $2, 2\frac{1}{2}, 3, 3\frac{1}{2}, \ldots$

   c) $1, 4, 9, 16, \ldots$

   d) $-2x^2, -5x^2, -8x^2, -11x^2, \ldots$

2. State the first five terms of the arithmetic sequence with the given t_1 and d.

   a) $t_1 = 1, d = -4$

   b) $t_1 = -6, d = 6$

   c) $t_1 = 5m, d = 3$

   d) $t_1 = c + 1, d = c - 2$

3. Determine the first term and common difference of the arithmetic sequence with the given terms.

   a) $t_5 = 16$ and $t_8 = 25$

   b) $t_{50} = 140$ and $t_{70} = 180$

   c) $t_2 = -12$ and $t_5 = 9$

   d) $t_7 = 37$ and $t_{10} = 22$

4. Determine the number of terms in the arithmetic sequences.

   a) $3, 5, 7, \ldots, 129$

   b) $-1, 2, 5, \ldots, 164$

   c) $-29, -24, -19, \ldots, 126$

   d) $p + 3q, p + 7q, p + 11q, \ldots, p + 111q$

5. A museum purchases a painting for \$15 000. The painting increases in value each year by 10% of the original price. What is the value of the painting after ten years?

1.2 Arithmetic Series, pages 14–21

6. Find the sum of the first ten terms of each arithmetic series.

a) $2 + 8 + 14 + \cdots$

b) $6 + 18 + 30 + \cdots$

c) $45 + 39 + 33 + \cdots$

d) $6 + 13 + 20 + \cdots$

7. Find the sum of each arithmetic series.

a) $2 + 7 + 12 + \cdots + 92$

b) $3 + 5.5 + 8 + \cdots + 133$

c) $20 + 14 + 8 + \cdots - 70$

d) $100 + 90 + 80 + \cdots - 100$

8. Find the first five terms of an arithmetic series with $S_{10} = 210$ and $S_{20} = 820$.

9. $S_n = -441$ for the series $19 + 15 + 11 + \cdots + t_n$. Determine the value of n.

1.3 Geometric Sequences, pages 22–31

10. Find the missing terms in each geometric sequence.

   a) _____, 5, _____, 125

   b) 3, _____, _____, 375

11. Find the number of terms, n, in each of the geometric sequences.

   a) 3, 6, 12, …, 1536

   b) −409.6, 102.4, −25.6, …, 0.025

   c) $\dfrac{1}{2}, \dfrac{1}{4}, \dfrac{1}{8}, \ldots, \dfrac{1}{2048}$

   d) $\dfrac{2}{81}, \dfrac{4}{27}, \dfrac{8}{9}, \ldots, 6912$

12. In a geometric sequence, $t_1 = 2$ and $t_5 = 162$. Find the common ratio, r, and the terms between t_1 and t_5.

13. Given two terms of each geometric sequence, find the general term for the sequence.

   a) $t_3 = 36$ and $t_4 = 108$

   b) $t_3 = 99$ and $t_5 = 11$

14. Most photocopiers can reduce the size an image by a maximum of 64% of the original dimensions. How many reductions, at the maximum setting, would it take to reduce an image to less than 10% of its original dimensions?

1.4 Geometric Series, pages 32–40

15. For each geometric series, state the values of t_1 and r. Then, determine each indicated sum. Express your answers as exact values in fraction form.

a) $24 - 12 + 6 - \cdots$ (S_{10})

b) $0.3 + 0.003 + 0.000\,03 + \cdots$ (S_{15})

c) $8 - 8 + 8 - \cdots$ (S_{40})

d) $1 - \frac{1}{3} + \frac{1}{9} - \cdots$ (S_{12})

16. What is S_n for each geometric series?

a) $t_1 = 6, r = 2, n = 9$

b) $t_1 = \frac{1}{2}, r = 4, n = 8$

17. Calculate the sum of each geometric series.

a) $960 + 480 + 240 + \cdots + 15$

b) $17 - 51 + 153 - \cdots - 334\,611$

18. Determine the number of terms in each geometric series.

a) $7\,971\,615 + 5\,314\,410 + 3\,542\,940 + \cdots + 92\,160$

b) $1 + 3x^2 + 9x^4 + \cdots + 243x^{10}$

19. A sweepstakes gives away $1 000 000, by giving away $25 in the first week, $75 in the second week, $225 in the third week, and so on. How many weeks will it take to give away all of the prize money?

1.5 Infinite Geometric Series, pages 41–49

20. Decide whether each infinite geometric series is convergent or divergent. State the sum of the series, if it exists.

a) $-64 + 16 - 4 + 2 - \cdots$

b) $\dfrac{5}{12} - \dfrac{5}{6} + \dfrac{5}{3} - \dfrac{10}{3} + \cdots$

c) $6.1 + 1.22 + 0.244 + 0.0488 + \cdots$

d) $\dfrac{24}{5} - 12 + 30 - 75 + \cdots$

21. The sum of an infinite series is 120 and the common ratio is $-\dfrac{2}{5}$. State t_1 and the first three terms of the series.

22. The length of an initial swing of a pendulum is 90 cm. Each successive swing is 0.70 times the length of the previous swing. If this process continues forever, how far will the pendulum swing?

Chapter 1 Skills Organizer

Complete the missing information in the chart.

Sequences	
Arithmetic	**Geometric**
A general arithmetic sequence is … Example:	A general geometric sequence is … Example:
Formula for Common Difference	Formula for Common Ratio
Formula for General Term	Formula for General Term

Series	
Arithmetic	**Geometric**
A general arithmetic series is … Example:	A general geometric series is … Example:
Formula for Sum of Series	Formulas for Sum of Series

Infinite Geometric Series
A general infinite geometric series is …
Condition for Convergent Geometric Series
Formula for Sum of Series

Chapter 2 Trigonometry

2.1 Angles in Standard Position

> ### « KEY IDEAS »

- An angle θ is in standard position when
  - the vertex of the angle is located at the origin $(0, 0)$ on a Cartesian plane
  - the initial arm of the angle lies along the positive x-axis

- Measure the angle θ in a counterclockwise direction from the initial arm to the terminal arm. The quadrants of the Cartesian plane are labelled with Roman numerals, also in a counterclockwise direction beginning from the positive x-axis.

- Angles in standard position have a corresponding acute angle called the reference angle, θ_R. The reference angle is the acute angle formed between the terminal arm and the x-axis.

- There are two special right triangles for which you can determine the exact values of the primary trigonometric ratios.

  Hint: The smallest angle is always opposite the shortest side.

$\sin 45° = \dfrac{1}{\sqrt{2}}$ $\cos 45° = \dfrac{1}{\sqrt{2}}$ $\tan 45° = 1$

$\sin 30° = \dfrac{1}{2}$ $\cos 30° = \dfrac{\sqrt{3}}{2}$ $\tan 30° = \dfrac{1}{\sqrt{3}}$

$\sin 60° = \dfrac{\sqrt{3}}{2}$ $\cos 60° = \dfrac{1}{2}$ $\tan 60° = \sqrt{3}$

Working Example 1: Sketch an Angle in Standard Position, $0° \leq \theta < 360°$

Sketch each angle in standard position. State the quadrant in which the terminal arm lies.

a) 80°　　　　　　　　　**b)** 120°　　　　　　　　　**c)** 266°

Solution

Consider the angle values for the axes: 0°, 90°, 180°, 270°, and 360°. Determine which region of the graph will contain the terminal arm of the angle.

a) For $\theta = 80°$, the angle lies between _____ (angle 1) and _____ (angle 2).

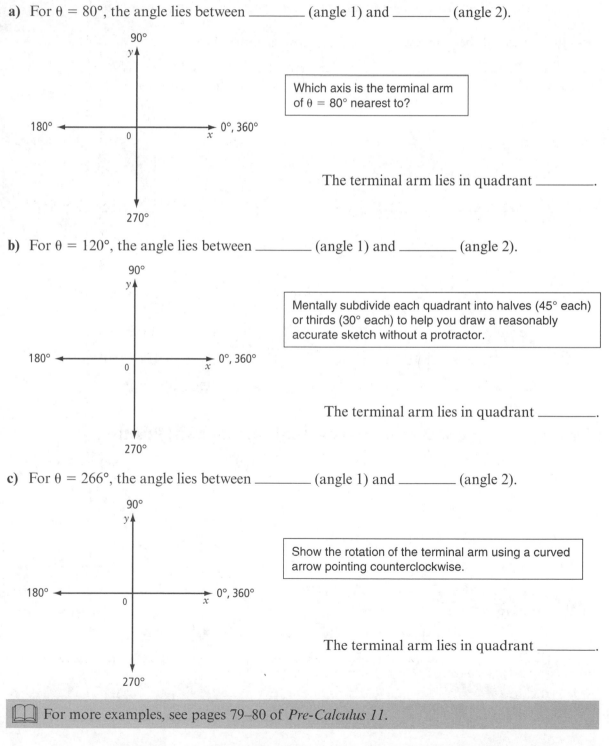

Which axis is the terminal arm of $\theta = 80°$ nearest to?

The terminal arm lies in quadrant _____.

b) For $\theta = 120°$, the angle lies between _____ (angle 1) and _____ (angle 2).

Mentally subdivide each quadrant into halves (45° each) or thirds (30° each) to help you draw a reasonably accurate sketch without a protractor.

The terminal arm lies in quadrant _____.

c) For $\theta = 266°$, the angle lies between _____ (angle 1) and _____ (angle 2).

Show the rotation of the terminal arm using a curved arrow pointing counterclockwise.

The terminal arm lies in quadrant _____.

📖 For more examples, see pages 79–80 of *Pre-Calculus 11*.

Working Example 2: Determine a Reference Angle

Determine the reference angle, θ_R, for each angle θ. Sketch θ in standard position and label the reference angle θ_R.

a) $\theta = 315°$ **b)** $\theta = 201°$

Solution

Sketch the angle θ in standard position.
Next, draw a vertical line from the terminal arm to the nearest part of the x-axis to make the reference triangle.
Label the acute angle between the x-axis and the terminal arm as θ_R.

In quadrants I and IV, the reference angle will be formed with the positive x-axis (0° or 360°).
In quadrants II and III, the reference angle will be formed with the negative x-axis (180°).

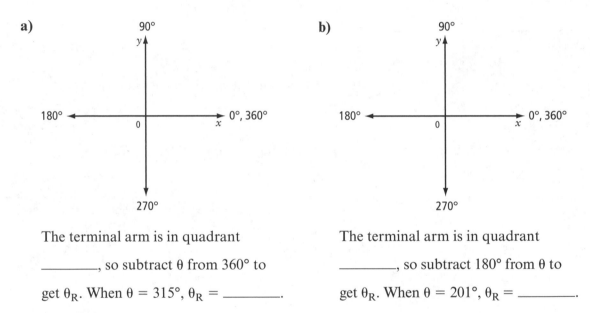

The terminal arm is in quadrant

_____, so subtract θ from 360° to

get θ_R. When $\theta = 315°$, $\theta_R = $ _____.

The terminal arm is in quadrant

_____, so subtract 180° from θ to

get θ_R. When $\theta = 201°$, $\theta_R = $ _____.

Working Example 3: Determine the Angle in Standard Position

Determine the measure of all angles in standard position, $0° < \theta < 360°$, that have a reference angle of 35°.

Solution

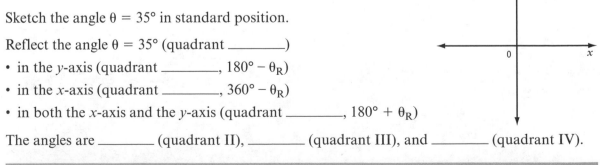

Sketch the angle $\theta = 35°$ in standard position.

Reflect the angle $\theta = 35°$ (quadrant _____)
• in the y-axis (quadrant _____, $180° - \theta_R$)
• in the x-axis (quadrant _____, $360° - \theta_R$)
• in both the x-axis and the y-axis (quadrant _____, $180° + \theta_R$)

The angles are _____ (quadrant II), _____ (quadrant III), and _____ (quadrant IV).

The example on page 81 of *Pre-Calculus 11* asks the same question in a different way.

Working Example 4: Find an Exact Distance

An 8-m boom is used to move a bundle of piping from point A to point B. Determine the exact horizontal displacement of the end of the boom when the operator raises it from 30° to 60°.

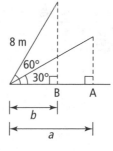

Solution

Use your knowledge of the exact trigonometric ratios in 30°-60°-90° triangles to calculate the exact distances a and b.

For distance a:

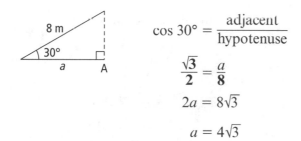

$$\cos 30° = \frac{adjacent}{hypotenuse}$$

$$\frac{\sqrt{3}}{2} = \frac{a}{8}$$

$$2a = 8\sqrt{3}$$

$$a = 4\sqrt{3}$$

Where did the value $\frac{\sqrt{3}}{2}$ come from?

For distance b:

Label the diagram with the given information.

Write the appropriate primary trigonometric ratio to solve for b.

Now solve for b, using exact values.

The total horizontal displacement is $a - b$ or exactly _____ m. (If you use your calculator to evaluate this exact value, you will find an approximate value of 2.93 m).

📖 A different situation using exact values can be found on page 82 of *Pre-Calculus 11*.

Check Your Understanding

Practise

1. Sketch each angle in standard position. State the quadrant in which the terminal arm lies.

a) 100°

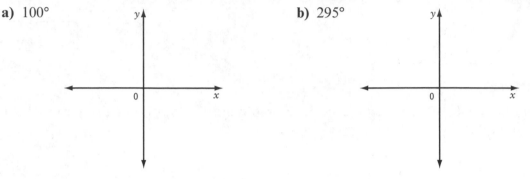

The terminal arm lies in

quadrant _____.

b) 295°

The terminal arm lies in quadrant

_____.

c) 25°

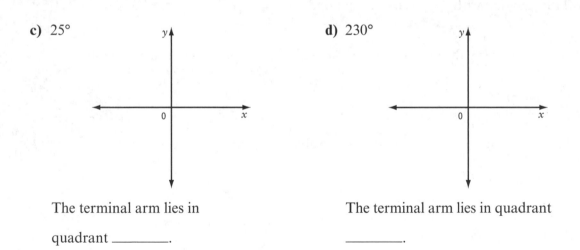

The terminal arm lies in

quadrant _____.

d) 230°

The terminal arm lies in quadrant

_____.

2. Determine the reference angle, θ_R, for each angle θ. Sketch θ in standard position and label the reference angle θ_R.

a) $\theta = 355°$　　　　$\theta_R = $ _____

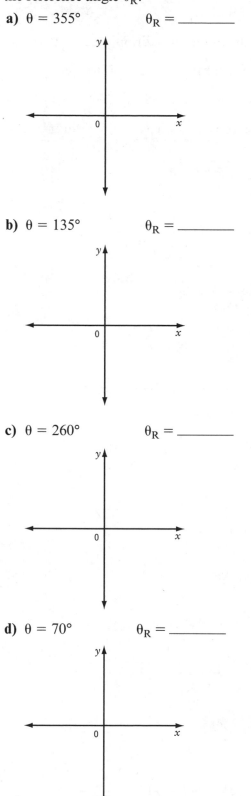

b) $\theta = 135°$　　　　$\theta_R = $ _____

c) $\theta = 260°$　　　　$\theta_R = $ _____

d) $\theta = 70°$　　　　$\theta_R = $ _____

3. Determine the measures of the three other angles in standard position, $0° < \theta < 360°$, that have the given reference angle.

a) 70°

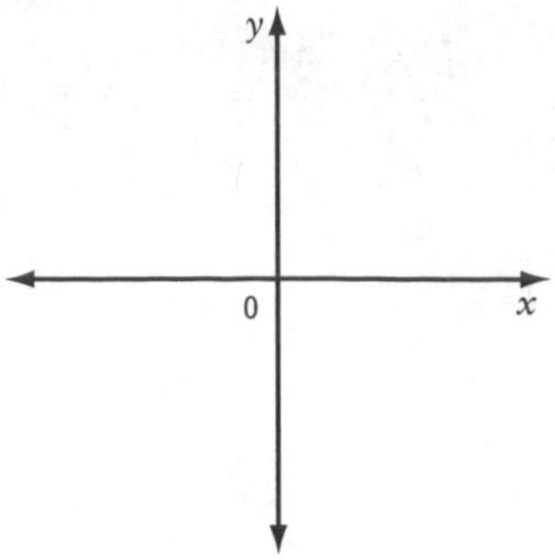

Reflect the angle $\theta = 70°$ (quadrant _____)

- in the y-axis (quadrant _____, $180° - \theta_R$)

- in the x-axis (quadrant _____, $360° - \theta_R$)

- in both the x-axis and the y-axis (quadrant _____, $180° + \theta_R$)

The angles are _____ (quadrant II), _____ (quadrant III), and _____ (quadrant IV).

b) 40°

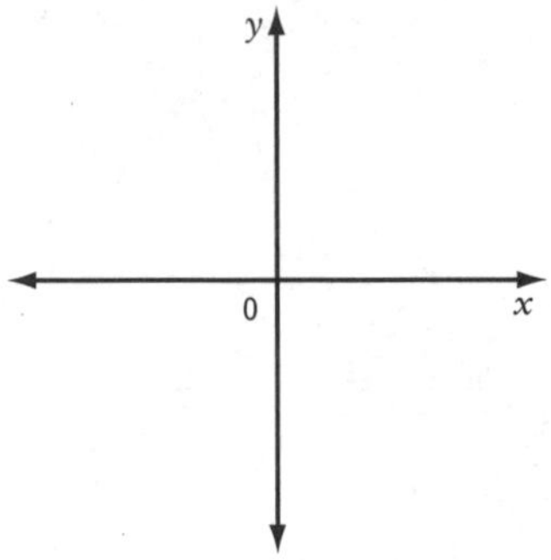

The angles are _____.

c) 50°

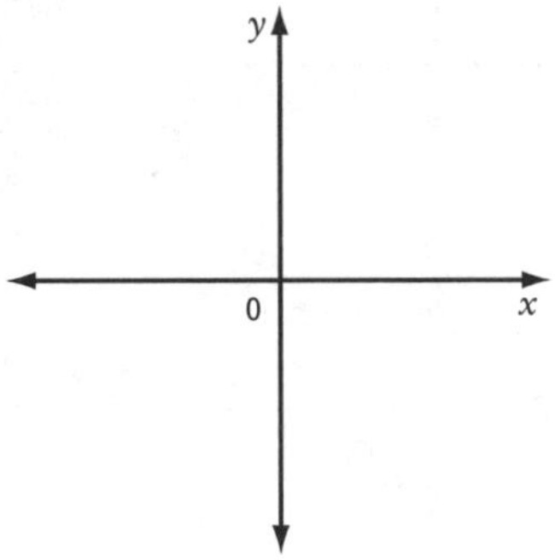

The angles are _____.

d) 89°

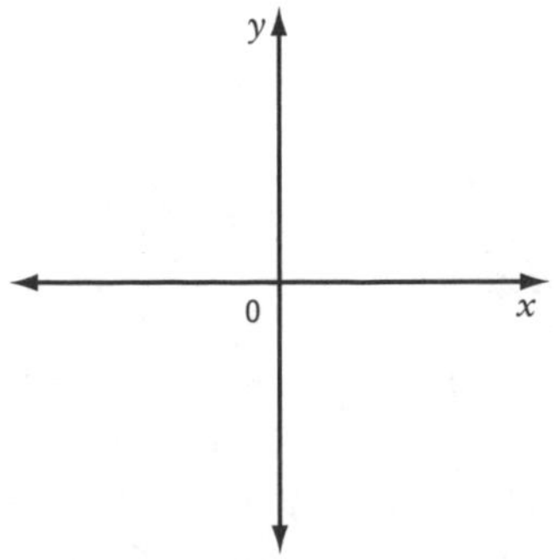

The angles are _____.

e) 27°

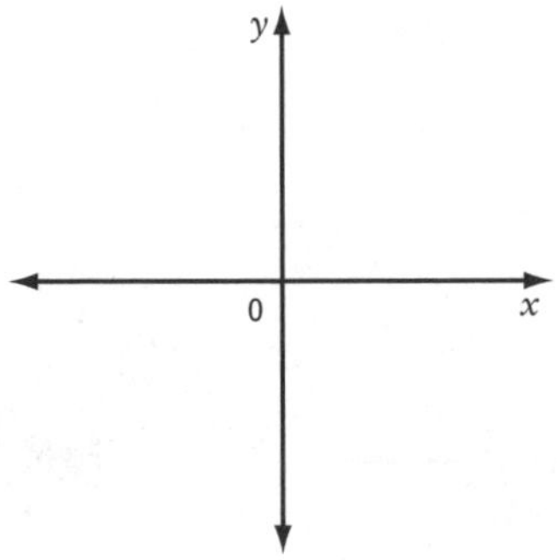

The angles are _____.

4. Determine the measure of each angle θ in standard position, $0° \leq \theta < 360°$, given its reference angle and the quadrant in which the terminal arm lies.

Hint: This is like the previous question, but working backward.

a) $\theta_R = 40°$, in quadrant II

b) $\theta_R = 37°$, in quadrant IV

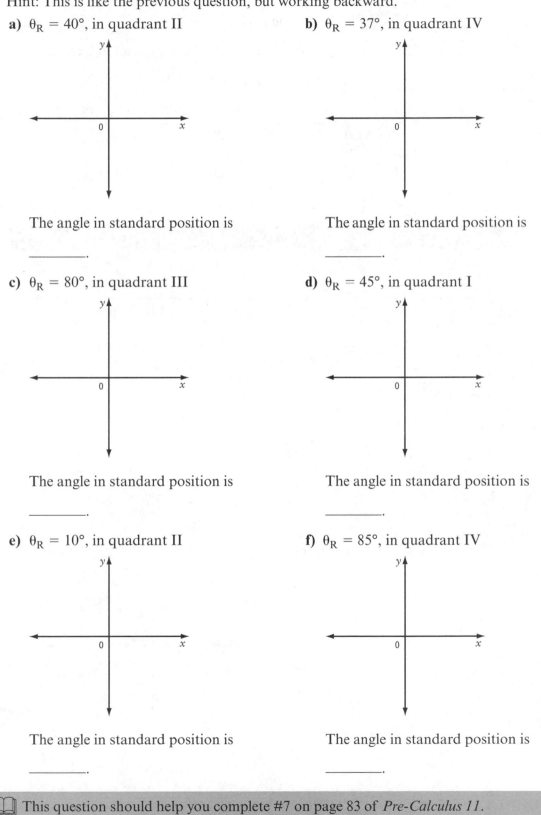

The angle in standard position is

_____.

The angle in standard position is

_____.

c) $\theta_R = 80°$, in quadrant III

d) $\theta_R = 45°$, in quadrant I

The angle in standard position is

_____.

The angle in standard position is

_____.

e) $\theta_R = 10°$, in quadrant II

f) $\theta_R = 85°$, in quadrant IV

The angle in standard position is

_____.

The angle in standard position is

_____.

📖 This question should help you complete #7 on page 83 of *Pre-Calculus 11*.

5. Label the sides of the right triangles shown with their exact lengths. The shortest side of each triangle should be 1 unit. Complete the table with the exact values of sine, cosine, and tangent for each angle.

The phrases "exact value" and "exact length" are clues that you should be thinking in terms of special triangles and square roots, rather than using your calculator.

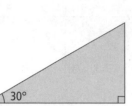 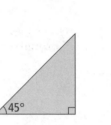 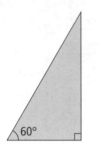

	$\theta = 30°$	$\theta = 45°$	$\theta = 60°$
sin θ			
cos θ			
tan θ			

6. Find the exact values of the missing side lengths.

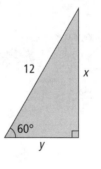

Write the primary trigonometric ratio you would use to solve for x.

Now solve for x, using exact values:

To find y, you could use the values y and 12 with the trigonometric ratio _____.

Or, you could use the values of x and y with the trigonometric ratio _____.

Or, you could use the Pythagorean Theorem.

Solve for y:

Apply

7. Find the exact area of the triangle shown.

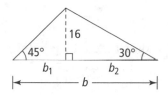

Formula for area of a triangle: $A = \frac{1}{2}bh$

From the diagram, $h =$ _____.

Calculate b. One strategy is to divide the big triangle into two parts, each consisting of a right triangle. Which primary trigonometric ratio (sine, cosine, tangent) is used?

In the 45°-45°-90° triangle, solve for b_1:   In the 30°-60°-90° triangle, solve for b_2:

The total base of the triangle is $b = b_1 + b_2$ or _____.

Now, find the area.

$A = \frac{1}{2}bh$

$A =$

The exact area of the triangle is _____ units.

8. Find the exact area of an equilateral triangle with a height of 9 units.

Diagram:

| What information is known? |
| What is unknown? |
| Which primary trigonometric ratio will you use? |

The total base of the triangle is:

The area of the triangle is:

9. A grandfather clock has a pendulum that is 1.40 m long and swings ±30° from centre. What are the minimum inner dimensions of the cabinet inside the clock that will accommodate the pendulum? Give exact values.

Label the diagram to model the information.

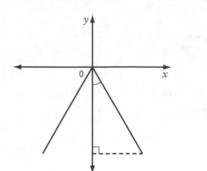

Let *a* represent the horizontal distance the pendulum travels from the centre to the end of its swing. Add this information to your diagram.

Write the primary trigonometric ratio you would use to solve for *a*:

Solve for *a*:

The total horizontal distance the pendulum travels is _____ m.

The pendulum is _____ m long, so the vertical dimension must be at least _____ m.

The cabinet must be at least _____ m wide and _____ m high.

📖 This question is similar to Example 4 on page 82 of *Pre-Calculus 11*.

10. An 8-m boom is used to move a bundle of piping from point A to point B. Determine the exact vertical displacement of the end of the boom when the operator raises it from 30° to 60°.

Hint: Use two triangles.

Connect

11. Complete the table for angles in standard position, $0° < \theta < 360°$.

Quadrant	Value of Angle θ	How to Calculate θ_R	Sketch
I	$0° < \theta < 90°$		
II	_____ $< \theta <$ _____		
	_____ $< \theta <$ _____		
	_____ $< \theta <$ _____	$\theta_R = 360° - \theta$	

KEY IDEAS

- Recall that you measure an angle θ in a counterclockwise direction from the initial arm (on the positive x-axis) to the terminal arm. The quadrants of the Cartesian plane are labelled with Roman numerals, also in a counterclockwise direction.

- If the terminal arm lies on an axis, the angle is called a quadrantal angle (it separates the quadrants).
  For example, 0°, 90°, 180°, 270°, and 360°.

- If point P(x, y) lies on the terminal arm of an angle θ in standard position, the primary trigonometric ratios are

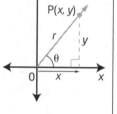

$$\sin \theta = \frac{y}{r} \qquad \cos \theta = \frac{x}{r} \qquad \tan \theta = \frac{y}{x}$$

  where the distance from point P(x, y) to the origin (0, 0) is represented by the variable r. Then, by the Pythagorean Theorem,

$$r = \sqrt{x^2 + y^2}$$

- Since r is a distance, it is always a positive number.

- $\sin \theta$ is positive in quadrants I and II.
  $\sin \theta = 0$ on the x-axis and ± 1 on the y-axis.

- $\cos \theta$ is positive in quadrants I and IV.
  $\cos \theta = \pm 1$ on the x-axis and 0 on the y-axis.

- $\tan \theta$ is positive in quadrants I and III.
  $\tan \theta = 0$ on the x-axis and is undefined on the y-axis.

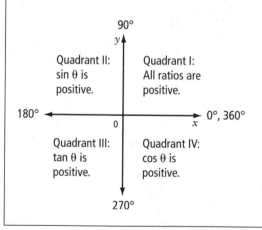

Working Example 1: Write Trigonometric Ratios for Angles in Any Quadrant

The point P(12, −9) lies on the terminal arm of an angle θ in standard position. Determine the exact trigonometric ratios for sin θ, cos θ, and tan θ.

Solution

Sketch the point P(12, −9) on the Cartesian plane.
Draw a line segment from the origin to P to represent the terminal arm of the angle.
Label the angle θ and the reference angle θ_R.

> To draw the right triangle containing θ_R, make a vertical line from P to the nearest part of the x-axis.

From the coordinates of point P, you know that $x =$ _____ and $y =$ _____.

Calculate r using the Pythagorean Theorem.

$$r = \sqrt{x^2 + y^2}$$

Substitute the values of x, y, and r into the formulas to calculate the three ratios.

> The wording "exact trigonometric ratios" means to leave your answer as a fraction in lowest terms.

$$\sin \theta = \frac{y}{r} \qquad \cos \theta = \frac{x}{r} \qquad \tan \theta = \frac{y}{x}$$

$\sin \theta =$ _____ $\cos \theta =$ _____ $\tan \theta =$ _____

📖 For another example, see page 91 of *Pre-Calculus 11*.

Working Example 2: Determine the Exact Value of Trigonometric Ratios

Determine the exact values of the sine, cosine, and tangent ratios for $\theta = 120°$.

Solution

Sketch the angle in standard position. Draw the reference angle, θ_R, and determine its measure.

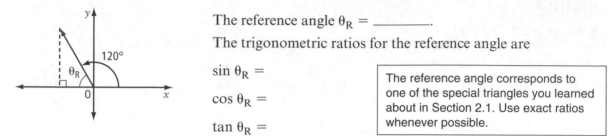

The reference angle $\theta_R =$ _____.

The trigonometric ratios for the reference angle are

$\sin \theta_R =$

$\cos \theta_R =$

$\tan \theta_R =$

> The reference angle corresponds to one of the special triangles you learned about in Section 2.1. Use exact ratios whenever possible.

In quadrant II, x is negative and y is positive (r is always positive). Determine the sign of each ratio.

$\sin \theta = \dfrac{y}{r}$ $\qquad$ $\cos \theta = \dfrac{x}{r}$ $\qquad$ $\tan \theta = \dfrac{y}{x}$

$\sin \theta = \dfrac{+}{+}$ $\qquad$ $\cos \theta = \dfrac{-}{+}$ $\qquad$ $\tan \theta = \dfrac{\boxed{}}{\boxed{}}$

$\sin \theta = +$ $\qquad$ $\cos \theta = -$ $\qquad$ $\tan \theta = \boxed{}$

Therefore, _____ is positive, and $\cos \theta$ and $\tan \theta$ are negative for angles in quadrant II.

$\sin 120° = +\sin 60°$ $\qquad$ $\cos 120° = -\cos 60°$ $\qquad$ $\tan 120° =$ _____

$\sin 120° =$ _____ $\qquad$ $\cos 120° =$ _____ $\qquad$ $\tan 120° =$ _____

Working Example 3: Determine Trigonometric Ratios

Suppose θ is an angle in standard position with terminal arm in quadrant IV and $\cos \theta = \dfrac{\sqrt{33}}{7}$. Determine the exact values of the other two trigonometric ratios.

Solution

Since $\cos \theta = \dfrac{x}{r}$, $x =$ _____ and $r =$ _____.

> In quadrant IV, is x positive or negative?

Solve for y using the Pythagorean Theorem.

$x^2 + y^2 = r^2$

> In quadrant IV, is y positive or negative? Select the positive or negative root accordingly.

The other two trigonometric ratios are $\sin \theta = \dfrac{y}{r} = \dfrac{\boxed{}}{\boxed{}}$ and $\tan \theta = \dfrac{y}{x} = \dfrac{\boxed{}}{\boxed{}}$.

Working Example 4: Solve for an Angle Given Its Sine, Cosine, or Tangent Value

Solve for θ.

a) $\tan \theta = -0.9004$, $0° \leq \theta < 360°$

b) $\cos \theta = -\dfrac{1}{\sqrt{2}}$, $0° \leq \theta < 360°$

Solution

a) Step 1: Determine which quadrants the solutions will be in by looking at the sign (+ or −) of the given ratio.

$\tan \theta$ is positive in quadrants _____ and _____.

$\tan \theta$ is negative in quadrants _____ and _____.

So, the solutions are in quadrants _____ and _____.

Step 2: Solve for the reference angle.

$\tan \theta_R = +0.9004$

> The reference angle is in quadrant I, where all three trigonometric ratios are positive.

$\theta_R = \tan^{-1}(0.9004)$

$\theta_R \approx$ _____ to the nearest tenth of a degree

Step 3: Sketch the reference angle in the appropriate quadrants. Use the diagram to determine the measures of the two related angles in standard position.

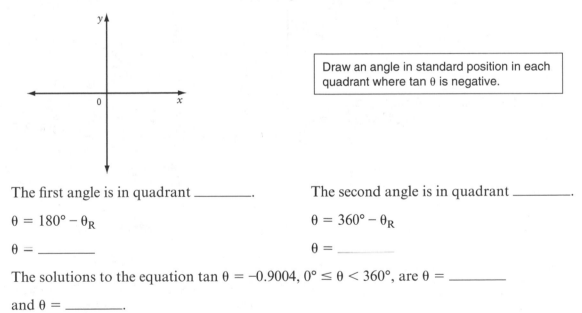

> Draw an angle in standard position in each quadrant where $\tan \theta$ is negative.

The first angle is in quadrant _____.

$\theta = 180° - \theta_R$

$\theta =$ _____

The second angle is in quadrant _____.

$\theta = 360° - \theta_R$

$\theta =$ _____

The solutions to the equation $\tan \theta = -0.9004$, $0° \leq \theta < 360°$, are $\theta =$ _____ and $\theta =$ _____.

b) $\cos \theta = -\dfrac{1}{\sqrt{2}}$, $0° \leq \theta < 360°$

Step 1: Determine which quadrants the solutions will be in by looking at the sign ($+$ or $-$) of the given ratio.

$\cos \theta$ is positive in quadrants _____ and _____.

$\cos \theta$ is negative in quadrants _____ and _____.

So, the solutions are in quadrants _____ and _____.

Step 2: Solve for the reference angle.

$\cos \theta_R = +\dfrac{1}{\sqrt{2}}$

$\qquad \theta_R = \cos^{-1}\left(\dfrac{1}{\sqrt{2}}\right)$

$\qquad \theta_R = $ _____

> The values 1 and $\sqrt{2}$ correspond to the 45°-45°-90° special triangle. You can find this answer without using a calculator.

Step 3: Sketch the reference angle in the appropriate quadrants. Use the diagram to determine the measure of the related angle in standard position.

The first angle is in quadrant _____.

$\theta = 180° - \theta_R$

$\theta = $ _____

The second angle is in quadrant _____.

$\theta = 180° + \theta_R$

$\theta = $ _____

The solutions to the equation $\cos \theta = -\dfrac{1}{\sqrt{2}}$, $0° \leq \theta < 360°$, are $\theta = $ _____ and $\theta = $ _____.

📖 For more examples, see pages 94–95 of *Pre-Calculus 11*.

Check Your Understanding

Practise

1. The coordinates of a point P on the terminal arm of an angle θ are shown.

   a) Determine the values of x, y, and r.

   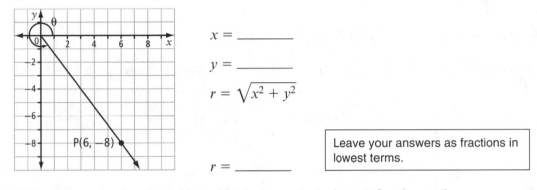

   $x =$ _____

   $y =$ _____

   $r = \sqrt{x^2 + y^2}$

   Leave your answers as fractions in lowest terms.

   $r =$ _____

   b) Write the exact trigonometric ratios $\sin \theta$, $\cos \theta$, and $\tan \theta$ for the angle.

   $\sin \theta = \dfrac{y}{r}$ $\cos \theta = \dfrac{x}{r}$ $\tan \theta = \dfrac{y}{x}$

   $\sin \theta =$ _____ $\cos \theta =$ _____ $\tan \theta =$ _____

2. Sketch an angle θ in standard position so that the terminal arm passes through P(−8, −15). Then, find the exact values of $\sin \theta$, $\cos \theta$, and $\tan \theta$ for the angle.

   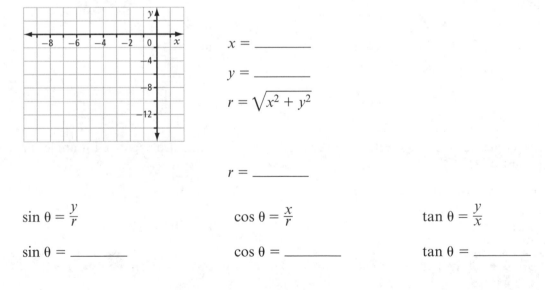

   $x =$ _____

   $y =$ _____

   $r = \sqrt{x^2 + y^2}$

   $r =$ _____

   $\sin \theta = \dfrac{y}{r}$ $\cos \theta = \dfrac{x}{r}$ $\tan \theta = \dfrac{y}{x}$

   $\sin \theta =$ _____ $\cos \theta =$ _____ $\tan \theta =$ _____

3. Determine the exact values of sin θ, cos θ, and tan θ if the terminal arm of an angle in standard position passes through the point P(1, 0).

x = _____   y = _____   r = _____

sin θ = _____   cos θ = _____   tan θ = _____

4. Determine the exact values of the sine, cosine, and tangent ratios for each angle.

a)

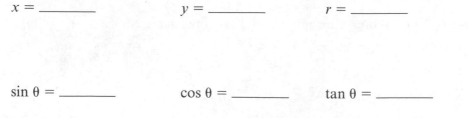

Draw in the special triangle that represents the reference angle.

The reference angle θ_R = _____.

The trigonometric ratios for the reference angle are

sin θ_R =   cos θ_R =   tan θ_R =

In quadrant _____, x and y are both negative (r is always positive). Determine the sign of each ratio.

$\sin \theta = \frac{y}{r}$ $\cos \theta = \frac{x}{r}$ $\tan \theta = \frac{y}{x}$

$\sin \theta = \frac{-}{+}$ $\cos \theta = \dfrac{\Box}{\Box}$ $\tan \theta = \dfrac{\Box}{\Box}$

$\sin \theta = -$ $\cos \theta = \Box$ $\tan \theta = \Box$

Therefore, _____ is positive, and _____ and _____ are negative for angles in quadrant III.

sin 210° = −sin 30°   cos 210° = _____   tan 210° = _____

sin 210° = _____   cos 210° = _____   tan 210° = _____

📖 Exact values for the trigonometric ratios in special right triangles can be found on page 79 of *Pre-Calculus 11*.

b)

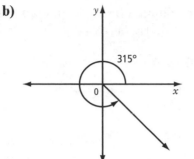

The reference angle $\theta_R =$ _____.

The trigonometric ratios for the reference angle are

$\sin \theta_R =$ _____ $\cos \theta_R =$ _____ $\tan \theta_R =$ _____

Determine the sign of each ratio in quadrant IV.

$\sin \theta = \dfrac{y}{r}$ $\cos \theta = \dfrac{x}{r}$ $\tan \theta = \dfrac{y}{x}$

$\sin \theta = -$ $\cos \theta = \boxed{}$ $\tan \theta = \boxed{}$

Therefore, _____ is positive, and _____ and _____ are negative for angles in quadrant IV.

$\sin 315° = -\sin \theta_R$ $\cos 315° =$ _____ $\tan 315° =$ _____

$\sin 315° = -\sin$ _____

$\sin 315° =$ _____ $\cos 315° =$ _____ $\tan 315° =$ _____

c)

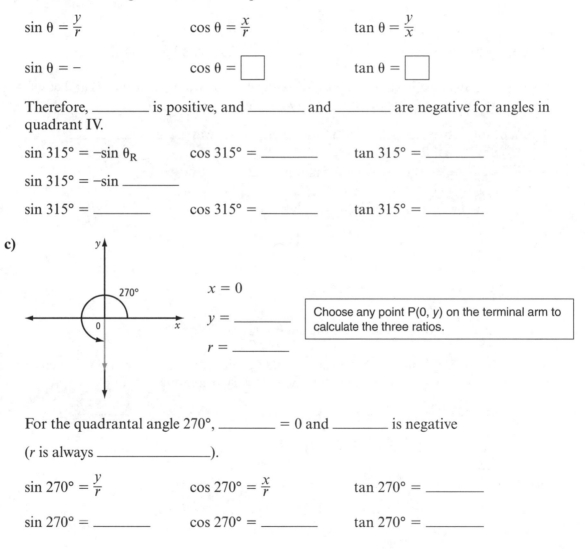

$x = 0$

$y =$ _____

$r =$ _____

Choose any point P(0, y) on the terminal arm to calculate the three ratios.

For the quadrantal angle 270°, _____ = 0 and _____ is negative

(r is always _____).

$\sin 270° = \dfrac{y}{r}$ $\cos 270° = \dfrac{x}{r}$ $\tan 270° =$ _____

$\sin 270° =$ _____ $\cos 270° =$ _____ $\tan 270° =$ _____

5. Suppose θ is an angle in standard position with terminal arm in quadrant III and $\tan \theta = \frac{6}{5}$. Determine the exact values of the other two primary trigonometric ratios.

In quadrant III, x is _____ and y is _____ (r is always positive).

Since $\tan \theta = \frac{y}{x}$, the known information is $x =$ _____ and $y =$ _____.

Solve for the unknown value using the Pythagorean Theorem.

$r = \sqrt{x^2 + y^2}$

The other two trigonometric ratios are $\sin \theta =$ _____ and $\cos \theta =$ _____.

6. Suppose θ is an angle in standard position with terminal arm in quadrant II and $\cos \theta = -\frac{7}{12}$. Determine the exact values of the other two primary trigonometric ratios.

In quadrant II, x is _____ and y is _____ (r is always _____).

Since $\cos \theta = \dfrac{\boxed{}}{\boxed{}}$, the known information is _____ and _____.

Solve for the unknown value using the Pythagorean Theorem.

The other two trigonometric ratios are $\sin \theta =$ _____ and $\tan \theta =$ _____.

7. Suppose θ is an angle in standard position with terminal arm in quadrant IV and $\cos \theta = \frac{40}{41}$. Determine the exact values of the other two primary trigonometric ratios.

In quadrant IV, x is _____ and y is _____ (r is always _____).

Since $\cos \theta = \dfrac{\boxed{}}{\boxed{}}$, the known information is _____ and _____.

Solve for the unknown value using the Pythagorean Theorem.

The other two trigonometric ratios are $\sin \theta =$ _____ and $\tan \theta =$ _____.

📖 These questions should help you complete #8 on page 96 of *Pre-Calculus 11*.

Apply

8. Solve for θ. Round your answer to the nearest degree.

   a) $\cos \theta = 0.8829$, $0° \leq \theta < 360°$

   $\cos \theta$ is positive in quadrants _____ and _____.

   The reference angle is $\theta_R = \cos^{-1}(0.8829)$ or _____.

   Sketch the reference angle in the appropriate quadrants.

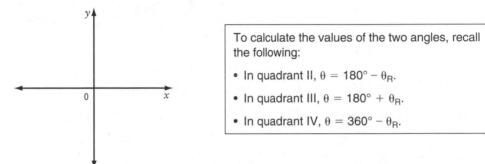

   To calculate the values of the two angles, recall the following:

   - In quadrant II, $\theta = 180° - \theta_R$.
   - In quadrant III, $\theta = 180° + \theta_R$.
   - In quadrant IV, $\theta = 360° - \theta_R$.

   The solutions to the equation $\cos \theta = 0.8829$, $0° \leq \theta < 360°$, are $\theta =$ _____ and

   $\theta =$ _____.

   b) $\tan \theta = -1.9626$, $0° \leq \theta < 360°$

   $\tan \theta$ is negative in quadrants _____ and _____.

   The reference angle is $\theta_R = \tan^{-1}(1.9626)$

   or _____.

   The reference angle is in quadrant I, where sine, cosine, and tangent are all positive.

   Sketch the reference angle in the appropriate quadrants. Then, calculate the values of the two angles.

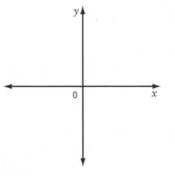

   The solutions to the equation $\tan \theta = -1.9626$, $0° \leq \theta < 360°$, are $\theta =$ _____

   and $\theta =$ _____.

📖 Question 9 on page 97 of *Pre-Calculus 11* is similar but involves special triangles.

9. Point P(−4, −5) is on the terminal arm of an angle θ in standard position.

   a) Sketch the angle.

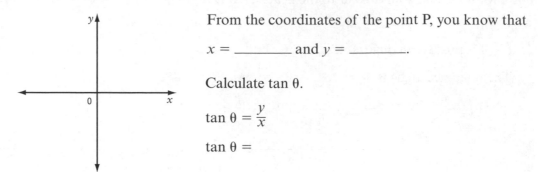

   From the coordinates of the point P, you know that

   $x =$ _____ and $y =$ _____.

   Calculate tan θ.

   $\tan \theta = \dfrac{y}{x}$

   $\tan \theta =$

   b) What is the measure of the reference angle, to the nearest degree?

   The reference angle is $\theta_R = \tan^{-1}($_____$)$ or _____.

   c) What is the measure of θ, to the nearest degree?

10. Point P(12, −3) is on the terminal arm of an angle θ in standard position.

   a) Sketch the angle.

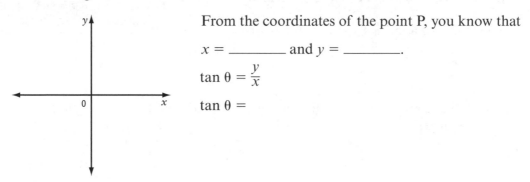

   From the coordinates of the point P, you know that

   $x =$ _____ and $y =$ _____.

   $\tan \theta = \dfrac{y}{x}$

   $\tan \theta =$

   b) What is the measure of the reference angle, to the nearest degree?

   The reference angle is $\theta_R = \tan^{-1}($_____$)$ or _____.

   c) What is the measure of θ, to the nearest degree?

📖 Question 27 on page 99 of *Pre-Calculus 11* asks you to explain the process used above.

Connect

11. Complete the table, using the following symbols where appropriate.

+ (positive)   − (negative)   0   1   −1   undefined

Trigonometric Ratio	$\sin \theta = \frac{y}{r}$	$\cos \theta = \frac{x}{r}$	$\tan \theta = \frac{y}{x}$
0°	0		
Quadrant I	+		
90°	1		undefined
Quadrant II			
180°			
Quadrant III			
270°			
Quadrant IV			
360°	0		

Chapter 2 Skills Organizer A

Complete the table for each point P on the terminal arm of an angle θ in standard position.

	Quadrant	Sketch	sin θ	cos θ	tan θ
P(x, y)	I				
P(0, 1)	N/A		$\sin \theta = 1$		
P(−x, y)			$\sin \theta = \dfrac{y}{r}$, $\sin \theta > 0$	$\cos \theta = \dfrac{-x}{r}$, $\cos \theta < 0$	$\tan \theta = \dfrac{y}{-x}$, $\tan \theta < 0$
P(−1, 0)	N/A				
P(−x, −y)					
P(0, −1)			$\sin \theta = -1$		
P(x, −y)					
P(1, 0)					

« **KEY IDEAS** »

- A triangle that does not contain a right angle is an oblique triangle. You can use the sine law to solve problems involving oblique triangles.

- To find a side length using the sine law, you must know the measure of the angle opposite that side, plus one other angle–opposite side pair (ASA).

$$\frac{a}{\sin A} = \frac{b}{\sin B} = \frac{c}{\sin C}$$

- To find an angle using the sine law, you must know the length of the side opposite that angle, plus one other angle–opposite side pair (SSA). Note that there are two solutions for any given $\sin \theta$, $0° \leq \theta < 180°$. One solution is an acute angle (in quadrant I), and the other solution is the obtuse angle (in quadrant II) with the same θ_R. This is known as the ambiguous case of the sine law.

- For an acute $\angle A$ and $a < b$, calculate the altitude $h = b \sin A$ to determine if there are 0, 1, or 2 triangles.

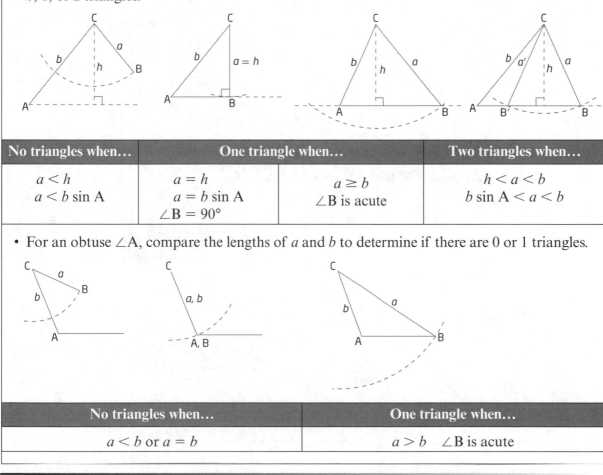

No triangles when...	One triangle when...		Two triangles when...
$a < h$ $a < b \sin A$	$a = h$ $a = b \sin A$ $\angle B = 90°$	$a \geq b$ $\angle B$ is acute	$h < a < b$ $b \sin A < a < b$

- For an obtuse $\angle A$, compare the lengths of a and b to determine if there are 0 or 1 triangles.

No triangles when...	One triangle when...
$a < b$ or $a = b$	$a > b$ $\quad \angle B$ is acute

Working Example 1: Determine an Unknown Side Length

Determine the length of side b, to the nearest millimetre.

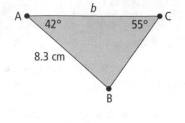

Solution

This is an oblique triangle, so you can use the sine law.
To solve for side b, you need to know its opposite
angle, $\angle B$.

The angles in a triangle sum to _____°, so

$\angle B = 180° - (42° + 55°)$

$\angle B = $ _____

You also know one other angle–opposite side pair: $\angle C = $ _____ and side $c = $ _____ cm.
According to the sine law,

$$\frac{b}{\sin B} \doteq \frac{c}{\sin C}$$

$$\frac{b}{\sin \boxed{}} = \frac{\textbf{8.3}}{\sin \textbf{55°}}$$

$$b = \sin \boxed{} \left(\frac{8.3}{\sin 55°}\right)$$

$$b = \underline{}\ldots$$

Side b is _____ cm.

> Rearrange the formula before you enter the numbers into your calculator, and complete the calculations all in one step.

> Is your calculator in "degree" mode?

> "To the nearest millimetre" means round your answer to the nearest 0.1 cm.

Working Example 2: Determine an Unknown Angle

Determine the measure of $\angle B$, to the nearest degree.

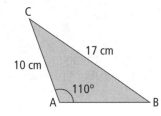

Solution

Use the sine law.

$$\frac{\sin A}{a} = \frac{\sin B}{b}$$

$$\frac{\sin \boxed{}°}{\textbf{17}} = \frac{\sin B}{\textbf{10}}$$

$$10\left(\frac{\sin \boxed{}°}{17}\right) = \sin B$$

$$\sin^{-1}\left(\frac{10 \sin \boxed{}°}{17}\right) = \angle B$$

$$\angle B = \underline{}$$

> Since $\angle A$ is obtuse and $a > b$, there is one triangle with an acute $\angle B$.

> Do the calculations all in one step on your calculator. Do not round off until the final answer.

Working Example 3: Determine the Number of Triangles

Determine the number of triangles that will satisfy the following conditions.

a) In $\triangle ABC$, $\angle A = 60°$, $a = 14$ units, and $b = 15$ units.

b) In $\triangle JKL$, $\angle J = 42°$, $j = 6.9$ cm, and $k = 10.3$ cm.

Solution

a) Sketch a possible diagram.

Hint: Place the known angle at the lower left corner of your diagram and the angle to be calculated at the lower right. Then, your altitude, h, will always be a vertical line.

In the diagram, label sides a (opposite $\angle A$) and b (opposite $\angle B$) with their lengths.

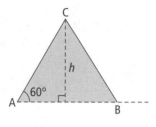

Since $\angle A$ is acute and $a < b$, calculate the altitude.

$h = b \sin A$

$h =$

> Make your sketch as close to scale as possible, especially in the measure of $\angle A$.

In order from smallest to largest, _____ (h) < _____ (a) < _____ (b).

Therefore, two triangles exist that satisfy the given conditions: one with acute $\angle B$ and one with obtuse $\angle B$. Sketch the two possible triangles.

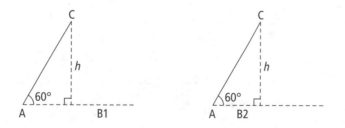

b) Sketch a possible diagram. Place the known $\angle J$ at the lower left corner of your diagram.

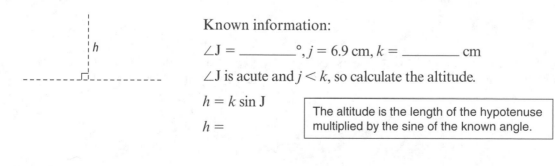

Known information:

$\angle J =$ _____°, $j = 6.9$ cm, $k =$ _____ cm

$\angle J$ is acute and $j < k$, so calculate the altitude.

$h = k \sin J$

$h =$

> The altitude is the length of the hypotenuse multiplied by the sine of the known angle.

Since $h = j$, there is/are _____ triangle(s). $\angle K$ is a right angle.
(zero, one, or *two)*

Working Example 4: Use the Sine Law in an Ambiguous Case

In $\triangle ABC$, $a = 3$, $b = 6$, and $\angle A = 70°$. Determine the measure of $\angle B$, to the nearest degree.

Solution

Sketch a possible diagram. Place the known $\angle A$ at the lower left corner of your diagram.

Known information:

$\angle A = \underline{\hspace{2cm}}°$, $a = \underline{\hspace{2cm}}$, $b = \underline{\hspace{2cm}}$

$\angle A$ is acute and $a < b$, so calculate the altitude.

$h = b \sin A$

$h = $

Since $a < h$, there is/are $\underline{\hspace{3cm}}$ triangle(s). You cannot calculate angle $\angle B$.
(*zero, one, or two*)

Working Example 5: Solve a Triangle

In $\triangle ABC$, $a = 4.8$ cm, $b = 6.4$ cm, and $\angle A = 18°$. Solve the triangle. Round angles to the nearest degree and sides to the nearest tenth of a centimetre.

Solution

Sketch a possible diagram. Place the known $\angle A$ at the lower left corner of your diagram.

Known information:

$\angle A = \underline{\hspace{2cm}}°$, $a = \underline{\hspace{2cm}}$ cm, $b = \underline{\hspace{2cm}}$ cm

$\angle A$ is acute and $a < b$, so calculate the altitude.

$h = b \sin A$

$h = $

Since $h < a < b$, there is/are $\underline{\hspace{3cm}}$ triangle(s).
(*zero, one, or two*)

Solving a triangle means to find the measures of all angles and all sides. Since there are two triangles that match the situation given, you will complete two full sets of calculations.

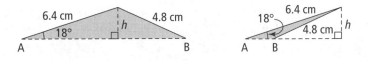

Triangle 1: $\angle B$ is acute

Calculate $\angle B$ using the sine law:

$$\frac{\sin A}{a} = \frac{\sin B}{b}$$

$$\frac{\sin 18°}{4.8} = \frac{\sin B}{6.4}$$

$$6.4\left(\frac{\sin 18°}{4.8}\right) = \sin B$$

$$\angle B = \sin^{-1}\left(\frac{6.4 \sin 18°}{4.8}\right)$$

$$\angle B = \underline{\hspace{2cm}}°$$

Find $\angle C$:

$\angle C = 180° - (18° + 24°)$

$\angle C = \underline{\hspace{2cm}}°$

Calculate side c using the sine law:

$$\frac{a}{\sin A} = \frac{c}{\sin C}$$

$$\frac{4.8}{\sin 18°} = \frac{c}{\sin 138°}$$

$$c = \sin 138°\left(\frac{4.8}{\sin 18°}\right)$$

$$c = \underline{\hspace{2cm}}$$

Triangle 2: $\angle B$ is obtuse

To calculate $\angle B$, find the angle in quadrant II with $\theta_R = 24°$:

$$\angle B = 180° - 24°$$

$$\angle B = \underline{\hspace{2cm}}°$$

Find $\angle C$:

Calculate side c using the sine law:

$$c = \underline{\hspace{2cm}}$$

The two possible triangles are as follows:

- acute $\triangle ABC$: $\angle A = \underline{\hspace{1.5cm}}°$, $\angle B = \underline{\hspace{1.5cm}}°$, $\angle C = \underline{\hspace{1.5cm}}°$, $a = \underline{\hspace{1.5cm}}$ cm,

  $b = \underline{\hspace{1.5cm}}$ cm, and $c = \underline{\hspace{1.5cm}}$ cm

- obtuse $\triangle ABC$: $\angle A = \underline{\hspace{1.5cm}}°$, $\angle B = \underline{\hspace{1.5cm}}°$, $\angle C = \underline{\hspace{1.5cm}}°$, $a = \underline{\hspace{1.5cm}}$ cm,

  $b = \underline{\hspace{1.5cm}}$ cm, and $c = \underline{\hspace{1.5cm}}$ cm

See a similar example on page 106–107 of *Pre-Calculus 11*.

Check Your Understanding

Practise

1. Solve for the unknown side (to one decimal place) or angle (to the nearest degree) in each.

a) $\dfrac{a}{\sin 48°} = \dfrac{20}{\sin 75°}$

$\qquad a = \sin 48° \left(\dfrac{20}{\sin 75°} \right)$

$\qquad a =$

b) $\dfrac{x}{\sin 125°} = \dfrac{15}{\sin 30°}$

c) $\dfrac{\sin B}{10} = \dfrac{\sin 45°}{16}$

$\qquad \sin B = 10 \left(\dfrac{\sin 45°}{16} \right)$

$\qquad \angle B = \sin^{-1} \left(\boxed{} \right)$

$\qquad \angle B =$

d) $\dfrac{\sin \theta}{5} = \dfrac{\sin 110°}{25}$

2. Determine the length of side x, to one decimal place, in each $\triangle$XYZ.

a)

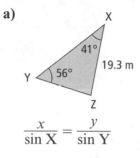

$$\frac{x}{\sin X} = \frac{y}{\sin Y}$$

The length of side x is _____ m.

b)

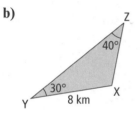

Find $\angle$X. Then, set up the sine law with pairs of angles and their opposite sides, and then solve.

The length of side x is _____ km.

3. Determine the measure of ∠Q, to the nearest degree, in each △PQR.

a)

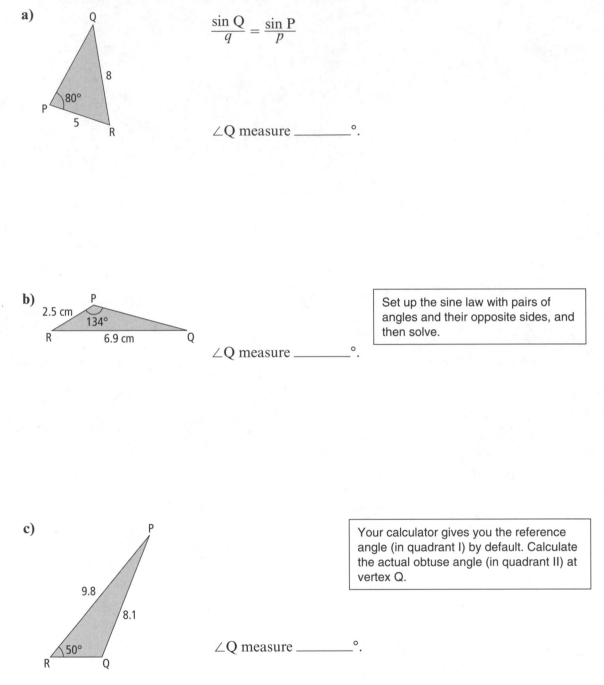

$$\frac{\sin Q}{q} = \frac{\sin P}{p}$$

∠Q measure _____°.

b)

Set up the sine law with pairs of angles and their opposite sides, and then solve.

∠Q measure _____°.

c)

Your calculator gives you the reference angle (in quadrant I) by default. Calculate the actual obtuse angle (in quadrant II) at vertex Q.

∠Q measure _____°.

4. Calculate the altitude, h, for each triangle, to two decimal places.

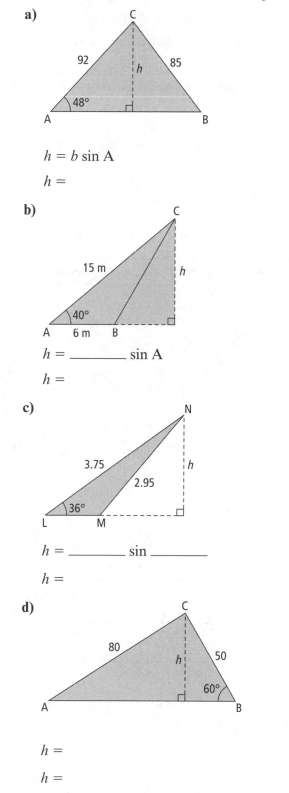

a)

$h = b \sin A$

$h =$

b)

$h = $ _____ $\sin A$

$h =$

c)

$h = $ _____ $\sin$ _____

$h =$

d)

$h =$

$h =$

> Caution! For this triangle, the known angle is $\angle B$, not $\angle A$.

5. Determine how many triangles satisfy the following conditions.

a) $\angle A = 65°$, $a = 4.0$ cm, and $b = 4.4$ cm

Sketch a possible diagram. Place the known $\angle A$ at the lower left corner of your diagram.

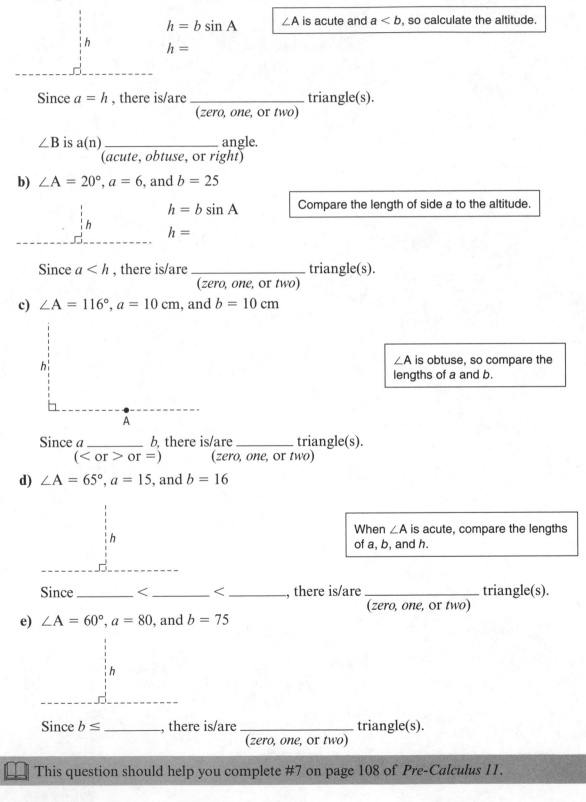

$h = b \sin A$

$h =$

> $\angle A$ is acute and $a < b$, so calculate the altitude.

Since $a = h$, there is/are _____ triangle(s).
(*zero, one,* or *two*)

$\angle B$ is a(n) _____ angle.
(*acute, obtuse,* or *right*)

b) $\angle A = 20°$, $a = 6$, and $b = 25$

$h = b \sin A$

$h =$

> Compare the length of side a to the altitude.

Since $a < h$, there is/are _____ triangle(s).
(*zero, one,* or *two*)

c) $\angle A = 116°$, $a = 10$ cm, and $b = 10$ cm

> $\angle A$ is obtuse, so compare the lengths of a and b.

Since a _____ b, there is/are _____ triangle(s).
(< or > or =)   (*zero, one,* or *two*)

d) $\angle A = 65°$, $a = 15$, and $b = 16$

> When $\angle A$ is acute, compare the lengths of a, b, and h.

Since _____ < _____ < _____, there is/are _____ triangle(s).
(*zero, one,* or *two*)

e) $\angle A = 60°$, $a = 80$, and $b = 75$

Since $b \leq$ _____, there is/are _____ triangle(s).
(*zero, one,* or *two*)

📖 This question should help you complete #7 on page 108 of *Pre-Calculus 11*.

Apply

6. Methane (CH_4) is the major component of natural gas. It can be found in underground gas reservoirs, oil wells, coal mines, marshland, agricultural sites, sewage sludge, and landfills. The molecule is highly symmetrical, with each C-H bond 1.087 Å (angstroms) long, and each H-C-H angle 109.5°. Calculate the distance, in angstroms, between H atoms.

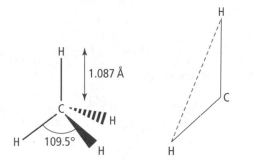

> Fill in the triangle with the known information. Which form of the sine law is best when solving for a distance?

> 📖 This question should help you complete #15 on page 110 of *Pre-Calculus 11*.

7. Determine the unknown side and angles in $\triangle ABC$, where $\angle A = 35°$, $a = 120$, and $b = 100$. If two solutions are possible, give both.

> Compare the lengths of a, b, and h.

Since b ≤ _____, there is/are _____ triangle(s).
                                   (*zero, one,* or *two*)

Solve for $\angle B$: $\dfrac{\sin B}{b} = \dfrac{\sin A}{a}$

Solve for c: $\dfrac{c}{\sin C} = \dfrac{a}{\sin A}$

Solve for $\angle C$: $\angle A + \angle B + \angle C = 180°$

In $\triangle ABC$, $\angle A = $ _____°,

$\angle B = $ _____°, $\angle C = $ _____°,

$a = $ _____, $b = $ _____,

and $c = $ _____.

8. Determine the unknown side and angles in $\triangle ABC$, where $\angle A = 41°$, $a = 12.3$ cm, and $b = 15.6$ cm. If two solutions are possible, give both.

Compare the lengths of a, b, and h.

Since _____ < _____ < _____, there is/are _____ triangle(s).
(zero, one, or two)

Triangle 1: $\angle B$ is acute	**Triangle 2:** $\angle B$ is obtuse
Calculate $\angle B_1$ using the sine law:	To calculate $\angle B_2$, find the angle in quadrant II with $\theta_R = \angle B_1$:
$$\frac{\sin A}{a} = \frac{\sin B_1}{b}$$	$\angle B_2 = 180° - \angle B_1$
$\angle B_1 = $ _____ $°$	$\angle B_2 = $ _____ $°$
Find $\angle C$:	Find $\angle C$:
$\angle A + \angle B_1 + \angle C = 180°$	
$\angle C = $ _____ $°$	$\angle C = $ _____ $°$
Calculate side c using the sine law:	Calculate side c using the sine law:
$$\frac{a}{\sin A} = \frac{c}{\sin C}$$	
$c = $ _____	$c = $ _____

The two possible triangles are as follows:

- acute $\triangle ABC$: $\angle A = $ _____ $°$, $\angle B = $ _____ $°$, $\angle C = $ _____ $°$, $a = $ _____ cm,

  $b = $ _____ cm, and $c = $ _____ cm

- obtuse $\triangle ABC$: $\angle A = $ _____ $°$, $\angle B = $ _____ $°$, $\angle C = $ _____ $°$, $a = $ _____ cm,

  $b = $ _____ cm, and $c = $ _____ cm

📖 For more practice, try #8 on page 109 of *Pre-Calculus 11.*

Connect

9. Solving a triangle means finding the measure of all unknown sides and angles. Create a flowchart or other graphic organizer describing how to use the sine law to solve triangles in the following situations. Include formulas and diagrams.

   a) You are given two angles and one side (ASA).

   b) You are given two sides and an angle opposite one of those sides (SSA). Be sure to include information on the ambiguous case.

📖 The Key Ideas on page 107 of *Pre-Calculus 11* may give you some helpful ideas.

> **≪≫ KEY IDEAS**

- A triangle that does not contain a right angle is called an oblique triangle. You can also use the cosine law to solve problems involving oblique triangles.

- To find a side length using the cosine law, you must know the measure of the angle opposite that side, plus the lengths of the other two sides (SAS). If the unknown side in $\triangle ABC$ is c, the cosine law is written as
$c^2 = a^2 + b^2 - 2ab \cos C$

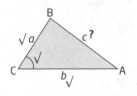

- To find an angle using the cosine law, you must know the length of all three sides in the triangle (SSS). If you are solving for the angle at vertex C in $\triangle ABC$, the cosine law is written as
$c^2 = a^2 + b^2 - 2ab \cos C$

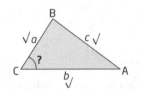

- You can choose to rearrange the formula before or after substituting the known values.

$$c^2 - a^2 - b^2 = -2ab \cos C$$

$$\frac{c^2 - a^2 - b^2}{-2ab} = \cos C$$

$$\cos^{-1}\left(\frac{c^2 - a^2 - b^2}{-2ab}\right) = \angle C$$

- There is no ambiguous case for the cosine law because acute angles (in quadrant I) have positive values of $\cos \theta$ and obtuse angles (in quadrant II) have negative values of $\cos \theta$.

- You can use cosine law in combination with the sine law to solve oblique triangles.

Working Example 1: Determine an Unknown Side Length

Determine the length of side b, to one decimal place.

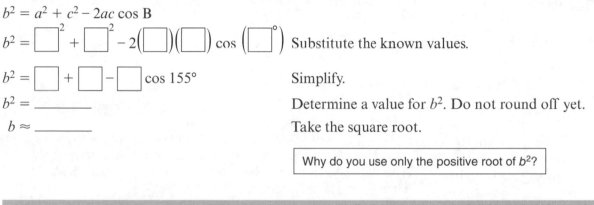

Solution

This is an oblique triangle. You know two sides and the angle at the vertex that joins them (SAS), so use the cosine law.

First, write the cosine law in terms of the unknown side, b. The known sides are a and c. The angle opposite the unknown side is $\angle B$.

$b^2 = a^2 + c^2 - 2ac \cos B$

$b^2 = \boxed{}^2 + \boxed{}^2 - 2\left(\boxed{}\right)\left(\boxed{}\right) \cos\left(\boxed{}^\circ\right)$ Substitute the known values.

$b^2 = \boxed{} + \boxed{} - \boxed{} \cos 155^\circ$ Simplify.

$b^2 = \underline{\hphantom{xxxxxx}}$ Determine a value for b^2. Do not round off yet.

$b \approx \underline{\hphantom{xxxxxx}}$ Take the square root.

> Why do you use only the positive root of b^2?

📖 See the example on pages 116–117 of *Pre-Calculus 11*, which is a word problem.

Working Example 2: Determine an Unknown Angle

Determine the measure of $\angle A$, to the nearest degree.

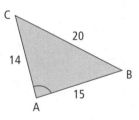

Solution

This is an oblique triangle. You know three sides and want to find an angle (SSS), so use the cosine law.

First, write the cosine law in terms of the unknown $\angle A$.
The side opposite the known angle, a, is isolated on the left side of the equation.
The two known sides are b and c, and they appear on the same side of the equation as the unknown angle.

$a^2 = b^2 + c^2 - 2ab \cos A$

$\boxed{}^2 = \boxed{}^2 + \boxed{}^2 - 2\left(\boxed{}\right)\left(\boxed{}\right) \cos A$ Substitute the known values.

$\boxed{} = \boxed{} + \boxed{} - \boxed{} \cos A$ Simplify.

$\boxed{} = -\boxed{} \cos A$ Isolate the term containing cos A. Subtract b^2 and c^2 from both sides.

$\cos A = \underline{\hphantom{xxxxxx}}$ Divide both sides by the coefficient of cos A. Do not round off yet.

$\angle A \approx \underline{\hphantom{xxxxxx}}$ Use the $\cos^{-1}$ function to find the angle.

Working Example 3: Choose Your Method

Determine the appropriate method to solve for the requested information.

a) In $\triangle ABC$, $\angle A = 60°$, $a = 15$ units, and $b = 14$ units. Find the measure of $\angle B$.

b) In $\triangle JKL$, $\angle L = 46°$, $j = 6.9$ cm, and $k = 10.3$ cm. Find the length of side l.

c) In $\triangle LMN$, $\angle L = 75°$, $\angle M = 28°$, and $m = 100$. Find the length of side l.

d) In $\triangle XYZ$, $\angle X = 90°$, $x = 5$ cm, and $z = 3$ cm. Find the measure of $\angle Z$.

Solution

a) What kind of triangle is $\triangle ABC$? _____
$\qquad\qquad\qquad\qquad\qquad\quad$ (*oblique* or *right*)

Sketch a diagram and label the known information.

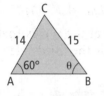

You are given information that deals with two pairs of angles and their opposite sides: $\angle A$ and a, $\angle B$ and b. So, use the sine law. Alternatively, you are given side a, side b, and $\angle A$, or SSA. Therefore, use the sine law.

b) What kind of triangle is $\triangle JKL$? _____
$\qquad\qquad\qquad\qquad\qquad\quad$ (*oblique* or *right*)

Sketch a diagram and label the known information.

You are given two sides (j and k) and the angle at the vertex that joins these sides, $\angle L$. So, use the cosine law to find the length of the third side.

Alternatively, you are given side j, $\angle L$, and side k, or SAS. Therefore, use the cosine law.

c) What kind of triangle is $\triangle LMN$? _____
$\qquad\qquad\qquad\qquad\qquad\quad$ (*oblique* or *right*)

Sketch a diagram and label the known information.

You know: _____

You want to find: _____

Therefore, use the _____.

Alternatively, you are given side m, $\angle L$, and $\angle M$, or _____.

So, use the _____.

d) What kind of triangle is $\triangle XYZ$? _____
(*oblique* or *right*)

Sketch a diagram and label the known information.

You know the opposite side and the hypotenuse, and you want to find: _____

Therefore, use the _____.

Working Example 4: Solve a Triangle

In $\triangle ABC$, $b = 14$ cm, $c = 15$ cm, and $\angle A = 110°$. Solve the triangle.

Solution

Sketch a diagram. Place the known $\angle A$ at the lower left corner of your diagram.

What kind of triangle is $\triangle ABC$? _____
(*oblique* or *right*)

You are given two sides and the angle at the vertex that joins them (SAS). To find the length of the third side,

use the _____.

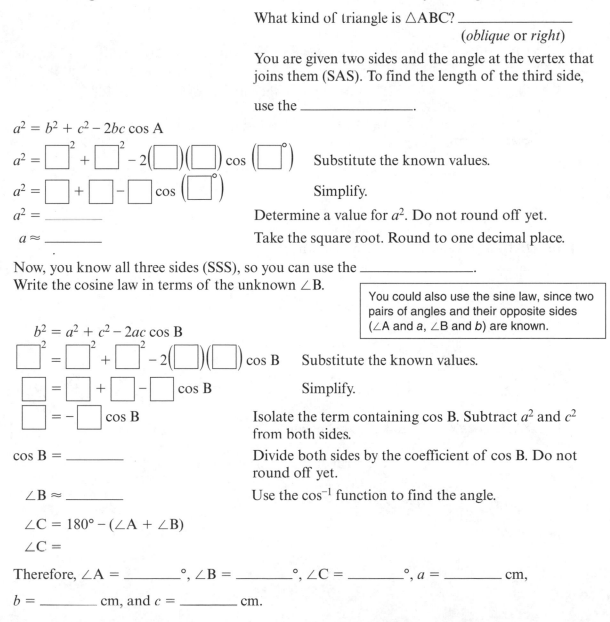

$a^2 = b^2 + c^2 - 2bc \cos A$

$a^2 = \boxed{}^2 + \boxed{}^2 - 2(\boxed{})(\boxed{}) \cos \left(\boxed{}^°\right)$ Substitute the known values.

$a^2 = \boxed{} + \boxed{} - \boxed{} \cos \left(\boxed{}^°\right)$ Simplify.

$a^2 = $ _____   Determine a value for a^2. Do not round off yet.

$a \approx $ _____   Take the square root. Round to one decimal place.

Now, you know all three sides (SSS), so you can use the _____.
Write the cosine law in terms of the unknown $\angle B$.

> You could also use the sine law, since two pairs of angles and their opposite sides ($\angle A$ and a, $\angle B$ and b) are known.

$b^2 = a^2 + c^2 - 2ac \cos B$

$\boxed{}^2 = \boxed{}^2 + \boxed{}^2 - 2(\boxed{})(\boxed{}) \cos B$ Substitute the known values.

$\boxed{} = \boxed{} + \boxed{} - \boxed{} \cos B$ Simplify.

$\boxed{} = -\boxed{} \cos B$ Isolate the term containing cos B. Subtract a^2 and c^2 from both sides.

$\cos B = $ _____   Divide both sides by the coefficient of cos B. Do not round off yet.

$\angle B \approx $ _____   Use the $\cos^{-1}$ function to find the angle.

$\angle C = 180° - (\angle A + \angle B)$

$\angle C = $

Therefore, $\angle A = $ _____°, $\angle B = $ _____°, $\angle C = $ _____°, $a = $ _____ cm,

$b = $ _____ cm, and $c = $ _____ cm.

Check Your Understanding

Practise

1. Write the cosine law in terms of the appropriate variables to solve for the unknown side.

   a) In △ABC, sides b and c and ∠A are known.

   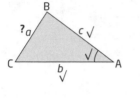

   The side opposite the known angle is _____.

   Use the form of the cosine law that starts and ends with that letter. The letters representing the other two sides go in the middle.

   $$\boxed{}^2 = b^2 + c^2 - 2bc \cos \boxed{}$$

   b) In △ABC, sides a and b and ∠C are known.

   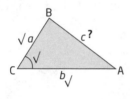

   The side opposite the known angle is _____.

   The form of the cosine law to use is

   $$c^2 = \boxed{}^2 + \boxed{}^2 - 2\left(\boxed{}\right)\left(\boxed{}\right) \cos C$$

   c) In △JKL, sides j and k and ∠L are known.

   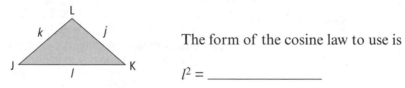

   The form of the cosine law to use is

   $$l^2 = \underline{\hspace{3cm}}$$

   d) In △XYZ, sides x and z and ∠Y are known.

   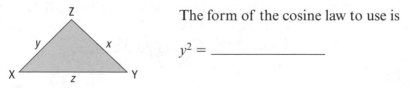

   The form of the cosine law to use is

   $$y^2 = \underline{\hspace{3cm}}$$

2. Determine the length of side x, to the nearest unit, in $\triangle$XYZ.

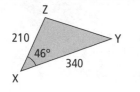

The form of the cosine law to use is

$$x^2 =$$

Substitute the known values into the formula and solve for x.

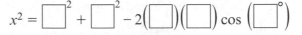

$$x^2 = \boxed{}^2 + \boxed{}^2 - 2\left(\boxed{}\right)\left(\boxed{}\right) \cos \left(\boxed{}^\circ\right)$$

3. In $\triangle$ABC, $a = 10$ cm, $b = 8$ cm, and $\angle C = 25°$. Determine the length of side c, to the nearest millimetre.

Sketch:

The form of the cosine law to use is

$$c^2 =$$

Substitute the known values into the formula and solve for c.

4. In $\triangle$XYZ, $x = 15$ cm, $z = 14$ cm, and $\angle Y = 60°$. Determine the length of side y, to the nearest millimetre.

Sketch:

The form of the cosine law to use is

$$y^2 =$$

Substitute the known values into the formula and solve for y.

5. Determine the measure of ∠Q, to the nearest degree, in each triangle.

a)

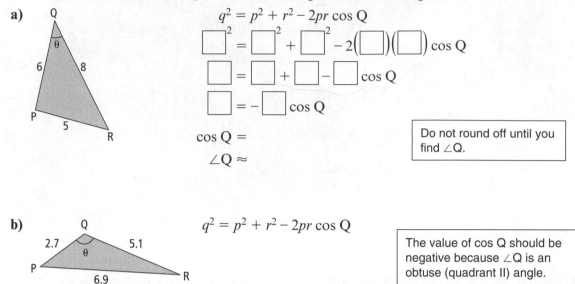

$$q^2 = p^2 + r^2 - 2pr \cos Q$$

$$\boxed{}^2 = \boxed{}^2 + \boxed{}^2 - 2\left(\boxed{}\right)\left(\boxed{}\right) \cos Q$$

$$\boxed{} = \boxed{} + \boxed{} - \boxed{} \cos Q$$

$$\boxed{} = - \boxed{} \cos Q$$

$\cos Q = $

∠Q ≈

> Do not round off until you find ∠Q.

b)

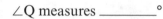

2.7   Q   5.1

θ

P   6.9   R

$$q^2 = p^2 + r^2 - 2pr \cos Q$$

> The value of cos Q should be negative because ∠Q is an obtuse (quadrant II) angle.

∠Q measures _____°

c) In △PQR, $p = 30$, $q = 20$, and $r = 15$.

Sketch:

Set up the cosine law for this triangle.

∠Q measures _____°

Apply

6. In parallelogram ABCD, the measure of the acute angle is 50°. If the sides are 10 cm and 9 cm, what is the measure of the shortest diagonal, to one decimal place?

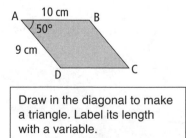

A   10 cm   B

50°

9 cm

D   C

The form of the cosine law to solve for the diagonal is

> Draw in the diagonal to make a triangle. Label its length with a variable.

The measure of the shortest diagonal is _____ cm.

7. Solve △ABC. Round angles to the nearest degree.

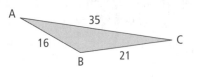

You know the measure of all three sides (SSS).

Therefore, use the _____
(*sine law* or *cosine law*)

to find any angle. Decide which angle you will find

first. _____

The form of the cosine law to solve for

_____ is _____.

Next, solve for _____ using the sine law
or cosine law.

Solve for the remaining angle using the fact that the sum of the angles in a triangle is 180°.

In △ABC, $\angle A =$ _____°, $\angle B =$ _____°, $\angle C =$ _____°, $a =$ _____,

$b =$ _____, and $c =$ _____.

8. In a baseball diamond, the bases are 90 ft apart. The second baseman stands back from the base line, AC, to cover the territory between first base, C, and second base, A. If the second baseman is standing at point B, which is 10 ft from the baseline at an angle of 9° to first base, how far is the player from second base?

To use the cosine law to find distance x, you need the opposite angle, $\angle C$, and the lengths of the two sides AC and BC.

You know AC = _____ ft and $\angle C =$ _____°. You need

to calculate BC (call this distance d).

The form of the cosine law to solve for x is

Therefore, the distance from the player to second base is _____ ft.

📖 Use a similar multiple-step approach in #10 to #23 on pages 121–123 of *Pre-Calculus 11*.

Connect

9. Write the form of the cosine law required to solve for each of the angles and sides of △LMN.

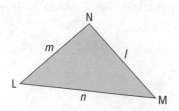

Given Information	Solve For	Formula
m, ∠L, n (SAS)		
	m	
	n	
l, m, n (SAS)	∠L	cos L =
	∠M	
	∠N	

Chapter 2 Review

2.1 Angles in Standard Position, pages 56–67

1. Sketch each angle in standard position. State which quadrant the angle terminates in and the measure of the reference angle.

   a) 35°   **b)** 165°   **c)** 216°

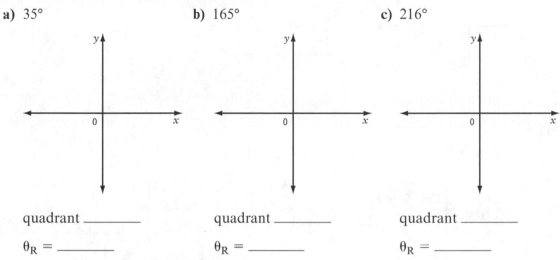

   quadrant _____   quadrant _____   quadrant _____

   θ_R = _____ θ_R = _____ θ_R = _____

2. Determine the exact value of the following ratios without using technology.

   a) cos 180° = _____   **b)** tan 210° = _____   **c)** sin 315° = _____

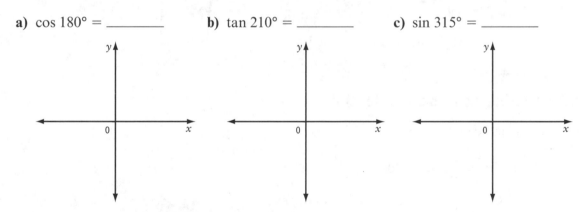

2.2 Trigonometric Ratios of Any Angle, pages 68–79

3. A point P(−4, 5) lies on the terminal arm of an angle θ in standard position. Determine the exact trigonometric ratios for sin θ, cos θ, and tan θ.

4. Suppose θ is an angle in standard position with terminal arm in quadrant II and $\sin \theta = \dfrac{15}{17}$. Determine the exact values of the other two primary trigonometric ratios.

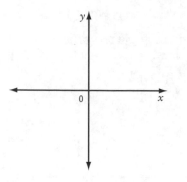

5. Solve for θ, $0° \leq \theta < 360°$.

    a) $\cos \theta = 0.5877$

    b) $\sin \theta = -\dfrac{\sqrt{3}}{2}$

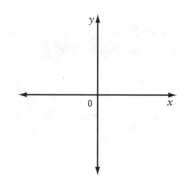

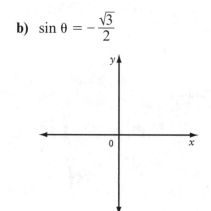

2.3 The Sine Law, pages 81–93

6. Find the indicated side or angle.

    a) $\angle B =$ _____

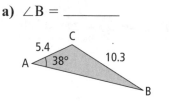

    b) side $b =$ _____

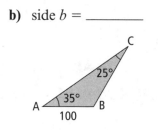

7. Determine how many △ABCs satisfy the following conditions.

a) ∠A = 69°, a = 10.1 cm, and b = 11.4 cm

b) ∠A = 28°, a = 4, and b = 6

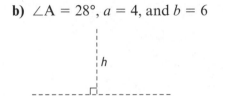

2.4 The Cosine Law, pages 94–102

8. Find the indicated side or angle.

a) side c = _____

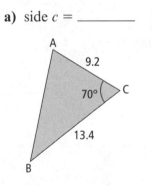

b) ∠A = _____

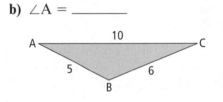

Solving a triangle means finding the measure of all unknown sides and angles. Complete the chart with all relevant formulas to solve any triangle.

Triangle	Known Info	How to Calculate Side	How to Calculate Angle	
  right triangle	$\angle C = 90°$	$a^2 =$ $b^2 =$ $c^2 = a^2 + b^2$	$\sin A = \dfrac{a}{c}$ $\cos A =$ $\tan A =$	$\sin B = \dfrac{b}{c}$ $\cos B =$ $\tan B =$
  oblique triangle	SSS or SAS	$a^2 = b^2 + c^2 - 2bc \cos A$ $b^2 =$ $c^2 =$	$\cos A = \dfrac{a^2 - b^2 - c^2}{-2bc}$ $\cos B =$ $\cos C =$	
	ASA or SSA*	$\dfrac{a}{\sin A} = \underline{\quad} = \underline{\quad}$	$\dfrac{\sin A}{a} = \underline{\quad} = \underline{\quad}$	

* Notes about the ambiguous case:

	Acute Angle	Obtuse Angle
0 triangles		
1 triangle		
2 triangles		

Chapter 3 Quadratic Functions

3.1 Investigating Quadratic Functions in Vertex Form

> ### KEY IDEAS

- For a quadratic function in vertex form, $f(x) = a(x - p)^2 + q$, $a \neq 0$, the graph
  - has the shape of a parabola
  - has its vertex at (p, q)
  - has an axis of symmetry with equation $x = p$
  - is congruent to $f(x) = ax^2$ translated horizontally by p units and vertically by q units
- You can sketch the graph of $f(x) = a(x - p)^2 + q$ by transforming the graph of $f(x) = x^2$.

The parameter a gives the direction of opening and the vertical stretch factor.	
$a > 0$	The parabola opens upward.
$a < 0$	The parabola is reflected in the x-axis; it opens downward.
$-1 < a < 1$	The parabola is compressed vertically; it is wider than the graph of $f(x) = x^2$ or $f(x) = -x^2$.
$a > 1$ or $a < -1$	The parabola is stretched vertically; it is narrower than the graph of $f(x) = x^2$ or $f(x) = -x^2$.
The parameter q gives the vertical translation.	
$q > 0$	The parabola is translated q units up.
$q < 0$	The parabola is translated q units down.
The parameter p gives the horizontal translation.	
$p > 0$	The parabola is translated p units to the right.
$p < 0$	The parabola is translated p units to the left.

Working Example 1: Sketch the Graph of a Quadratic in Vertex Form

State the vertex, the direction of opening, the equation of the axis of symmetry, the domain and range, and the maximum or minimum value of the graph of $y = -3(x + 4)^2 + 1$. Then, sketch the graph.

Solution

Use the values of a, p, and q to determine some characteristics of the function and sketch the graph.

$y = -3(x + 4)^2 + 1$
       a p q

> Which of the parameters a, p, and q determine the coordinates of the vertex?

The vertex is (_____, _____).

Since $a < 0$, the graph opens _____.
                    (*upward* or *downward*)

The equation of the axis of symmetry is _____.

> Which of the parameters a, p, and q determine the equation of the axis of symmetry?

The domain of the quadratic is $\{x \mid x \in \mathbf{R}\}$.

The range is $\{y \mid y \leq$ _____, $y \in \mathbf{R}\}$.

> How can you use the value of q to help you determine the range?

The _____ value is _____.
  (*maximum* or *minimum*)

Determine the coordinates of a point (other than the vertex) on the graph.
Choose an x-coordinate and determine the corresponding y-coordinate.
Choose $x = -3$. Substitute this value of x into the function to determine y.
$y = -3(x + 4)^2 + 1$
$y = -3(\mathbf{-3} + 4)^2 + 1$
$y = -3(1)^2 + 1$
$y = -2$

So, one point on the graph is (_____, _____).

Since every parabola is symmetric about its axis of symmetry, this means that another point on the

graph is (_____, -2).

Plot the vertex and these two other points to sketch the graph.

📖 Compare this method with the two methods shown on pages 148–149 of *Pre-Calculus 11*.

Working Example 2: Determine a Quadratic Function in Vertex Form Given Its Graph

Determine a quadratic function, in vertex form, for the graph.

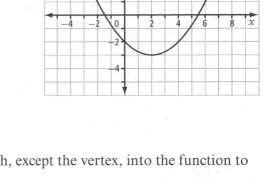

Solution

The vertex of the graph is _____.

So, $p =$ _____ and $q =$ _____.

The equation of the function in the form

$y = a(x - p)^2 + q$ is _____.

Substitute the coordinates of any point from the graph, except the vertex, into the function to determine the value of a.
Use $(0, -2)$:

$y = a(x - 2)^2 - 3$
$\mathbf{-2} = a(\mathbf{0} - 2)^2 - 3$
$-2 = 4a - 3$
$1 = 4a$
$\dfrac{1}{4} = a$

Substitute the parameters a, p, and q to write the equation of the function.

$y =$ _____

Working Example 3: Determine the Number of x-Intercepts Using a and q

Determine the number of x-intercepts for the quadratic function $f(x) = 4(x - 3)^2$.

Solution

Use the value of a to determine if the graph opens upward or downward.
Use the value of q to determine if the vertex is above, below, or on the x-axis.

a _____ 0 The graph opens _____.
   ($<$ or $>$)   (*upward* or *downward*)

q _____ 0 The vertex is _____ the x-axis.
($<$ or $=$ or $>$)   (*on* or *below* or *above*)

How many x-intercept(s) does the function have? _____

> How many times does the graph touch the x-axis?

📖 See pages 153–154 of *Pre-Calculus 11* for more examples.

Check Your Understanding

Practise

1. State the coordinates of the vertex and the number of x-intercepts for each of the following functions.

    a) $y = (x - 3)^2 + 5$

    $p =$ _____ $q =$ _____

    vertex: (_____ , _____)

    a _____ 0; the graph opens _____
       (< or >)   (*upward* or *downward*)

    q _____ 0; there are _____ x-intercepts.
       (< or >)

    b) $y = -4x^2 + 1$

    c) $y = \frac{2}{3}(x - 11)^2$

    d) $y = -\left(x + \frac{1}{2}\right)^2 + \frac{7}{3}$

2. State the direction of opening, the equation of the axis of symmetry, and the maximum or minimum value for each of the following.

a)

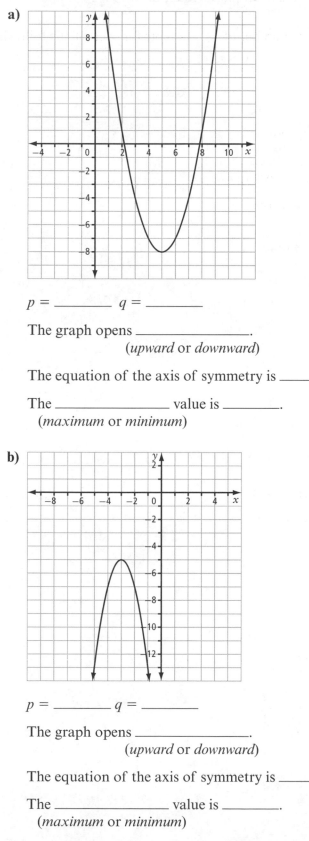

$p =$ _____ $q =$ _____

The graph opens _____.
                      (*upward* or *downward*)

The equation of the axis of symmetry is _____.

The _____ value is _____.
  (*maximum* or *minimum*)

b)

$p =$ _____ $q =$ _____

The graph opens _____.
                      (*upward* or *downward*)

The equation of the axis of symmetry is _____.

The _____ value is _____.
  (*maximum* or *minimum*)

3. Describe how to obtain the graph of each function from the graph of $y = x^2$. State the domain and the range for each. Then, graph the function.

a) $y = (x + 4)^2 - 2$

$a =$ _____ $p =$ _____ $q =$ _____

The graph opens _____.
                     (*upward* or *downward*)

The _____ value is _____.
  (*maximum* or *minimum*)

The graph of $y = x^2$ is translated _____ units to the _____ and
                                                      (*left* or *right*)

_____ units _____.
              (*up* or *down*)

The domain is _____. The range is _____.

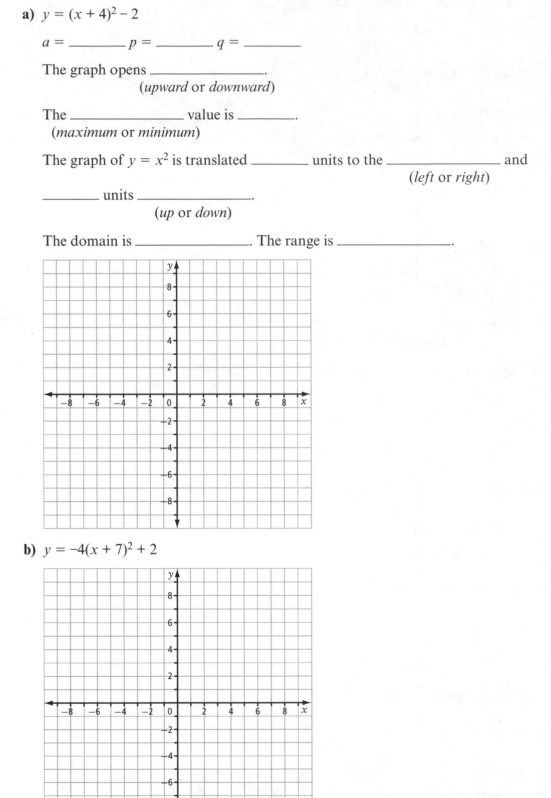

b) $y = -4(x + 7)^2 + 2$

4. Sketch each of the following. Label the vertex and axis of symmetry. State the domain and range.

a) $y = -2(x + 5)^2 + 4$

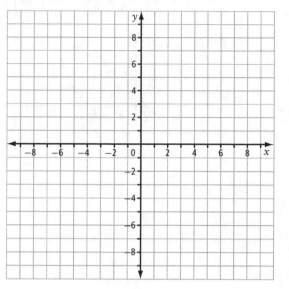

b) $y = \frac{1}{2}(x - 3)^2 - 4$

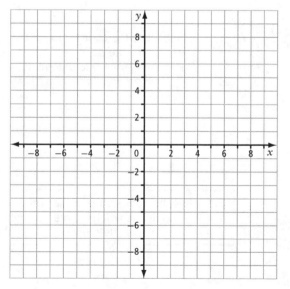

5. Determine the quadratic function in vertex form for each parabola.

a)

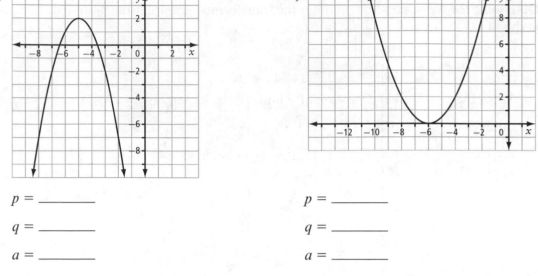

$p =$ _____

$q =$ _____

$a =$ _____

b)

$p =$ _____

$q =$ _____

$a =$ _____

function: _____

function: _____

6. Write the quadratic function in vertex form that has the given characteristics.

a) vertex at $(0, 4)$, congruent to $y = 5x^2$

$a =$ _____ $p =$ _____ $q =$ _____

function: _____

b) vertex at $(3, 0)$, passing through $(4, -2)$

> Substitute the coordinates of the vertex and the point $(4, -2)$ into $y = a(x - p)^2 + q$ to determine a.

c) vertex $(1, -1)$, with y-intercept 3

> Substitute the coordinates of the vertex and the coordinates of the y-intercept into $y = a(x - p)^2 + q$ to determine a.

Apply

7. Determine the corresponding point on the transformed graph for the point $(-1, 1)$ on the graph of $y = x^2$.

a) $y = x^2$ is transformed to $y = (x + 5)^2 - 1$.

For $y = (x + 5)^2 - 1$, $p = $ _____ and $q = $ _____.

Apply the horizontal translation of 5 units to the left and the vertical translation of

1 unit down to the point $(-1, 1)$: $(-1 + $ _____, $1 + $ _____$)$

The corresponding point of $(-1, 1)$ after the graph is transformed is ($\underline{\hspace{1.5cm}}$, $\underline{\hspace{1.5cm}}$).

📖 This question should help you complete #10 on page 158 of *Pre-Calculus 11*.

b) $y = x^2$ is transformed to $y = 2(x - 2)^2 - 3$.

For $y = 2(x - 2)^2 - 3$, $a = $ _____, $p = $ _____, and $q = $ _____.

Apply the multiplication of the y-values by a factor of 2 to the point $(-1, 1)$:

$(-1, $ _____ $(1))$

Then, apply the horizontal translation of 2 units to the right and the vertical translation

of 3 units down to the point $(-1, 2)$: $(-1 + $ _____, $2 + $ _____$)$

The corresponding point of $(-1, 1)$ after the graph is transformed is ($\underline{\hspace{1.5cm}}$, $\underline{\hspace{1.5cm}}$).

c) $y = x^2$ is transformed to $y = \frac{1}{2}(x + 1)^2 + 4$.

8. Parabolic mirrors are often used in lights because they give a focused beam. Suppose a parabolic mirror is 6 cm wide and 1 cm deep, as shown.

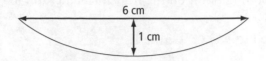

a) Suppose the vertex of the mirror is at the origin. Determine the quadratic function in vertex form that describes the shape of the mirror.

The coordinates of the vertex are _____.

The coordinates of one endpoint of the mirror are _____.

Use the coordinates of the vertex and the endpoint to determine a.

If the vertex is at the origin, the function is _____.

b) Now suppose the origin is at the left outer edge of the mirror. Determine the quadratic function in vertex form that describes the mirror.

The coordinates of the vertex are _____.

If the origin is at the left endpoint, the function is _____.

c) Compare your functions in parts a) and b). How are they similar? How are they different?

9. The points $(0, 0)$ and $(8, 0)$ are on a parabola.

   a) How many different parabolas do you think pass through these points?

   b) Choose a point to be the maximum for a parabola passing through $(0, 0)$ and $(8, 0)$. Determine the quadratic function in vertex form with this maximum.

   c) Choose a different point to be the maximum. Determine the quadratic function of the resulting parabola.

   d) How many of the parameters in a quadratic function in vertex form change when you change the location of the vertex? Explain.

Question 15 on page 159 of *Pre-Calculus 11* uses the same concepts as #8 and #9.

Connect

10. The horizontal distance, d, in metres, that a projectile travels is given by $d = -\dfrac{v^2 \cos \theta \sin \theta}{4.9}$, where v is the initial speed in metres per second and θ is the angle at which the object leaves the ground.

a) Choose an angle, substitute into the formula, and simplify. List the characteristics of the resulting quadratic function.

b) Choose a different angle and repeat your work in part a). How do your two resulting quadratic functions compare?

c) List the characteristics that all quadratics resulting from this formula will have in common. Which characteristics will vary?

11. Student council sells school T-shirts for $12 each. If they raise prices, they hope to make more money. If x represents the price increase and y represents revenue, then the quadratic function $y = -10(x - 9)^2 + 4510$ models this situation.

   a) If the price does not change ($x = 0$), what is the current revenue?

   b) Sketch a graph of this function.

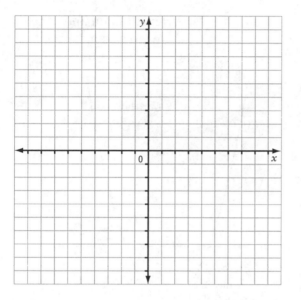

   c) Explain why it is reasonable for a quadratic to represent this situation.

   d) Determine the price for T-shirts that gives the maximum revenue for the student council. What is this maximum revenue? Justify your answer.

KEY IDEAS

- The standard form of a quadratic function is $f(x) = ax^2 + bx + c$ or $y = ax^2 + bx + c$, where $a \neq 0$.

- The graph of a quadratic function is a parabola that
  - is symmetric about a vertical line, called the axis of symmetry, that passes through the vertex
  - opens upward and has a minimum value if $a > 0$
  - opens downward and has a maximum value if $a < 0$
  - has a y-intercept at $(0, c)$ that has a value of c

- Use the graph of a quadratic function to determine the vertex, domain and range, direction of opening, axis of symmetry, x-intercepts, y-intercept, and maximum or minimum value.

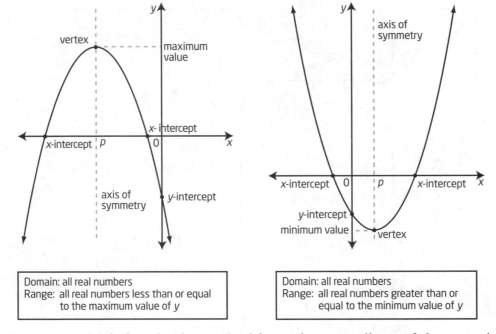

Domain: all real numbers
Range: all real numbers less than or equal to the maximum value of y

Domain: all real numbers
Range: all real numbers greater than or equal to the minimum value of y

- For any quadratic function in standard form, the x-coordinate of the vertex is $x = -\dfrac{b}{2a}$.

📖 See page 166 of *Pre-Calculus 11* to see how to derive the formula for x-coordinate of the vertex.

- For quadratic functions in applied situations,
  - the y-intercept represents the value of the function when the independent variable is 0
  - the x-intercept(s) represent(s) the value(s) of the independent variable when the function is 0
  - the vertex represents the point at which the function reaches its maximum or minimum
  - the domain and range may need to be restricted based on the possible values in the situation

Working Example 1: Characteristics of a Quadratic Function in Standard Form

For each graph of a quadratic function given, identify the following:
• the direction of opening
• the coordinates of the vertex
• the maximum or minimum value
• the equation of the axis of symmetry
• the x-intercepts and y-intercept
• the domain and range

> How can you use the x-coordinate of the vertex to determine the y-coordinate of the vertex?

> What is the relationship between the x-coordinate of the vertex and the axis of symmetry?

a) $f(x) = x^2 + 4x$

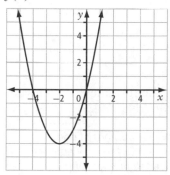

b) $f(x) = -x^2 - 2x + 3$

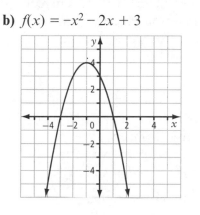

Solution

a) The graph opens _____.

The x-coordinate of the vertex is _____.

The y-coordinate of the vertex is _____.

The minimum value of the function is

_____.

The equation of the axis of symmetry is

$x =$ _____.

The factored form of the function is $f(x) = x(x + 4)$, so the x-intercepts

are _____ and _____.

The y-intercept is 0 because

_____.

The domain is $\{x \mid x \in R\}$.

The range is $\{y \mid y \geq -4, y \in R\}$

because _____.

b) The graph opens _____.

The x-coordinate of the vertex is _____.

The y-coordinate of the vertex is _____.

The maximum value of the function is

_____.

The equation of the axis of symmetry is

$x =$ _____.

The factored form of the function is

$f(x) =$ _____, so the

x-intercepts are _____ and _____.

The y-intercept is _____

because _____.

The domain is _____.

The range is _____

because _____.

📖 After completing this example, you should be able to explain the solutions to Example 1 on pages 167–168 of *Pre-Calculus 11*.

Working Example 2: Using a Quadratic Function to Model a Situation

A student council sells memberships for $6 per year and has 700 members. To increase revenue, they decide to increase the membership cost. The results of a survey indicates that 50 fewer students will buy a membership for every $1 increase in the membership cost.

a) Write a quadratic function in standard form to model this situation.

b) Graph the quadratic function. What does the shape of the graph communicate about the situation?

c) What are the coordinates of the vertex? What information does it give the student council?

d) Determine if there are any x-intercepts that are relevant. What do these intercepts, if they exist, represent in the situation?

e) What domain and range are logical for this situation? Explain.

Solution

a) Let x represent the number of price increases and $r(x)$ represent the revenue after a given price increase. Then,
revenue = (price)(number of members)
$$r(x) = (6 + x)(700 - 50x)$$

$$r(x) = 4200 - 300x + \text{_____}$$

$$r(x) = \text{_____}$$

> The new price is $6 plus the number of price increases times $1, or 6 + 1x. The new number of members is 700 minus the number of price increases times 50, or 700 – 50x.

b) Enter the function on a graphing calculator.

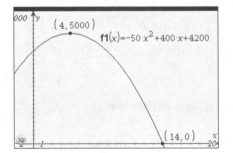

> Think about the maximum number of price increases possible and revenue amounts to help you determine window settings.

The shape of the quadratic confirms that if the council raises the membership price, revenue at first increases, but then decreases.

c) The vertex of the graph is located at (4, 5000). This means that a price increase of _____, to a new price of _____, will give the maximum revenue of $5000.

d) The x-intercept of _____ indicates that if the price is increased by $ _____, the student council will have no revenue. So, there will be no sales at this price.

e) The domain for this situation is _____, as 0 is the smallest possible price increase and 14 is the greatest possible price increase.

The range is _____, as revenue is positive and the maximum revenue is $5000.

📖 See pages 168–172 of *Pre-Calculus 11* for more examples.

Check Your Understanding

Practise

1. Which of the following functions are quadratic? Rewrite the quadratic functions in standard form.

   a) $f(x) = -5(x + 2)^2 + 8$

   b) $f(x) = 3x^2 + 4^x + 1$

   c) $f(x) = (8x + 11)(x - 5)$

   d) $f(x) = (3x - 7)(x - 4)(x + 1)$

2. For each graph, identify the following:
   - the coordinates of the vertex
   - the equation of the axis of symmetry
   - the x-intercepts and y-intercept
   - the maximum or minimum value and how it relates to the direction of opening
   - the domain and range

   a)

   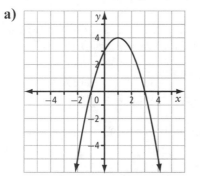

   - The vertex is (_____, _____).
   - The x-coordinate of the vertex gives the equation of the axis of symmetry as $x = $ _____.
   - The graph has a y-intercept of _____, and the x-intercepts are _____ and _____.
   - Since the graph opens downward, it has a _____, and that value is given by the y-coordinate of the vertex.
   - The domain is _____. Using the vertex, the range is _____.

b)

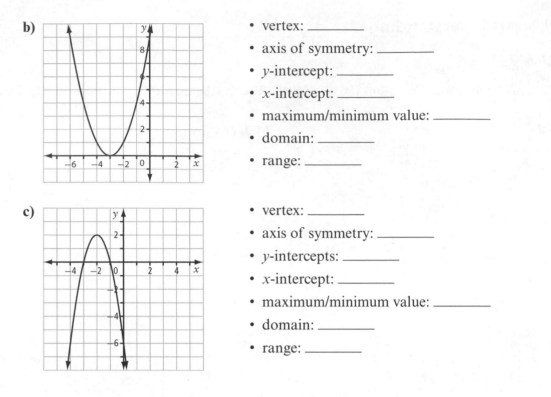

- vertex: _____
- axis of symmetry: _____
- y-intercept: _____
- x-intercept: _____
- maximum/minimum value: _____
- domain: _____
- range: _____

c)

- vertex: _____
- axis of symmetry: _____
- y-intercepts: _____
- x-intercept: _____
- maximum/minimum value: _____
- domain: _____
- range: _____

3. Use technology to graph each of the following functions. Identify the vertex, the axis of symmetry, the maximum or minimum value, the domain and range, and all intercepts. Round values to the nearest tenth, if necessary.

   a) $y = x^2 - 5x - 1$

   - The vertex is (_____, _____).

   - The x-coordinate of the vertex gives the axis of symmetry as $x = $ _____.

   - Since the graph opens _____, it has a _____ value and that
                  (*upward* or *downward*)   (*maximum* or *minimum*)

     value is given by the y-coordinate of the vertex, which is _____.

   - The domain is _____, and using the vertex, the range is _____.

   - The x-intercepts are _____ and _____, and the y-intercept is _____.

   b) $y = -2x^2 + x + 3$

   - vertex: _____
   - axis of symmetry: _____
   - y-intercept: _____
   - x-intercepts: _____
   - maximum/minimum value: _____
   - domain: _____
   - range: _____

c) $y = 0.25x^2 - 5.5x + 27.25$

- vertex: _____
- axis of symmetry: _____
- y-intercept: _____
- x-intercept: _____
- maximum/minimum value: _____
- domain: _____
- range: _____

4. Determine the vertex of each quadratic function.

> The x-coordinate of the vertex is given by $x = -\dfrac{b}{2a}$. Find the y-coordinate by substituting that value of x into the function.

a) $y = x^2 - 4x - 12$

b) $y = 3x^2 + 6x - 1$

c) $y = -x^2 + 8x + 25$

d) $y = 2x^2 - 6x - 5$

5. Determine the number of x-intercepts for each function. Explain how you know.

a) $y = x^2 + 2x - 35$

   The vertex of this function is at (_____, _____).

   The parabola opens _____.

   There are _____ x-intercepts.

b) a quadratic function with a maximum value at its y-intercept of 12

c) a quadratic function with its vertex located on the x-axis

d) a quadratic function with an axis of symmetry of $x = 2$ and passing through the point $(5, 0)$

e) a quadratic function with vertex $(-2, 5)$ and passing through the point $(1, 18)$

f) a quadratic function with a range of $y \leq -7$

📖 See #8 on page 175 of *Pre-Calculus 11* for more practice with this concept.

Apply

6. The graph approximates the height of a soccer ball kicked by the goalkeeper. Use the graph to answer the following questions. Explain what property of the graph led to your answer.

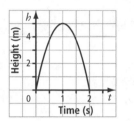

a) From what height is the ball kicked?

b) What is the maximum height of the ball? When does it occur?

c) How long is the ball in the air?

d) What are the domain and range for this situation?

7. When determining the maximum allowable speed for a curve in a road, engineers use the equation $a = \frac{v^2}{r}$, where a is the acceleration, in metres per second squared, experienced by the vehicle as it turns, v is the road speed of the vehicle in metres per second, and r is the radius of the curve, in metres.

   a) Suppose that a particular curve has a radius of 25 m. Write the equation for the acceleration of vehicles around this curve.

   b) Identify the vertex, the equation of the axis of symmetry, and the intercepts of the function. Sketch the graph of the function.

      vertex: _____

      axis of symmetry: _____

      x-intercept: _____

      y-intercept: _____

   c) Determine the domain of the function. Explain your answer.

   d) Determine the range of the function. Explain your answer.

   e) The speed limit on the road is equivalent to 14 m/s. The maximum acceleration the engineer wants vehicles to experience on the curve is 6 m/s². Does the curve fit the criterion? Explain your answer.

8. Sketch the graph of a quadratic function that has the characteristics given. Is it possible to have more than one correct answer?

a) axis of symmetry $x = 3$ and x-intercepts of 0 and 6

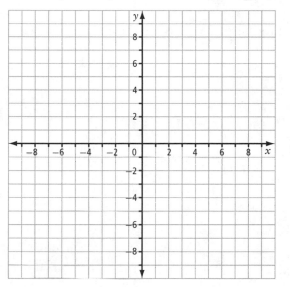

b) x-intercepts of -2 and 3 and range $y \geq -6.25$

See #10 on page 175 of *Pre-Calculus 11* for a similar question.

9. A manufacturer has determined that demand, *d*, for its product is given by $d = -p^2 + 24p + 56$, where *p* is the price of the product, in dollars.

a) Determine the coordinates of the vertex of this function.

b) Sketch the graph of the function.

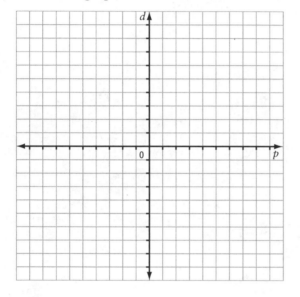

c) What does the vertex represent in this situation?

d) What does the shape of the graph tell the manufacturer in this situation?

10. Brooklyn has 24 m of fencing. She wants to build a rectangular enclosure for her dog with the maximum possible area.

   a) Write a function to represent the rectangular area of the enclosure. How do you know that the function is quadratic?

   b) Sketch a graph of the function.

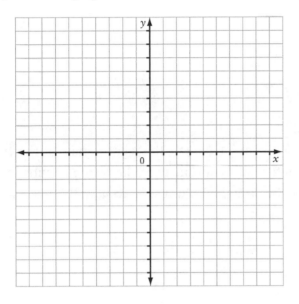

   c) Determine the coordinates of the vertex. What do these coordinates represent?

   d) What are the dimensions of the enclosure that achieve Brooklyn's goals? What area will be available to her dog?

   📖 Your work on this question should help you answer #15 and #17 on page 177 of *Pre-Calculus 11*.

Connect

11. a) Explain how knowing the vertex and direction of opening allows you to determine the number of x-intercepts of a quadratic function.

b) Does knowing the equation of the axis of symmetry and direction of opening allow you to determine the number of x-intercepts? Explain using examples.

12. For a quadratic function in standard form $y = ax^2 + bx + c$, the x-coordinate of the vertex is given by $x = -\dfrac{b}{2a}$. Obtain an expression for the y-coordinate of the vertex by substituting this value into the quadratic. Explain whether you think it is useful to have this expression.

KEY IDEAS

- To convert a quadratic function from standard form to vertex form, use an algebraic process called completing the square.

$y = 5x^2 - 30x + 7$	← Standard form
$y = 5(x^2 - 6x) + 7$	Group the first two terms. Factor out the leading coefficient if $a \neq 1$.
$y = 5(x^2 - 6x + \mathbf{9} - \mathbf{9}) + 7$	Add and then subtract the square of half of the coefficient of the x-term to create a perfect square trinomial.
$y = 5[(x^2 - 6x + 9) - 9] + 7$	Group the perfect square trinomial.
$y = 5[(x - 3)^2 - 9] + 7$	Rewrite using the square of a binomial.
$y = 5(x - 3)^2 - 45 + 7$	Simplify.
$y = 5(x - 3)^2 - 38$	← Vertex form

- Converting a quadratic function to vertex form, $y = a(x - p)^2 + q$, reveals the coordinates of the vertex, (p, q).

- You can use information derived from the vertex form to solve problems such as those involving maximum and minimum values.

Working Example 1: Convert from Standard Form to Vertex Form

Rewrite each function in vertex form by completing the square. State the vertex for each.

a) $y = x^2 - 8x + 13$

b) $y = -2x^2 + 12x + 2$

c) $y = 3x^2 + 2x - 1$

Solution

a) Group the first two terms.

$y = (x^2 - 8x) + 13$

Then, add and subtract the square of half the coefficient of the x-term to create a perfect square trinomial.

$y = (x^2 - 8x + 16 - 16) + 13$

$$\left(\frac{-8}{2}\right)^2 = (-4)^2$$
$$= 16$$

Factor the first three terms, which will always be a perfect square trinomial.

$y = (x - 4)^2 - 16 + 13$

Simplify.

$y = (x - 4)^2 - 3$

The vertex is at $(4, -3)$.

b) After grouping the first two terms, factor out the coefficient -2 from the group.

$y = -2(x^2 - 6x) + 2$

Complete the square as in part a).

$y = -2(x^2 - 6x + \underline{\hspace{1.5cm}} - \underline{\hspace{1.5cm}}) + 2$

> Determine the quantity to be added and subtracted by calculating the square of half the coefficient of the x-term.

$y = -2[(x - \underline{\hspace{1.5cm}})^2 - \underline{\hspace{1.5cm}}] + 2$

$y = -2(x - \underline{\hspace{1.5cm}})^2 + 18 + 2$

> Remember that the distributive property applies to the fourth term in the parentheses.

$y = -2(x - \underline{\hspace{1.5cm}})^2 + \underline{\hspace{1.5cm}}$

The vertex is at $(3, 20)$.

c) Though 2 is not a factor of 3, you can still begin by grouping and factoring.

$y = 3\left(x^2 + \frac{2}{3}x\right) - 1$

$y = 3\left(x^2 + \frac{2}{3}x + \underline{\hspace{1.5cm}} - \underline{\hspace{1.5cm}}\right) - 1$

$y = 3[(x + \underline{\hspace{1.5cm}})^2 - \underline{\hspace{1.5cm}}] - 1$

$y = 3(x + \underline{\hspace{1.5cm}})^2 - \underline{\hspace{1.5cm}} - 1$

$y = 3(x + \underline{\hspace{1.5cm}})^2 - \underline{\hspace{1.5cm}}$

The vertex is at \underline{\hspace{3cm}}.

📖 See pages 184–186 of *Pre-Calculus 11* for similar examples.

Working Example 2: Convert to Vertex Form and Verify

a) Convert the function $y = -3x^2 - 24x - 19$ to vertex form.

b) Verify that the two forms are equivalent.

Solution

a) Complete the square for the function $y = -3x^2 - 24x - 19$.

$y = ($ _____ $-$ _____ $) -$ _____

$y = -3($ _____ $+$ _____ $) -$ _____

$y = -3[(x +$ _____ $)^2 -$ _____ $] -$ _____

$y = -3(x +$ _____ $)^2 +$ _____ $-$ _____

$y = $ _____

b) **Method 1: Use Algebra**

To verify that the two forms are equivalent, expand and simplify the vertex form of the function.

$y = -3(x + 4)^2 + 29$
$y = -3(x + 4)(x + 4) + 29$
$y = -3(x^2 + 4x + 4x + 16) + 29$
$y = -3(x^2 + 8x + 16) + 29$
$y = -3x^2 - 24x - 48 + 29$
$y = -3x^2 - 24x - 19$

Method 2: Use Technology

Use graphing technology to graph each function.

$y = -3x^2 - 24x - 19$ $\qquad\qquad\qquad$ $y = -3(x + 4)^2 + 29$

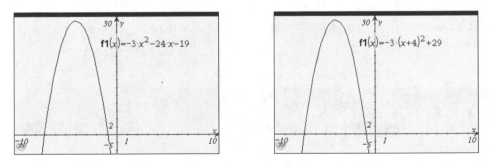

Since the graphs appear identical, the two forms are equivalent.

Working Example 3: Optimization

Rylee has 12 m of edging material to place along the three sides of the garden to separate it from her lawn. What dimensions will give the maximum area for the garden?

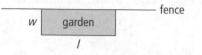

Solution

Let w represent the width of the garden and l represent the length of the garden.

The expression _____ + _____ = 12 models the edging material available.

Isolate l: $l = 12 -$ _____.

The area of the garden is given by $A = lw$. Substitute the expression above for l.

$A = ($_____$)w$
$A = 12w - 2w^2$

Rearrange the area formula and complete the square.
$A = -2w^2 + 12w$

$A = -2($_____ $-$ _____$)$

$A = -2($_____ $-$ _____ $+$ _____ $-$ _____$)$

$A = -2[($_____ $-$ _____$)^2 -$ _____$]$

$A = -2($_____ $-$ _____$)^2 +$ _____

The quadratic function representing all possible widths of Rylee's garden has its vertex at (3, 18). Rylee's garden will have a width of 3 m, a length of 6 m, and a maximum area of 18 m².

> How is the length of 6 m determined? How do you know that the area is a maximum and not a minimum?

📖 See pages 190–191 of *Pre-Calculus 11* for an example of optimization in a different context.

Check Your Understanding

Practise

1. Write each quadratic function in vertex form. State the coordinates of the vertex.

   a) $y = x^2 + 2x + 3$

   b) $y = x^2 + 12x + 20$

   c) $y = -x^2 + 8x - 7$

   d) $y = -x^2 - 10x - 31$

2. Write each function in vertex form by completing the square. State the coordinates of the vertex.

   a) $y = 2x^2 + 8x + 1$

   b) $y = 5x^2 - 60x + 166$

   c) $y = -4x^2 + 24x - 21$

   d) $y = -7x^2 - 42x + 3$

3. Write each function in vertex form. Sketch the graph of the function, and label the vertex.

   a) $y = x^2 - 10x + 18$

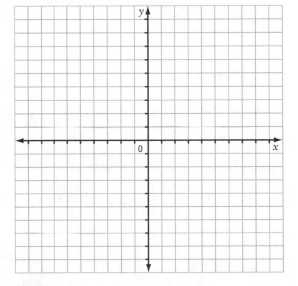

b) $y = -2x^2 + 8x + 3$

4. Indicate which are quadratic functions. For the quadratic functions, expand and state the coordinates of the vertex.

   a) $y = (x - 4)(x - 12)(x + 2)$

   b) $y = 3(x + 8) - 2(x + 2)(x - 1) + 3x$

   c) $y = 2(x - 6)(x - 3) - x + 5$

   d) $y = (x - 3)(3x^2 + 6x - 1)$

5. Verify in two different ways that each pair of functions represents the same parabola.

   a) $y = x^2 + 2x - 35$ and $y = (x + 1)^2 - 36$

   b) $y = -2x^2 + 16x - 29$ and $y = -2(x - 4)^2 + 3$

   c) $y = \frac{1}{2}(x - 5)^2 - 4$ and $y = \frac{1}{2}x^2 - 5x + \frac{17}{2}$

6. State the maximum or minimum value of each quadratic function, correct to the nearest hundredth, and the x-value at which it occurs.

a) $y = 3x^2 - 4x - 5$

b) $y = \frac{1}{3}x^2 - 4x + 10$

c) $y = -0.25x^2 + 2x + 3$

d) $y = 2x^2 - \frac{1}{4}x + 1$

📖 See #7 and #8 on page 193 of *Pre-Calculus 11* for more practice in completing the square with fractions and decimals.

Apply

7. A manufacturer determines that the cost, c, in dollars, of producing a particular component can be modelled by the function $c(n) = 50n^2 - 8000n + 3\,300\,000$, where n is the number of components made. Determine the number of components that should be made so that the manufacturer has the minimum possible cost.

This quadratic function has a minimum because _____.
The minimum value occurs at the vertex of the function. So, determine the minimum by completing the square.

$c(n) = 50n^2 - 8000n + 3\,300\,000$

$c(n) = 50(n^2 - \underline{\hspace{1cm}} n) + 3\,300\,000$

> What information does the coordinates of the vertex give the manufacturer?

📖 For more practice with this concept, complete #13 on page 194 of *Pre-Calculus 11*.

8. When an object is thrown in the air, its height, h, in metres after t seconds can be approximated by the function $h(t) = -5t^2 + vt + d$, where v is its starting speed in metres per second and d is its initial height, in metres, above the ground.

a) Suppose a ball is thrown from a height of 2 m at a speed of 20 m/s. Determine algebraically the maximum height of the ball and the time it takes to reach that height.

b) Use technology to verify your answer to part a).

c) A better model for the height of an object is $h(t) = -4.905t^2 + vt + d$. Use this model to determine the maximum height of this ball. Explain whether you prefer to use an algebraic or technological approach.

9. A sales manager wants to increase his sales revenue. Currently, he sells his product for $12 and sells 500 each month. His research indicates that for every $1 price increase, he will sell 25 fewer products.

a) Write a quadratic function that models this situation.

b) Rewrite the function in vertex form.

c) What does the vertex represent in this situation?

d) What price should the sales manager set for the product? How much revenue can he expect?

If you need help setting up the function to model this situation, see Example 4 on page 190 of *Pre-Calculus 11*.

10. An animal rescue society needs to build a new rectangular enclosure for 9 animals. The budget allows for the purchase of 100 m of fencing. The design of the enclosure is shown. What dimensions will provide the maximum area?

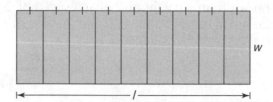

a) Write a function that represents the fencing used to build this enclosure.

b) Isolate one variable in your expression from part a).

c) Write a quadratic function that models the area of the enclosure.

d) Determine the vertex of the quadratic function you wrote in part c).

e) What dimensions give the maximum area for the enclosure?

Chapter 3 Review

3.1 Investigating Quadratic Functions in Vertex Form, pages 107–119

1. For each of the following, determine the number of x-intercepts, the equation of the axis of symmetry, and the domain and range.

   a) $y = -2(x + 5)^2 + 6$

   b) $y = 5(x - 8)^2$

2. For each of the following, determine the coordinates of the vertex and whether the graph has a maximum or minimum value.

   a) $y = -(x - 3)^2 - 7$

   b) $y = 0.5(x + 11)^2 + 8$

3. Sketch each of the following functions. Label the vertex and axis of symmetry.

   a) $y = -4(x + 1)^2$

   b) $y = \frac{1}{4}(x + 2)^2 - 3$

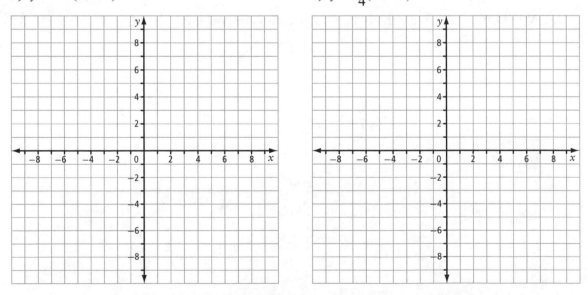

4. Suppose a sculptor wants to create a parabolic arch with a height of 5 m and a width at the base of 8 m.

   a) Determine the quadratic function that represents the arch if the vertex of the parabola is at the origin.

   b) Determine the quadratic function that represents the arch if the origin is at the lower left end of the arch.

   c) Explain the similarities and differences between your two functions.

3.2 Investigating Quadratic Functions in Standard Form, pages 120–132

5. State the x-intercepts and y-intercept for each function.

   a) $y = x^2 + 2x - 8$

   b) $y = x^2 + 10x + 9$

6. Determine the x-coordinate of the vertex of each of the quadratic functions.

   a) $y = 2x^2 + 6x - 5$

   b) $y = -3x^2 - 5x + 9$

7. State the equation of the axis of symmetry and the direction of opening for each quadratic function.

   a) $y = -0.5x^2 - 5x + 2$

   b) $y = 6x^2 - 8x - 11$

3.3 Completing the Square, pages 133–141

8. Write each function in vertex form. State the domain and range.

 a) $y = x^2 + 6x + 15$

 b) $y = -3x^2 - 36x - 100$

 c) $y = 2x^2 - 16x + 22$

 d) $y = \frac{1}{2}x^2 - x + 3$

9. The profit, p, earned from the sale of a particular product by a business is given by $p(d) = -0.25d^2 + 5d + 80$, where d is the number of days the product has been for sale.

 a) Determine the vertex of the profit function.

 b) Explain what the vertex means in the context of this problem.

10. A student club is planning a fundraising car wash. Last year they charged $10 per vehicle and washed 120 vehicles. They would like to earn more money this year. For every $1 increase in price, they know they will wash 5 fewer vehicles.

 a) Write a quadratic function to model this situation using v as the number of vehicles and r as the revenue.

 b) Determine the best price to charge for the car wash and the revenue expected at that price.

Chapter 3 Skills Organizer

Complete the table for quadratic functions in vertex form, $f(x) = a(x - p)^2 + q$.

Parameter	Possible Value	Effect on Graph	Sketch
a	$a < -1$		
	$-1 < a < 0$		
	$0 < a < 1$		
	$a > 1$		
p	$p > 0$		
	$p < 0$		
q	$q > 0$		
	$q < 0$		

Complete the table for quadratic functions.

Equation	Coordinates of Vertex	Direction of Opening	y-Intercept
$y = ax^2 + bx + c$			
$y = a(x - p)^2 + q$			

Chapter 4 Quadratic Equations

4.1 Graphical Solutions of Quadratic Equations

<table>
<tr><th colspan="3">KEY IDEAS</th></tr>
<tr><th colspan="3">Definition</th></tr>
<tr><th>Term</th><th>Description</th><th>Examples</th></tr>
<tr>
<td>Quadratic equation</td>
<td>

• an equation in which one of the terms is squared, and no other term is raised to a higher power: $ax^2 + bx + c = 0$, $a \neq 0$
</td>
<td>

$x^2 - 5x + 6 = 0$ and $-x^2 + 5x + 1 = 0$
</td>
</tr>
<tr>
<td>Root(s) of a quadratic equation</td>
<td>

• the solution(s) to a quadratic equation

• correspond to the point(s) where the graph of the corresponding quadratic function intersects with the x-axis, the x-intercepts of the graph or the zeros of the quadratic function

• Check the solution(s) by substituting them into the original equation.
</td>
<td>

For $x^2 - 5x + 6 = 0$, graph the corresponding function, $f(x) = x^2 - 5x + 6$.

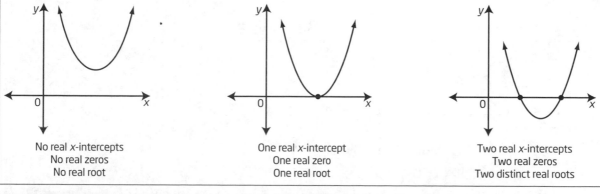

The x-intercepts occur at $(2, 0)$ and $(3, 0)$, so $x = 2$ or $x = 3$ satisfies the equation $x^2 - 5x + 6 = 0$.

Check:
$(2)^2 - 5(2) + 6 = 0$ ✓
$(3)^2 - 5(3) + 6 = 0$ ✓
</td>
</tr>
</table>

The graph of a quadratic function can have zero, one, or two x-intercepts (or zeros of the quadratic function). The zeros represent the solutions to the corresponding quadratic equation, so a quadratic equation can have zero, one, or two solutions.

No real x-intercepts No real zeros No real root	One real x-intercept One real zero One real root	Two real x-intercepts Two real zeros Two distinct real roots

Working Example 1: Solve a Quadratic Equation Graphically

Determine the roots of each equation by graphing the corresponding function. Use either paper and pencil or technology. If necessary, round answers to the nearest tenth.

a) $x^2 + 6x + 3 = 0$ **b)** $-x^2 = 2x + 1$ **c)** $2x^2 + 22 = 12x$

Solution

a) Use technology to graph the function $f(x) = x^2 + 6x + 3$. Adjust the window settings, if necessary, so that all x-intercepts are visible. Use the trace or zero function of your technology to find the x-intercepts of the graph.

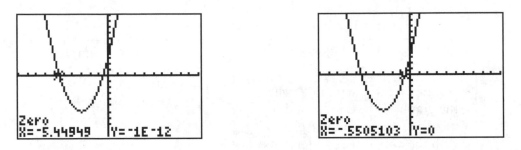

The x-intercepts of the graph correspond to the solutions to the equation. Thus, the solutions to $x^2 + 6x + 3 = 0$ expressed to the nearest tenth are $x = $ _____

and $x = $ _____.

Check by substituting your solutions in the equation, _____.
For $x = -5.5$:

Left Side	Right Side
$x^2 + 6x + 3$	0
$= ($_____$)^2 + 6($_____$) + 3$	
$=$ _____ $+ (-32.4) + 3$	
$= -0.24$	

Left Side ≈ Right Side

Note that the two sides are not exactly equal in this case. Why? Why is this acceptable? What could you do to be more certain that −5.4 is a solution to the equation?

For $x = -0.6$:

Left Side	Right Side
$x^2 + 6x + 3$	0
$= ($_____$)^2 + 6($_____$) + 3$	
$= 0.36 + ($_____$) + 3$	
$= -0.24$	

Left Side ≈ Right Side

b) Use pencil and paper to graph the function. Begin by rewriting the equation in the form $ax^2 + bx + c = 0$.

Create a table of values. Plot the coordinate pairs and use them to sketch the graph of the function.

$-x^2 - 2x - 1 = 0$

x	$f(x)$
-4	-9
-3	-4
-2	-1
-1	0
0	-1
1	-4
2	-9

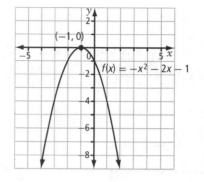

Since the graph intersects the x-axis at $(-1, 0)$, the solution to the equation is $x = -1$.

Check by substituting $x = -1$:
$-x^2 = 2x + 1$

Left Side	Right Side
x^2	$2x + 1$
$= -(\mathbf{-1})^2$	$= 2(\mathbf{-1}) + 1$
$= -1$	$= -1$

Left Side = Right Side

The solution is $x = -1$.

c) Begin by rewriting the equation in the form $ax^2 + bx + c = 0$.

Then, use technology to graph the corresponding function.

$2x^2 - 12x + 22 = 0$

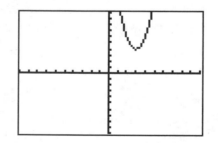

Because the graph does not intersect the x-axis, you know

that the equation has _____ solution(s).

(*one*, *two*, or *no*)

Compare this example with the Examples on pages 208–212 of *Pre-Calculus 11*.

Working Example 2: Solve a Quadratic Equation That Models a Situation

The profit, p, a particular company makes from selling its product is modelled by $p(n) = -0.1n^2 + 100n - 21\ 000$, where n is the number of products sold each month.

a) Graph the business's profit function. Explain why it is reasonable to model this situation with a quadratic equation.

b) A business hits a break-even point when its profits are $0. At this point, the business neither makes nor loses money. Determine how many sales the company needs to reach this break-even point.

c) What should the business owner conclude from the solution to this quadratic equation?

Solution

a)

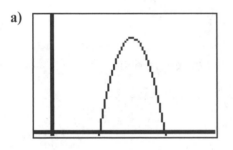

You can assume that the company initially sets a price so that it makes a profit on each item. This would mean that the more product it sells, the greater the profit. However, as sales increase, the company may find that it has to hire more workers, buy more equipment, or move into a bigger facility. These expenses would cause profits to decrease.

b)

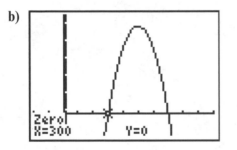 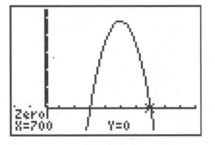

How can you check these solutions?

By using the trace or zero features of a graphing calculator, you can determine that the

solutions to the equation $-0.1n^2 + 100n - 21\ 000 = 0$ are $n =$ _____ and $n =$ _____.
The business will break even if they sell 300 products or 700 products each month.

c) The business owner should conclude that the company

will make a profit if it sells more than _____

products, but fewer than _____ products each month.

Assume that because of competition, the company cannot charge more for its product. Why, then, might the point at the vertex of this parabola be of special interest to the owner?

📖 See pages 208–213 of *Pre-Calculus 11* for more examples.

Check Your Understanding

Practise

1. How many roots does each graph have? Explain how you know. State the root(s).

a)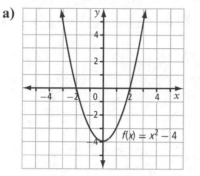

b)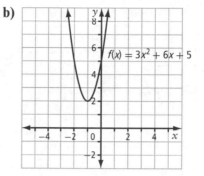

c)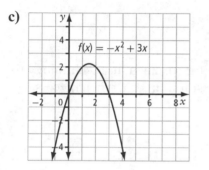

d)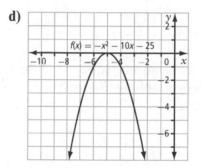

2. Solve each equation by graphing.

a) $x^2 - 9x + 8 = 0$

b) $x^2 + 14x + 45 = 0$

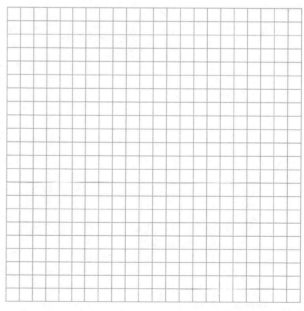

c) $2x^2 - 16x = 0$

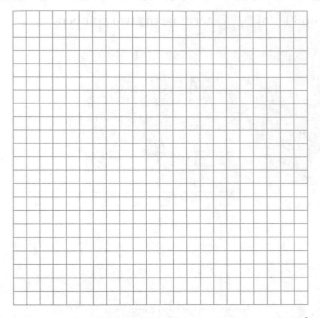

3. Rewrite each quadratic equation in the form $ax^2 + bx + c = 0$. Then, use technology to solve each by graphing. Round your answers to the nearest hundredth, where necessary.

   a) $3x^2 + 30 = -19x$

   b) $12x^2 + 23x = 24$

   c) $6x^2 = 25x - 24$

   d) $-33 - 23x = 4x^2$

Apply

4. Two numbers have a sum of 12 and a product of 32. Determine the two numbers.

Step 1: Assign variables.

Let x represent one number.

The second number is _____ $- x$.

Step 2: Set up an equation for the product.

$x(\underline{\hspace{1.5cm}}) = \underline{\hspace{1.5cm}}$

$x(\underline{\hspace{1.5cm}}) = 32$

$\underline{\hspace{1.5cm}} - x^2 = 32$

$\underline{\hspace{2.5cm}} = 0$

Step 3: Solve for x by graphing.

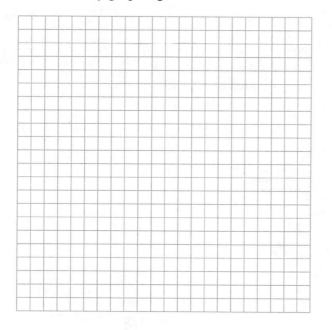

The two x-intercepts are _____ and _____, so the two numbers are _____

and _____.

> You can use a similar approach to solve #6 on page 215 of *Pre-Calculus 11*.

5. When a basketball is thrown, its height can be modelled by the function $h(t) = -4.9t^2 + 15t + 1$, where h is the height of the ball, in metres, and t is time, in seconds.

   a) Write a quadratic equation that you can use to determine how long the basketball is in the air.

   b) Use graphing technology to solve the equation you wrote in part a). If necessary, round your answers to the nearest tenth of a second.

   $t =$ _____ and $t =$ _____

   > What is the height of the ball when it lands on the ground?

   c) Do both solutions to the quadratic equation make sense in the context of this problem? Explain.

6. Madisen stores her all-terrain vehicles (ATVs) in a storage shed. The walls and roof of the shed form a parabolic shape, so the shape of the building can be represented by a quadratic function. The height of the building, h, in metres is modelled by $h = -\frac{1}{3}(d-3)^2 + 3$, where d is the distance along the floor, in metres, from the edge of the building.

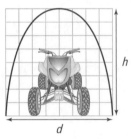

   a) Use graphing technology to determine the roots of the equation corresponding to the shape of the building.

   b) What is the width of the floor of Madisen's storage building, to the nearest tenth of a metre?

   > What does the equation $-\frac{1}{3}(d-3)^2 + 3 = 0$ represent in this situation?
   > What do the roots of the equation represent?

📖 See #9 on page 216 of *Pre-Calculus 11* for a similar question.

7. Parabolic arches are often used in architecture because they provide great strength and durability. The height, h, in metres, of a certain parabolic bridge support is modelled by $h = -\dfrac{w^2}{9} + \dfrac{4w}{3}$, where w is the distance, in metres, from the side of the arch.

   a) Write a quadratic equation that you can use to determine the width of the arch at the widest point.

   b) Use graphing technology to graph the quadratic equation from part a). What is the width of the arch? Express your answer to the nearest tenth of a metre.

   > What is the significance of the two x-intercepts of the graph, or zeros of the function?
   >
   > How could you use the zeros to determine the highest point of this bridge?

8. The height, h, in metres, of a BMX rider t seconds after leaving a jump can be modelled by the function $h(t) = -4.5t^2 + 8.3t + 2.1$.

   a) State a quadratic equation that can be used to find the time that elapses before the rider lands.

   b) Create a graph with technology to determine how long the rider remains in the air, to the nearest tenth of a second.

Connect

9. In your work with quadratics, you have used equations of the form $y = a(x - p)^2 + q$ in some places, and equations of the form $ax^2 + bx + c = 0$ in other places.

   a) Are there any coefficients that are the same in both forms?

   b) Describe a situation in which one of these forms of a quadratic equation is more useful than the other. Justify your answer.

10. **a)** Write a quadratic equation that has exactly one real root.

    b) Explain how you know that it only has one root.

<< KEY IDEAS >>

Definition		
Term	**Description**	**Examples**
Zero product property	• If two real numbers have a product of zero, then one or both of the factors must be equal to zero. • If the factors of a quadratic equation have a product of zero, then one or both of the factors must be equal to zero.	• $(x)(y) = 0$, so $x = 0$ or $y = 0$ • $(x + 3)(x - 9) = 0$, so $(x + 3) = 0$ or $(x - 9) = 0$

Strategies for Factoring Quadratics		
Task	**Description**	**Examples**
Solve a quadratic equation by factoring	• Three steps for solving: Step 1: Write the equation in the form $ax^2 + bx + c = 0$. Step 2: Factor the left side. Step 3: Set each factor equal to zero and solve for the unknown.	$x^2 + 12x = 27$ $x^2 + 12x - 27 = 0$ $(x + 3)(x - 9) = 0$ Either $(x + 3) = 0$ or $(x - 9) = 0$, so $x = -3$ or 9.
Factor polynomials in quadratic form	• The squared term in a quadratic function may be an expression, such as $(x + 3)^2$. To solve this type of quadratic expression, Step 1: Replace the expression with a variable. Step 2: Factor. Step 3: Substitute the expression back into the factored expression. Step 4: Simplify the final factors, if possible.	Factor $2(x + 3)^2 - 11(x + 3) + 15$. Let $r = x + 3$. Replace $x + 3$ with r: $2r^2 - 11r + 15$ $= 2r^2 - 5r - 6r + 15$ $= (2r^2 - 5r) + (-6r + 15)$ $= r(2r - 5) - 3(2r - 5)$ $= (2r - 5)(r - 3)$ Substitute $(x + 3)$ back in for r: $= [2(x + 3) - 5][x + 3 - 3]$ $= (2x + 1)(x)$ $= x(2x + 1)$
Factor a difference of squares	Consider the following: $9^2 - 5^2 \qquad (9 - 5)(9 + 5)$ $= 81 - 25 \qquad = (4)(14)$ $= 56 \qquad\quad = 56$ This is true for any two expressions: $P^2 - Q^2 = [P - Q][P + Q]$.	$25x^2 - 100y^2$ $= (5x - 10y)(5x + 10y)$

Working Example 1: Factor Quadratic Polynomials

Factor each polynomial.

a) $\frac{x^2}{16} - 25y^2$

b) $9(x-1)^2 - 100y^2$

c) $4(x+3)^2 + 8(x+3) - 5$

Solution

a) This is a difference of squares:

$$\sqrt{\frac{x^2}{16}} = \frac{x}{4} \text{ and } \sqrt{25y^2} = \underline{\hspace{1.5cm}}$$

So, $\frac{x^2}{16} - 25y^2 = (\underline{\hspace{1cm}} + \underline{\hspace{1cm}})(\underline{\hspace{1cm}} - \underline{\hspace{1cm}})$.

> You can factor a difference of squares, $(ax)^2 - (by)^2$, into $(ax - by)(ax + by)$.

> How can you verify that the factored form is correct?

b) This is a difference of squares:

$$\sqrt{9(x-1)^2} = 3(\underline{\hspace{1cm}}) \text{ and } \sqrt{100y^2} = \underline{\hspace{1cm}} y.$$

So, $9(x-1)^2 - 100y^2 = (3(\underline{\hspace{1cm}}) + 10y)(\underline{\hspace{1cm}}(x-1) - \underline{\hspace{1cm}})$.

Simplify by using the distributive property.

$(3x - 3 + \underline{\hspace{1.5cm}})(\underline{\hspace{1.5cm}} - 10y)$.

c) This is a quadratic in $(x + 3)$. This means that you can view $(x + 3)$ as a single variable. Replace $x + 3$ in the equation with a variable, such as a: $4a^2 + 8a - 5$.

Determine two factors of -20 that have a sum of 8: $\underline{\hspace{1.5cm}}$ and $\underline{\hspace{1.5cm}}$.

Write the equation using these factors:

$$4a^2 + 8a - 5 = 4a^2 - 2a + 10a - 5$$
$$= (4a^2 - 2a) + (10a - 5)$$
$$= \underline{\hspace{1.5cm}}(2a - 1) + 5(\underline{\hspace{1cm}})$$
$$= (2a - 1)(\underline{\hspace{1cm}})$$

> How do you factor a quadratic where the leading coefficient is something other 1?
> Explain why you find factors of -20 in this case.

Replace a with $x + 3$ and simplify.

$$(\underline{\hspace{1.5cm}} + \underline{\hspace{1.5cm}})(2(x + 3) - 1)$$
$$= (\underline{\hspace{1cm}})(\underline{\hspace{1cm}})$$

📖 For additional factoring examples, see pages 220–222 of *Pre-Calculus 11*.

Working Example 2: Solve a Quadratic Equation by Factoring

Factor to determine the roots of each quadratic equation. Verify your solutions.

a) $x^2 + 2x - 24 = 0$ **b)** $6x^2 - 11x - 35 = 0$ **c)** $x^2 = 10x - 16$

Solution

a) The factors of -24 that have a sum of 2 are _____ and _____.

$$x^2 + 2x - 24 = 0$$

$$(\underline{\hspace{2cm}})(\underline{\hspace{2cm}}) = 0$$

Either $(x + 6) = 0$ or _____ $= 0$. So, $x =$ _____ or $x =$ _____.

Check your solutions.

For $x = -6$:

Left Side	Right Side
$x^2 + 2x - 24$	0
$= (-6)^2 + 2(-6) - 24$	
$= 0$	

Left Side = Right Side

For $x =$ ___:

Left Side	Right Side
$x^2 + 2x - 24$	0
$= (\underline{\hspace{1cm}})^2 + 2(\underline{\hspace{1cm}}) - 24$	
$= 0$	

Left Side = Right Side

b) The factors of -210 that have a sum of -11 are _____ and _____.

$$6x^2 - 11x - 35 = 0$$

$$6x^2 - 21x + \underline{\hspace{2cm}} x - 35 = 0$$

$$\underline{\hspace{2cm}} (2x - 7) + 5(\underline{\hspace{1.5cm}}) = 0$$

$$(\underline{\hspace{2.5cm}})(\underline{\hspace{2.5cm}}) = 0$$

$2x - 7 = 0$ or _____ $= 0$

$x =$ _____ $x =$ _____

> Why do you use factors of -210?

Check your solutions.

For $x = \frac{7}{2}$:

Left Side	Right Side
$6x^2 - 11x - 35$	0
$= 6\left(\frac{7}{2}\right)^2 - 11\left(\frac{7}{2}\right) - 35$	
$= \frac{147}{2} - \frac{77}{2} - \frac{70}{2}$	
$= 0$	

Left Side = Right Side

For $x =$ ___:

Left Side	Right Side
$6x^2 - 11x - 35$	0
$= 6(\underline{\hspace{1cm}})^2 - 11(\underline{\hspace{1cm}}) - 35$	
$= \underline{\hspace{1cm}} + \underline{\hspace{1cm}} - \underline{\hspace{1cm}}$	
$= \underline{\hspace{1cm}}$	

Left Side _____ Right Side

c) Begin by writing the equation as $x^2 -$ _____ $= 0$. Then, factor the left-hand side.

$(x -$ _____$)(x$_____$) = 0$

(_____$) = 0$ or (_____$) = 0$

$x =$ _____ $x =$ _____

Check your solutions.

For $x =$ ____: For $x =$ ____:

Left Side	Right Side
x^2	$10x - 16$
$= ($_____$)^2$	$= -10($_____$) - 16$
$=$ _____	$=$ _____

Left Side $=$ Right Side

Left Side	Right Side
x^2	$10x - 16$
$= ($_____$)^2$	$= 10($_____$) - 16$
$=$ _____	$=$

Left Side $=$ Right Side

Working Example 3: Solve a Quadratic Equation That Models a Situation

Bobbi is building a rectangular concrete patio. Her budget allows her to buy enough cement to fill an area 48 m^2 at a depth of 3 inches. She wants the length of the patio to be 2 m longer than its width.

a) Sketch a diagram of this situation.

b) Write a quadratic equation that models this situation.

c) Solve the quadratic equation. What are the dimensions of the patio that Bobbi should build?

Solution

a)

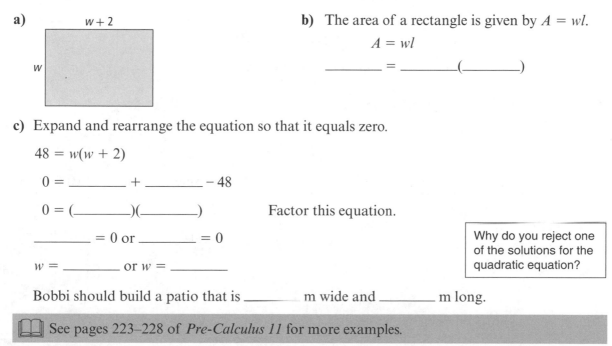

$w + 2$

w

b) The area of a rectangle is given by $A = wl$.

$$A = wl$$

_____ $=$ _____(_____)

c) Expand and rearrange the equation so that it equals zero.

$48 = w(w + 2)$

$0 =$ _____ $+$ _____ $- 48$

$0 = ($_____$)($_____$)$ Factor this equation.

_____ $= 0$ or _____ $= 0$

$w =$ _____ or $w =$ _____

> Why do you reject one of the solutions for the quadratic equation?

Bobbi should build a patio that is _____ m wide and _____ m long.

See pages 223–228 of *Pre-Calculus 11* for more examples.

Check Your Understanding

Practise

1. Factor completely.

   a) $x^2 - 9x + 18$

   b) $5b^2 - 5b - 30$

   > First remove the common factor.

2. Factor

   a) $3n^2 - 11n - 4$

   b) $4x^2 + 11x + 6$

   c) $2t^2 - 17t + 30$

   d) $12x^2 - x - 6$

3. Factor each quadratic equation.

   a) $\frac{1}{2}x^2 - 2x - 6$

   $= \frac{1}{2}(x^2 - \underline{\hspace{1.5cm}} x - \underline{\hspace{1.5cm}})$

   $= \frac{1}{2}(\underline{\hspace{1.5cm}})(\underline{\hspace{1.5cm}})$

   b) $\frac{1}{4}x^2 + \frac{1}{2}x - 6$

   c) $0.1a^2 - 0.1a - 3$

   d) $0.5z^2 - 5.4z + 4$

4. Factor, using a difference of squares.

   a) $0.81x^2 - 0.25y^2$

   b) $1.21k^2 - 0.01x^2$

   c) $\frac{1}{25}d^2 - \frac{1}{49}f^2$

   d) $8a^2 - 18b^2$

5. Factor completely.

a) $(x + 1)^2 + 2(x + 1) - 15$

Treat $x + 1$ as a single variable, m.
Substitute m for $x + 1$.

_____ + _____ − 15

Factor the resulting quadratic.

$m^2 + 2m - 15 = ($_____$)($_____$)$.

Replace m with $x + 1$ and simplify.

$($_____$)($_____$) = $ _____

b) $(2x - 1)^2 + 16(2x - 1) + 63$

c) $2(x + 2)^2 + 3(x + 2) - 20$

d) $4(5x - 1)^2 - 12(5x - 1) + 5$

6. Solve each equation. Note that they are already factored for you.

a) $(x - 5)(x + 9) = 0$

b) $(2x + 9)(x - 4) = 0$

c) $\left(x + \dfrac{3}{4}\right)\left(x - \dfrac{11}{2}\right) = 0$

d) $x(3x - 14) = 0$

7. Solve each equation by factoring. Verify your answers.

   a) $x^2 - 9x + 20 = 0$

   b) $x^2 + 12x = -36$

   c) $3x^2 + 11x = 42$

   d) $8x^2 = 18x - 9$

   e) $2x^2 + 12x = 0$

   f) $\frac{1}{3}x^2 = -5x - 18$

See *Pre-Calculus 11* page 230 for more practice factoring and solving quadratic equations.

Apply

8. A rectangular picture frame has dimensions w and $w + 3$. The area of the glass in the frame is 154 in.^{2}.

a) What equation could you use to determine the width of the frame?

b) What are the dimensions of the frame, in inches?

9. Two consecutive integers have a product of 156.

a) Assign a variable for one number. Express the second number in terms of the variable.

Let x represent the first number. The second number is _____.

b) Write a single-variable quadratic equation that represents the product of these numbers.

c) Solve the quadratic equation to determine the two numbers.

10. When a football is kicked, its height can be modelled by the function $h(d) = -0.1d^2 + 4.8d$, where d is the horizontal distance that the ball has travelled, in metres, and h is the height of the ball, in metres.

a) Write a quadratic equation that can be used to determine the distance that the ball has been kicked.

> What is the height of the ball when it lands on the ground?

b) Solve the quadratic equation to determine the distance the ball travels.

11. Aaryn has built a play area for his children that is 12 m long and 8 m wide. He wants to install a rubberized safety border around the area. This border will be the same width all the way around, as shown in the diagram. He has enough of the safety material to construct a border with a total area of 44 m².

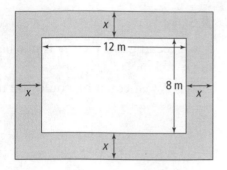

a) What is the total area of the play area plus the border in square metres?

_____ + 44 = _____

b) Let x be the width of the border. Write a quadratic equation to represent the total area of the play area plus the border. Then, solve your equation to determine the width of the border Aaryn can install.

📖 See #23 on page 232 of *Pre-Calculus 11* for a similar question.

Connect

12. How can you tell when a quadratic equation of the form $ax^2 + bx + c = 0$ has 0 as one solution? Justify your answer.

13. In Section 4.2, you verified the solutions to quadratic equations by substituting the roots into the original quadratic. How can you use your work in Section 4.1 to verify your solutions in another way?

<<< **KEY IDEAS** >>>

Definition	
Term	**Description**
Completing the square	The process of rewriting a quadratic polynomial from the standard form, $ax^2 + bx + c$, to the vertex form, $a(x - p)^2 + q$.

Strategy for Applying Completing the Square	Example
Step 1: If the coefficient of x^2 is not 1, check for a common factor. In the example, remove the common factor, 2.	$2x^2 - 12x - 4 = 0$ $x^2 - 6x - 2 = 0$
Step 2: Isolate the variable terms on the left side.	$x^2 - 6x = 2$
Step 3: Determine what value to add to the left side to make it a perfect square. Do this by taking half of b (the coefficient of x) and squaring it.	$\left(\frac{1}{2}(6)\right)^2 = 3^2$ $\qquad = 9$
Step 4: Add the value you calculated in step 3 to both sides of the equation.	$x^2 - 6x + 9 = 2 + 9$ $x^2 - 6x + 9 = 11$
Step 5: Factor the left side.	$(x - 3)^2 = 11$
Step 6: Take the square root of both sides.	$x - 3 = \pm\sqrt{11}$
Step 7: Solve for x. Express roots of quadratic equations as exact roots or as decimal approximations.	$x - 3 = \sqrt{11}$ $\quad x = 3 + \sqrt{11}$ $\quad x \approx 6.32$ or $x - 3 = -\sqrt{11}$ $\quad x = 3 - \sqrt{11}$ $\quad x \approx -0.32$

Working Example 1: Take Square Roots to Solve Quadratic Equations

Solve each equation.

a) $x^2 = 36$

b) $(x - 4)^2 = 64$

Solution

a) Take the square root of both sides of the equation.

$$x^2 = 36$$

$$x = \pm\sqrt{36}$$

$$x = \pm \underline{\hspace{2cm}}$$

b) Take the square root of each side of the equation.

$$(x - 4)^2 = 64$$

$$x - 4 = \pm\sqrt{64}$$

$$\underline{\hspace{2cm}} = \underline{\hspace{2cm}}$$

Solve for x.

$$x - 4 = \underline{\hspace{2cm}} \text{ or } x - 4 = \underline{\hspace{2cm}}$$

$$x = \underline{\hspace{2cm}} \qquad x = \underline{\hspace{2cm}}$$

Working Example 2: Solve Quadratic Equations by Completing the Square

Complete the square to solve each of the following. Express your answers as exact values.

a) $a^2 + 18a = -32$ **b)** $t^2 - 8t = 4$

Solution

a)
$$a^2 + 18a = -32$$

$$a^2 + 18a + \underline{\hspace{2cm}} = -32 + \underline{\hspace{2cm}}$$

$$(a + 9)^2 = \underline{\hspace{2cm}}$$

$$(a + 9) = \pm\sqrt{\boxed{}}$$

$$\underline{\hspace{3cm}} = \pm 7$$

> How do you use the coefficient of a to find the value needed to complete the square?

Solve for a.

$$a + 9 = \underline{\hspace{2cm}} \text{ or } a + 9 = \underline{\hspace{2cm}}$$

$$a = 7 - \underline{\hspace{1.5cm}} \qquad a = \underline{\hspace{1.5cm}} - 9$$

$$a = \underline{\hspace{2cm}} \qquad a = \underline{\hspace{2cm}}$$

b) $t^2 - 8t = 4$

$$t^2 - 8t + \underline{\hspace{1.5cm}} = 4 + \underline{\hspace{1.5cm}}$$

$$(\underline{\hspace{1.5cm}})^2 = 20$$

$$\underline{\hspace{1.5cm}} = \pm\sqrt{20}$$

$$\underline{\hspace{1.5cm}} = \pm 2\sqrt{5}$$

Why is $\pm\sqrt{20}$ rewritten as $\pm 2\sqrt{5}$?

Solve for t.

$$t - 4 = 2\sqrt{5} \qquad \text{or } t - 4 = -2\sqrt{5}$$

$$t = 2\sqrt{5} + \underline{\hspace{1.5cm}} \quad t = -\underline{\hspace{1.5cm}} + 4$$

Working Example 3: Apply Completing the Square When $a \neq 1$

Pumpkin chunking is a competition in which competitors use various ways to throw a pumpkin as far as possible. Winning teams often fling their pumpkins more than a thousand metres. A pumpkin chunking team has determined that the height, h, in metres, of their pumpkin is modelled by $h(d) = -0.000\,25d^2 + 0.3d + 2.5$, where d is the horizontal distance, in metres. How far does the team's pumpkin travel, to the nearest tenth of a metre?

Solution

When the pumpkin hits the ground, its height is \underline{\hspace{1.5cm}} m. So, at this point

$$-0.000\,25d^2 + 0.3d + 2.5 = \underline{\hspace{1.5cm}}.$$

Begin by moving the constant to the other side of the equal sign.

$$-0.000\,25d^2 + 0.3d + 2.5 - 2.5 = 0 - 2.5$$

$$-0.000\,25d^2 + 0.3d = -2.5$$

Since the quadratic term has a coefficient other than 1, divide through by the coefficient.

$$d^2 - \underline{\hspace{1.5cm}}d = 10\,000$$

$$d^2 - \underline{\hspace{1.5cm}} + 360\,000 = 10\,000 + \underline{\hspace{1.5cm}}$$

$$(d - \underline{\hspace{1.5cm}})^2 = \underline{\hspace{1.5cm}}$$

$$d - 600 = \pm\sqrt{\boxed{}}$$

Solve for d.

$$d - \underline{\hspace{1.5cm}} = \sqrt{370\,000} \qquad \text{or} \qquad d - \underline{\hspace{1.5cm}} = \underline{\hspace{1.5cm}}$$

$$d = \sqrt{370\,000} + \underline{\hspace{1.5cm}} \qquad\qquad d = \underline{\hspace{1.5cm}} + 600$$

$$d \approx \underline{\hspace{1.5cm}} \qquad\qquad\qquad d \approx \underline{\hspace{1.5cm}}$$

Since a negative horizontal distance is not reasonable in this problem, the pumpkin travels a

horizontal distance of \underline{\hspace{1.5cm}} m.

📖 For additional examples, see pages 236–239 of *Pre-Calculus 11*.

Check Your Understanding

Practise

1. State the value of c that makes each of the following a perfect square.

   a) $x^2 - 12x + c$ **b)** $x^2 - 3x + c$

   c) $x^2 + \frac{1}{4}x + c$ **d)** $x^2 + 0.8x + c$

2. Solve each of the following by completing the square. Express your answers as exact values.

   a) $x^2 - 8x = 9$

   Determine the value that must be added to make the left side a perfect square.

   $$\left(\frac{1}{2}(8)\right)^2 = \underline{\hspace{2cm}}$$

   > What value in the equation have you multiplied by half and then squared?

   Add this value to both sides of the equation.

   $$x^2 - 8x + 16 = 9 + \underline{\hspace{2cm}}$$

   $$(x - \underline{\hspace{2cm}})^2 = 25$$

   Take the square root of both sides.

   $$x - \underline{\hspace{2cm}} = \pm \underline{\hspace{3cm}}$$

   So, $x - \underline{\hspace{2cm}} = \underline{\hspace{2cm}}$ or $x - \underline{\hspace{2cm}} = \underline{\hspace{2cm}}$.

   $$x = \underline{\hspace{2cm}} \text{ or } \qquad\qquad x = \underline{\hspace{2cm}}$$

   b) $x^2 + 6x = 27$ **c)** $x^2 + 10x + 5 = 0$

   d) $x^2 - 2x - 39 = 0$ **e)** $x^2 + 3x = \frac{15}{4}$

3. Solve each of the following. Express your answers as exact values.

   a) $(x-2)^2 = 9$ **b)** $(x+5)^2 = 49$

   c) $\left(x + \dfrac{2}{3}\right)^2 = 1$ **d)** $\left(x - \dfrac{7}{5}\right)^2 = \dfrac{36}{25}$

4. Solve. Express your answers as exact values.

   a) $2x^2 - 12x = 110$ **b)** $3x^2 - 12x = 18$

      Remove a common factor of _____.

      _____$(x^2 - $_____$) = 110$

      Divide both sides of the equation by 2.

      $x^2 - 6x = $ _____

      Complete the square and solve for x.

   c) $0.5x^2 + 8.5 = 5x$ **d)** $\dfrac{1}{4}x^2 + x - \dfrac{7}{2} = 0$

Completing #3 and 4 will help you answer #6 and 7 on page 241 of *Pre-Calculus 11*.

Apply

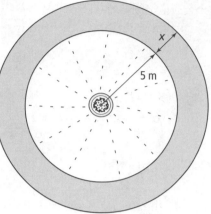

5. A sprinkler waters a circular area of diameter 10 m. A designer wants to make a sprinkler that will spray over a larger circular area.

a) If the radius of the new circle will be *x* metres more than the radius of first circle, write a quadratic expression for the area of the larger circle.

$$A = \pi r^2$$

b) If the new circle is to have an area of 150 m², determine the amount that the radius needs to increase, to the nearest tenth of a metre.

6. A rectangular storage room measures 6 feet by 8 feet. Aimee wants to triple the area of the room by moving each wall by the same amount.

a) Sketch and label a diagram for this situation.

b) Write an equation to determine the new area.

c) Solve your equation to determine the dimensions of the new storage room. Express your answer to the nearest tenth of a foot.

📖 Your work on this question should help you solve 8 on page 241 of *Pre-Calculus 11*.

7. Kara solved the equation $x^2 - x - 5 = 0$ as shown. Identify Kara's error. Then, write the correct solution to the quadratic as an exact value.

$$x^2 - x = 5$$
$$x^2 - x + 1 = 5 + 1$$
$$(x - 1)^2 = 6$$
$$x = \sqrt{6} + 1 \text{ or } x = -\sqrt{6} + 1$$

8. A Pythagorean triple is a set of three natural numbers that satisfy the Pythagorean Theorem. For example, the numbers 3, 4, and 5 form a Pythagorean triple because $3^2 + 4^2 = 5^2$. Another Pythagorean triple can be written as $8^2 + x^2 = (x + 2)^2$. Determine the numbers in this Pythagorean triple.

9. The height of a golf ball, in yards, is $h(d) = -0.02d^2 + 2d$, where d is the horizontal distance the ball has travelled, in yards, after being struck. Determine how far the ball travels before it first strikes the ground.

$-0.02d^2 + 2d =$ _____

How high is the ball when it hits the ground?

Connect

10. Write a quadratic equation that cannot be solved by completing the square. Justify your answer.

11. In Chapters 3 and 4, you have used the process of completing the square in different ways. Explain how you know when to complete the square to find solutions to quadratic equations and when to complete the square to find other properties of quadratic functions.

⟪ **KEY IDEAS** ⟫

Definition		
Term	**Description**	**Examples**
Quadratic formula	$x = \dfrac{-b \pm \sqrt{b^2 - 4ac}}{2a}$ • You can use this formula to solve a quadratic equation of the form $ax^2 + bx + c = 0,\ a \neq 0$.	For the quadratic equation $2x^2 - 12x - 4 = 0,$ $a = 2, b = -12,$ and $c = -4.$ $x = \dfrac{-b \pm \sqrt{b^2 - 4ac}}{2a}$ $x = \dfrac{-(-\mathbf{12}) \pm \sqrt{(-\mathbf{12})^2 - 4(\mathbf{2})(-\mathbf{4})}}{2(\mathbf{2})}$ $x = \dfrac{12 \pm \sqrt{144 - (-32)}}{4}$ $x = \dfrac{12 \pm \sqrt{176}}{4}$ $x \approx 6.32$ or $x \approx -0.32$
Discriminant	• the expression under the radical sign in the quadratic formula: $b^2 - 4ac$	For the above example: $(-\mathbf{12})^2 - 4(\mathbf{2})(-\mathbf{4}) = 144 + 32$ $\qquad\qquad\qquad\qquad = 176$

Working With the Quadratic Formula	Example
If exact values are required, use your skills for reducing radicals to write the value resulting from $\sqrt{b^2 - 4ac}$ in simplest radical form. Then, write any resulting fractions in lowest terms.	$x = \dfrac{12 \pm \sqrt{176}}{4}$ $x = \dfrac{12 \pm \sqrt{(16)(11)}}{4}$ $x = \dfrac{12 \pm 4\sqrt{11}}{4}$ $x = 3 \pm \sqrt{11}$

Working With the Discriminant		
If $b^2 - 4ac > 0$, there are two distinct real roots. The graph intersects the x-axis at two points. 	If $b^2 - 4ac = 0$, there is one distinct real root or two equal real roots. The graph intersects the x-axis at one point. 	If $b^2 - 4ac < 0$, there are no real roots. The graph does not intersect the x-axis.

Working Example 1: Use the Discriminant to Determine the Nature of the Roots

Determine the nature of the roots for each quadratic equation. Check your answer.

a) $5x^2 - 7x + 4 = 0$

b) $x^2 + 8 = -6x$

c) $4x^2 = 20x - 25$

> Note that the question does not ask you to determine the roots. The question just asks you to determine how many roots there are.

Solution

a) For $5x^2 - x + 4 = 0$, $a =$ _____, $b =$ _____, and $c =$ _____.
Substitute the values of a, b, and c into the discriminant.

$b^2 - 4ac = ($_____$)^2 - 4($_____$)($_____$)$

$b^2 - 4ac =$ _____

Since the discriminant is _____ 0,
$\quad\quad\quad\quad\quad$ (=, <, or >)
the equation has _____ root(s).

Check your answer by graphing the corresponding function $f(x) = 5x^2 - 7x + 4$. You can see that there are no x-intercepts, thus there are no real roots.

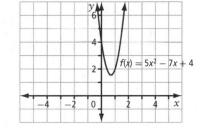

b) First, rewrite the equation in the form $ax^2 + bx + c = 0$.

$$x^2 + 8 = -6x$$

$x^2 +$ _____ $+$ _____ $= 0$

So, $a =$ _____, $b =$ _____, and $c =$ _____.

Calculate the value of the discriminant.

$b^2 - 4ac = ($_____$)^2 - 4($_____$)($_____$)$

$b^2 - 4ac =$ _____

Since the value of the discriminant is _____ 0, the equation has _____ root(s).
$\quad\quad\quad\quad\quad\quad\quad\quad\quad\quad$ (=, <, or >)

Check your answer by factoring.

$$x^2 + 6x + 8 = 0$$

($_____$)($_____$) $= 0$

This confirms that the equation has _____ roots. Note that you do not need to know the values of the roots in this case; this check simply confirms how many roots exist.

c) First, rewrite the equation in the form $ax^2 + bx + c = 0$.

$4x^2 - 20x + 25 = 0$

$a = \underline{\hspace{1cm}}, b = \underline{\hspace{1cm}}, c = \underline{\hspace{1cm}}$

The value of the discriminant, $b^2 - 4ac$, is

$(\underline{\hspace{1cm}})^2 - 4(\underline{\hspace{1cm}})(\underline{\hspace{1cm}}) = \underline{\hspace{1cm}}.$

Since the value of the discriminant is $\underline{\hspace{2cm}}$ 0, the equation has $\underline{\hspace{1cm}}$ root(s). $\qquad\quad (=, <, \text{ or } >)$

You can check your solution by writing the quadratic function in vertex form, $y = a(x - p)^2 + q$.

$$y = 4x^2 - 20x + 25$$

$$y = (4x^2 - 20x) + 25$$

$$y = \underline{\hspace{1cm}}(x^2 - \underline{\hspace{1cm}} x) + 25$$

$$y = 4(x^2 - 5x + 6.25 - 6.25) + 25$$

$$y = 4(x - \underline{\hspace{1cm}})^2 - 4(6.25) + 25$$

$$y = \underline{\hspace{1cm}}$$

The coordinates of the vertex are (p, q) in the vertex form. Therefore, the vertex for this

parabola is at ($\underline{\hspace{1.5cm}}$). Since the vertex of the parabola is on the $\underline{\hspace{1cm}}$-axis, you

know that the graph has one real root or $\underline{\hspace{2cm}}$ roots.

📖 For additional examples about the nature of roots, see pages 246–247 of *Pre-Calculus 11*.

Working Example 2: Use the Quadratic Formula to Solve Quadratic Equations

Use the quadratic formula to solve each of the following. Express your answers as exact values.

a) $x^2 + 6x = 1$ **b)** $3x^2 = 8x - 3$

Solution

a) First, rewrite the equation in the form $ax^2 + bx + c = 0$.

$x^2 + 6x - 1 = 0$

$a = \underline{\hspace{1cm}}, b = \underline{\hspace{1cm}}, c = \underline{\hspace{1cm}}$

$x = \dfrac{-b \pm \sqrt{b^2 - 4ac}}{2a}$

> Substitute the values of a, b, and c in the quadratic formula.

$x = \dfrac{-6 \pm \sqrt{\boxed{}^2 - 4(\boxed{})(\boxed{})}}{2(\boxed{})}$

$x = \dfrac{-6 \pm \sqrt{40}}{2}$

Write $\sqrt{40}$ as a mixed radical.

> What factors of 40 are used to rewrite $\sqrt{40}$ as a mixed radical?

$x = \dfrac{-6 \pm \underline{\hspace{1cm}} \sqrt{\underline{\hspace{1cm}}}}{2}$

$x = -3 \pm \underline{\hspace{1.5cm}}$ Divide through by 2.

The two roots of the equation are $x = -3 + \underline{\hspace{1.5cm}}$ or $x = -3 - \underline{\hspace{1.5cm}}$.

b) First, rewrite the equation in the form $ax^2 + bx + c = 0$.

$\underline{\hspace{3.5cm}} = 0$

$x = \dfrac{-b \pm \sqrt{b^2 - 4ac}}{2a}$

$x = \dfrac{-(\boxed{}) \pm \sqrt{(\boxed{})^2 - 4(\boxed{})(\boxed{})}}{2(\boxed{})}$

$x = \dfrac{(\boxed{}) \pm \sqrt{(\boxed{})^2 - 4(\boxed{})(\boxed{})}}{2(\boxed{})}$

$x = \dfrac{8 \pm \sqrt{28}}{6}$

Reduce the radical in the expression to a mixed radical.

$x = \dfrac{8 \pm \boxed{}\sqrt{7}}{\boxed{}}$

$x = \dfrac{\boxed{} \pm \sqrt{\boxed{}}}{3}$ Divide through by 2.

So, $x = \underline{\hspace{2.5cm}}$ or $x = \underline{\hspace{2.5cm}}$.

Working Example 3: Use a Quadratic to Model a Situation

The drama club is painting a set of parabolic arches on a backdrop. To make sure that the arches are identical, they use the equation $y = 2x^2 - 3.66x + 0.93025$, where all measurements are in metres. They need to find the width of the bottom of each arch to know if the arches will properly fit on the backdrop.

a) Determine the roots of the quadratic equation. Express your answer to the nearest hundredth of a metre.

b) State the width of each arch where it touches the floor. Express your answer to the nearest hundredth of a metre.

Solution

a) $-2x^2 + 3.66x - 0.93025 = 0$

$a =$ _____ , $b =$ _____ , $c =$ _____

To find the roots, substitute the values of a, b, and c into the quadratic formula and solve.

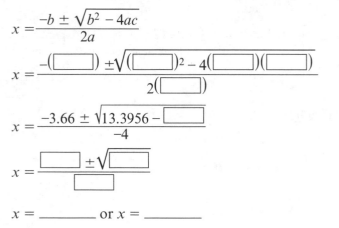

$$x = \frac{-b \pm \sqrt{b^2 - 4ac}}{2a}$$

$$x = \frac{-(\boxed{}) \pm \sqrt{(\boxed{})^2 - 4(\boxed{})(\boxed{})}}{2(\boxed{})}$$

$$x = \frac{-3.66 \pm \sqrt{13.3956 - \boxed{}}}{-4}$$

$$x = \frac{\boxed{} \pm \sqrt{\boxed{}}}{\boxed{}}$$

$x =$ _____ or $x =$ _____

| How do you make sure that your calculator performs the operations in the intended order? |

b) To calculate the distance across the bottom of the arch, subtract the roots.

| Why does subtracting the two roots result in the width of the arch at its base? |

_____ – _____ = _____

The width of each arch at its widest point, to the nearest hundredth of a metre, is _____ m.

📖 For additional examples using the quadratic formula, see pages 248–252 of *Pre-Calculus 11*.

Check Your Understanding

Practise

1. Use the discriminant to determine the number of roots for each. Use technology to check your answers graphically.

   a) $16x^2 + 8x + 1 = 0$

   b) $2x^2 + 7x - 3 = 0$

   c) $-2x^2 + 7x - 9 = 0$

   d) $3x^2 - 6x + 3 = 0$

2. Use the quadratic formula to solve each of the following. Express your answers as exact values.

   a) $3x^2 + 2 = 6x$

   b) $6x^2 + x = 2$

   c) $9x^2 = 12x - 2$

   d) $4x^2 - 5x = 2$

3. Solve each of the following using the quadratic formula. Express your answers as approximate values, to the nearest tenth.

  a) $-x^2 + 1 = -x$

  b) $3x^2 + 1 = 7x$

  c) $2x^2 - 17x - 30 = 0$

  d) $0.25x^2 - 0.5x = 1.3$

📖 For more practice using the quadratic formula, see page 254 of *Pre-Calculus 11*.

Apply

Use the quadratic formula to answer the following. For questions 4 to 8, decide whether to express your answer as an exact value or a decimal approximation.

4. Five times a number less the square of the number is equal to the negative of the number. Determine the number.

5. Two numbers have a sum of 15 and a product of 36. Determine the numbers.

6. Tee-Jay has a photo that measures 10 cm by 15 cm. He wants to fix it to a mat, so that there is a border of uniform width around the photo. The mat and photo will have an area of 500 cm². What should the width of the mat be?

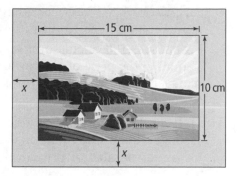

7. A batter hits a baseball straight up. The ball's height, h, in metres, is given by $h(t) = -4.9t^2 + 21t + 1.2$, where t is time, in seconds. (Hint: Draw a sketch of this situation.)

   a) How long, to the nearest hundredth of a second, will the ball be in the air before it lands on the ground?

   b) How long is the ball in the air, to the nearest hundredth of a second, if a fielder catches it when it is 1 m from the ground?

   c) Why do you disregard one of the roots in parts a) and b)?

8. The path of a firework that is launched from the ground can be approximated by the quadratic function $h = -0.05d^2 + 3d + 15$, where d is the horizontal distance, in metres. Determine the width of the opening of the parabola formed by the smoke trail of the firework. Express your answer to the nearest hundredth of a metre.

Connect

9. A store sells 100 calculators every year at $125 each. The revenue that these sales create is equal to the price of the calculator times the number of calculators sold. The store's manager wants to raise the price, but has learned that for every $5 price increase he can expect to sell two fewer calculators.

   a) If n is the number of $5 price increases, fill in the following table. In the last cell, you will have a quadratic equation that can be used to calculate the revenue from calculator sales for any number of price increases.

	Present Price ($)	Changed Price ($)
Cost of a calculator	_____	$(125 + \text{_____}n)$
Number sold	_____	$(100 - \text{_____}n)$
Revenue	$r = (\text{_____})(\text{_____})$	$r(n) = (\text{_____})(\text{_____})$

   b) Explain the expression in each cell in the third column of the table.

   c) Explain how you would determine the range of prices at which calculators must be sold if the store needs to generate at least $14 000 annually from calculator sales. Do the calculation and state the range of prices.

Chapter 4 Review

4.1 Graphical Solutions of Quadratic Equations, pages 147–155

1. Use the graph to state the roots of each equation.

a)

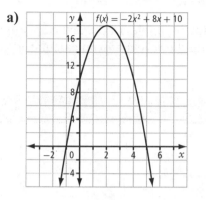

b)

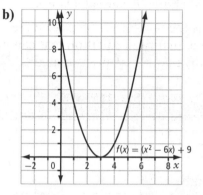

2. Explain which properties dictate the number of x-intercepts for each of the following. Then, sketch a sample of each type of graph on the same set of axes.

   a) two distinct real roots

   b) one real root

   c) no real roots

3. Graph the following. From your graph, state the roots to the nearest tenth.

a) $y = x^2 - 10x + 20$

b) $y = 0.5(x - 11)^2 - 3$

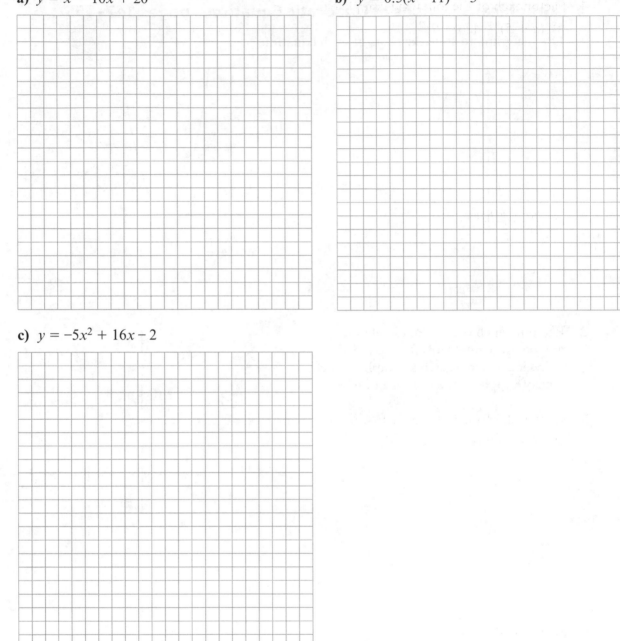

c) $y = -5x^2 + 16x - 2$

4.2 Factoring Quadratic Equations, pages 156–164

4. Factor each of the following completely.

    a) $(a + 5)^2 - 49(b - 9)^2$
    b) $(x - 6)^2 + 10(x - 6) + 9$

    c) $\dfrac{9m^2}{16} - \dfrac{100n^2}{81}$

5. Solve each of the following equations by factoring. Verify your answers.

    a) $x^2 + 6x + 8 = 0$
    b) $3x^2 - 5x + 2 = 0$

    c) $4x^2 + 27 = 24x$
    d) $36x^2 - 81 = 0$

6. One side of an envelope is 3 inches longer than the other side. The area of the envelope is 108 in.^{2}. Determine the dimensions of the envelope. (Sketch a diagram to help you with your solution.)

4.3 Solving Quadratic Equations by Completing the Square, pages 165–171

7. Solve each of the following. State your answers as exact values.

   a) $x^2 = 169$

   b) $(x + 7)^2 = 121$

   c) $(x - 12)^2 = 80$

   d) $-3(x + 1)^2 = -48$

8. Solve each of the following by completing the square. State your answers as exact values and as approximations to the nearest tenth.

   a) $x^2 + 8x = 7$

   b) $2x^2 - 20x + 14 = 0$

9. The profit, p, earned from the sale of a particular product by a business is given by $p(d) = -0.25d^2 + 5d + 80$, where d is the number of days the product has been for sale. Solve this equation by completing the square to determine the last day on which the product will be profitable.

4.4 The Quadratic Formula, pages 172–180

10. Use the discriminant to decide the nature of the roots for each of the following.

What is the discriminant? What can it tell you?

   a) $2x^2 + 5x = 8$

   b) $x^2 = x + 12$

   c) $16x^2 + 49 = -56x$

   d) $7x^2 = 3x - 2$

11. Use the quadratic formula to solve each of the following. State your answers as exact values and as approximations to the nearest tenth.

   a) $x^2 + 10 = 10x$

   b) $5x^2 = 8 - 2x$

12. Solve each of the following using an algebraic method. Explain your choice of method.

   a) $x^2 + 4x = 21$

   b) $5x^2 - 13x - 6 = 0$

   c) $2x^2 + 9x = -3$

Chapter 4 Skills Organizer

Complete the missing information in the graphic organizer.

To solve graphically, I …	To solve by factoring, I …
Example:	Example:

A quadratic equation is …

To determine the nature of the roots, I …	To solve with the quadratic formula, I …
Example:	Example:

Chapter 5 Radical Expressions and Equations

5.1 Working With Radicals

<table>
<tr><td colspan="3">⟪   KEY IDEAS   ⟫</td></tr>
</table>

	Definitions	
Term	**Description**	**Examples**
Mixed radical	• the product of a monomial and a radical	index radical sign $-8\sqrt[3]{45}$ coefficient radicand
Entire radical	• radical with a coefficient of 1 or −1	$\sqrt{30},\ -\sqrt[3]{100},\ \sqrt{98y^3}$
Like radicals	• radicals with the same index and the same radicand	$9\sqrt{2}$ and $-5\sqrt{2}$ $\frac{1}{4}\sqrt[3]{7x^2}$ and $-\sqrt[3]{7x^2}$
Radical in simplest form	a radical term where the • radicand does not contain a fraction • radicand does not contain a factor that can be removed • denominator does not contain a radical	$\begin{aligned}\sqrt{20} &= \sqrt{4(5)}\\ &= \sqrt{4}(\sqrt{5})\\ &= 2\sqrt{5}\end{aligned}$

	Working With Radicals	
	Strategies	**Examples**
Compare and order radicals	• Convert mixed radicals to entire radicals. If the radicals have the same index, compare the radicands.	• Order $5\sqrt[3]{4},\ \sqrt[3]{153},\ \sqrt[3]{46}$ $\begin{aligned}5\sqrt[3]{4} &= \sqrt[3]{5^3(4)}\\ &= \sqrt[3]{125(4)}\\ &= \sqrt[3]{500}\end{aligned}$ So, $\sqrt[3]{46},\ \sqrt[3]{153},\ 5\sqrt[3]{4}$ are in ascending order.
	• Compare the coefficients of like radicals.	• $5\sqrt[3]{4},\ 7\sqrt[3]{4},\ 11\sqrt[3]{4}$ are in ascending order
	• Compare the indices of radicals with equal radicands. When the radicands are equal, the higher the indices, the smaller the number.	• $\sqrt[4]{16},\ \sqrt[3]{16},\ \sqrt[2]{16}$ are in ascending order
Adding and subtracting radicals	• Combine the coefficients of like radicals: $q\sqrt[n]{x} \pm r\sqrt[n]{x} = (q \pm r)\sqrt[n]{x}$, where n is a natural number $q, r,$ and x are real numbers • If n is even, then $x \geq 0$.	• $6\sqrt{2} + 4\sqrt{2} = 10\sqrt{2}$ • $6\sqrt{2} - 4\sqrt{2} = 2\sqrt{2}$

| Restrictions on variables in radicand | • Identify the values of the variables that make the radical a real number. For radicals to be real numbers,
  – denominators cannot be equal to zero
  – if the index is even, the radicand must be positive
  – if the index is odd, the radicand may be any real number | • $\dfrac{8}{\sqrt{0}}$ is undefined
• $\sqrt[4]{xy}$, $x \geq 0$, $y \geq 0$
• $\sqrt[5]{xy}$, no restrictions
• $\sqrt{-4}$ is undefined, but $\sqrt[3]{-8} = -2$ |

Working Example 1: Convert Mixed Radicals to Entire Radicals

Express each **mixed** radical in **entire** radical form. State the restrictions on the variables.

a) $5\sqrt{3}$ **b)** $2b\sqrt{b}$ **c)** $-4x\sqrt[3]{7x^2}$

Solution

a) $5\sqrt{3}$

$5 = \sqrt{\boxed{}}$ Write the coefficient, 5, as a square root.

$5\sqrt{3} = (\sqrt{5^2})(\sqrt{3})$ Multiply the radicands of the square roots.

$\phantom{5\sqrt{3}} = \sqrt{\boxed{}(3)}$

$\phantom{5\sqrt{3}} = \sqrt{\boxed{}}$

The entire radical form of $5\sqrt{3}$ is _____.

b) $2b\sqrt{b}$

$2b = \sqrt{\boxed{}}$ Write the coefficient, $2b$, as a square root.

> Is there any restriction on the value of b? Explain.

$2b\sqrt{b} = (\sqrt{4b^2})(\sqrt{b})$ Multiply the radicands.

$\phantom{2b\sqrt{b}} = \sqrt{\boxed{}(b)}$

$\phantom{2b\sqrt{b}} = \sqrt{\boxed{}}$

The entire radical form of $2b\sqrt{b}$ is $\sqrt{\boxed{}}$. Since the index is _____,

then b _____ 0.   (*odd* or *even*)

c) $-4x\sqrt[3]{7x^2}$

$-4x = \sqrt[3]{\boxed{}}$ Write the coefficient, $-4x$, as a cube root.

$-4x\sqrt[3]{7x^2} = (\sqrt[3]{-64x^3})(\sqrt[3]{7x^2})$ Multiply the radicands.

$\phantom{-4x\sqrt[3]{7x^2}} = \sqrt[3]{\boxed{}}$

The entire radical form of $-4x\sqrt[3]{7x^2}$ is $\sqrt[3]{\boxed{}}$. Since the index of the radical is

_____, the value of the variable x can be _____.
(*odd* or *even*)

📖 See page 274 of *Pre-Calculus 11* for more examples.

Working Example 2: Express Entire Radicals as Mixed Radicals

Express each entire radical as a mixed radical in simplest form.

a) $\sqrt{192}$ **b)** $\sqrt[3]{y^7}$

Solution

a) $\sqrt{192}$

Method 1: Use the Greatest Perfect-Square Factor

The following perfect squares are factors of 192: 1, _____, _____, and _____.
Write $\sqrt{192}$ as a product using the greatest perfect-square factor.

$\sqrt{192} = \sqrt{\boxed{}(3)}$

$\phantom{\sqrt{192}} = (\sqrt{64})(\sqrt{3})$

$\phantom{\sqrt{192}} = \underline{}\sqrt{3}$

> How might a table help you find the greatest perfect square?

Therefore, $\sqrt{192}$ written as a mixed radical is _____.

> How can you verify the answer?

Method 2: Use Prime Factorization

Express 192 as a product of prime factors.

$\sqrt{192} = \sqrt{(2)(2)(2)(2)(2)(2)(\boxed{})}$

Since the index is 2, combine pairs of identical factors.

$\sqrt{192} = \sqrt{(2^2)(2^2)(2^2)(\boxed{})}$

$\phantom{\sqrt{192}} = (2)(2)(2)\sqrt{\boxed{}}$

$\phantom{\sqrt{192}} = \underline{}\sqrt{3}$

Therefore, $\sqrt{192}$ written as a mixed radical is _____.

b) $\sqrt[3]{y^7}$

Method 1: Use Prime Factorization

Express the radicand as a product of prime factors.

$\sqrt[3]{y^7} = \sqrt[3]{(y)\boxed{}}$

Since the index is _____, combine triplets (groups of three) of identical factors.

$\sqrt[3]{y^7} = \sqrt[3]{(y)(\boxed{})(\boxed{})}$

$\phantom{\sqrt[3]{y^7}} = (y)(y)\sqrt[3]{\boxed{}}$

$\phantom{\sqrt[3]{y^7}} = y^2\sqrt[3]{\boxed{}}$

Therefore, $\sqrt[3]{y^7}$ written as a mixed radical is _____.

Method 2: Use Powers

$$\sqrt[3]{y^7} = y^{\frac{7}{3}}$$

Write the rational exponent as the sum of a whole number and a fraction.

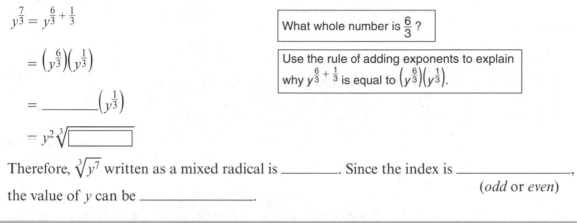

$$y^{\frac{7}{3}} = y^{\frac{6}{3} + \frac{1}{3}}$$

What whole number is $\frac{6}{3}$?

$$= \left(y^{\frac{6}{3}}\right)\left(y^{\frac{1}{3}}\right)$$

Use the rule of adding exponents to explain why $y^{\frac{6}{3} + \frac{1}{3}}$ is equal to $\left(y^{\frac{6}{3}}\right)\left(y^{\frac{1}{3}}\right)$.

$$= \underline{\hspace{1.5cm}} \left(y^{\frac{1}{3}}\right)$$

$$= y^2 \sqrt[3]{\boxed{}}$$

Therefore, $\sqrt[3]{y^7}$ written as a mixed radical is _____. Since the index is _____, the value of y can be _____.

(*odd* or *even*)

📖 Compare these methods to those on page 275 of *Pre-Calculus 11*.

Working Example 3: Compare and Order Radicals

Without using technology, arrange the following real numbers in ascending order.

$\sqrt{149}$, 13, $4\sqrt{10}$, $2(42)^{\frac{1}{2}}$, $3\sqrt{19}$

Ascending is from least to greatest. What is the arrangement greatest to least called?

Solution

Express each number as an entire radical.

$\sqrt{149}$ is already written as an _____.

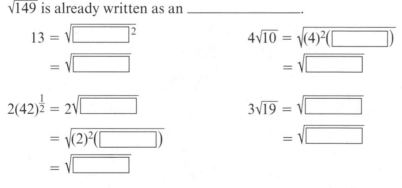

$$13 = \sqrt{\boxed{}^2}$$
$$= \sqrt{\boxed{}}$$

$$4\sqrt{10} = \sqrt{(4)^2(\boxed{})}$$
$$= \sqrt{\boxed{}}$$

$$2(42)^{\frac{1}{2}} = 2\sqrt{\boxed{}}$$
$$= \sqrt{(2)^2(\boxed{})}$$
$$= \sqrt{\boxed{}}$$

$$3\sqrt{19} = \sqrt{\boxed{}}$$
$$= \sqrt{\boxed{}}$$

All these radicals have the same indices. Compare the five radicands and order them from least to greatest: $\sqrt{149} < \sqrt{\boxed{}} < \sqrt{\boxed{}} < \sqrt{\boxed{}} < \sqrt{171}$.

The real numbers written in ascending order are _____.

📖 Compare these methods to those on page 276 of *Pre-Calculus 11*.

Working Example 4: Add and Subtract Radicals

Simplify the radicals and combine like terms.

a) $\sqrt{27} + 2\sqrt{12}$ **b)** $5\sqrt{8} - 3\sqrt{18} + \sqrt{3}$ **c)** $3\sqrt{32a} - 4\sqrt{162a}$, $a \geq 0$

> Explain the restriction on the variable for part c).

Solution

a) $\sqrt{27} + 2\sqrt{12}$

Rewrite each radical as a mixed radical in simplest form.

$\sqrt{27} = \sqrt{(\boxed{})(3)}$ $2\sqrt{12} = 2\sqrt{(\boxed{})(3)}$

$\quad = \underline{}\sqrt{3}$ $\quad = \underline{}\sqrt{3}$

$3\sqrt{3}$ and $4\sqrt{3}$ are like radicals because _____.
Therefore, add the coefficients.

$\sqrt{27} + 2\sqrt{12} = 3\sqrt{3} + 4\sqrt{3}$

$\qquad\qquad = \underline{}$

b) $5\sqrt{8} - 3\sqrt{18} + \sqrt{3}$

Rewrite each radical as a mixed radical in simplest form.

$5\sqrt{8} = \underline{}$, $3\sqrt{18} = \underline{}$, $\sqrt{3}$ is already in simplest form

The like radicals are _____ and _____. Since $\sqrt{3}$ has a different _____, it is not a like radical with the other two terms.

$5\sqrt{8} - 3\sqrt{18} + \sqrt{3} = \underline{}\sqrt{2} - 9\sqrt{2} + \sqrt{3}$

$\qquad\qquad = \underline{}$

c) $3\sqrt{32a} - 4\sqrt{162a}$

$3\sqrt{32a} = 3\sqrt{16(\boxed{})a}$ $4\sqrt{162a} = 4\sqrt{(\boxed{})2a}$

$\quad = (3)(\underline{})\sqrt{2a}$ $\quad = (4)(\underline{})\sqrt{2a}$

$\quad = \underline{}$ $\quad = \underline{}$

Since $12\sqrt{2a}$ and _____ have the same radicand, they are _____ radicals. Therefore,

add their _____.

$3\sqrt{32a} - 4\sqrt{162a} = \underline{} - \underline{}$

$\qquad\qquad = \underline{}$

📖 Compare these methods to those on pages 276–277 of *Pre-Calculus 11*.

Check Your Understanding

Practise

1. Complete the table.

Mixed Radical Form	$\sqrt{125} = \sqrt{(25)(5)}$ $= \underline{}\sqrt{5}$	$6\sqrt{7}$		$-5\sqrt{15}$		$3\sqrt[4]{6}$
Entire Radical Form	$\sqrt{125}$	$6\sqrt{7} = \sqrt{(6)^2(7)}$ $= \sqrt{\boxed{}}$	$\sqrt{63}$		$\sqrt[3]{-56}$	

2. Write each entire radical as a mixed radical in simplest form. Write each mixed radical as an entire radical. State any restrictions on the variables.

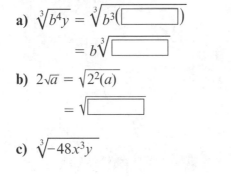

a) $\sqrt[3]{b^4y} = \sqrt[3]{b^3(\boxed{})}$

$= b\sqrt[3]{\boxed{}}$

> When the index is odd, is there any restriction on the variables? Explain.

b) $2\sqrt{a} = \sqrt{2^2(a)}$

$= \sqrt{\boxed{}}$

> When the index is even, what restriction is there on the variable?

c) $\sqrt[3]{-48x^3y}$

d) $\sqrt[4]{32a^5}$

e) $7y\sqrt{2z}$

f) $-3m^2\sqrt{5m}$

📖 #1 and 2 use the same concepts as #1 and 4 on pages 278 and 279 of *Pre-Calculus 11*.

3. From the following list, identify like radicals. Show your method.

> Like radicals have the same indices and the same radicands.

$\sqrt{63}, \sqrt[3]{250}, 4\sqrt[3]{16}, \sqrt{7}, -\sqrt{27}, 3\sqrt{75}$

4. State a radical expression that would form a like radical pair for each given expression.

a) $\sqrt{28} =$ _____ $\sqrt{7}$

$\sqrt{28}$ and _____ are like radicals.

> What is the index and radicand of $\sqrt{28}$ when it is reduced to its simplest form?

b) $7\sqrt[3]{2}$ and _____ are like radicals.

c) $-4\sqrt{2m}$ and _____ are like radicals.

d) $\sqrt[4]{32a^5}$ and _____ are like radicals.

> For parts d), e), and f), what do you need to do before you can find a like radical?

e) $-8x\sqrt{18}$ and _____ are like radicals.

f) $\sqrt{20xy^3}$ and _____ are like radicals.

📖 The concepts used in #3 and 4 are also used in #5 on page 279 of *Pre-Calculus 11*.

5. Arrange each set of numbers in descending order without using technology.

a) $-\sqrt{60}, -2\sqrt{17}, -5\sqrt{3}, -8$

b) $\sqrt{300}, \frac{3}{10}\sqrt{3500}, 18, 9\sqrt{\frac{15}{4}}$

c) $5, 3\sqrt[4]{8}, \sqrt[4]{615}, 4\sqrt[4]{\frac{9}{4}}$

6. Simplify each expression.

a) $\sqrt{7} - \sqrt{28} + 3\sqrt{63}$

b) $3\sqrt{175} - 6\sqrt{32} + \sqrt{98}$

c) $\sqrt[3]{9} + \sqrt{9} - 1$

d) $\sqrt[4]{48} - \frac{2}{3}\sqrt[4]{243}$

📖 #6 is similar to #8 and 9 on page 279 of *Pre-Calculus 11*.

7. Simplify each expression. State any restrictions on the variable.

a) $8\sqrt{m} - \sqrt{m} + 6\sqrt{m} = $ _____ $\sqrt{m}$, $m \geq$ _____

b) $5\sqrt{3x^3} - 3\sqrt{12x^3} = 5$ _____ $\sqrt{3\boxed{}} - 3$ _____ $\sqrt{\boxed{}}$

           $= $ _____ , $x \geq 0$

c) $\sqrt{32a^2b^3} - ab\sqrt{98b}$

d) $\frac{\sqrt{64y^3}}{2} - \sqrt{9y^3} + \frac{1}{5}\sqrt{25y^3}$

📖 #7 is similar to #10 on page 279 of *Pre-Calculus 11*.

Apply

Unless otherwise stated, express all answers as radicals in simplest form.

8. The flow-rate equation of a nozzle of a hose is $r = 6d^2P$, where r is the flow rate in gallons per minute, d is the diameter of the nozzle in inches, and P is the pressure of the nozzle in pounds per square inch. What is the diameter of a hose with nozzle pressure of 3 lb/in.^{2} and flow rate of 162 gal/min?

   The quantities in the formula I know are _____ and _____.

   > How do you rewrite the formula to isolate d?

9. The formula $t = \sqrt{\dfrac{2d}{g}}$ can be used to find the time, t, in seconds, it takes for an object to fall from a height or distance, d, in metres, using the force of gravity, g (9.8 m/s^2). A ball is dropped from the top of a building 122.5 m in height. How long does it take for the ball to reach the ground (ignoring other forces, such as air pressure)?

   > What values in the formula do you know?

10. Tyson has a square dog run with a perimeter of 32 ft. He wants to split the dog run diagonally. What is the length of the diagonal section of fencing that Tyson will need to install? Show your reasoning.

> Consider drawing a diagram when solving word problems.

11. Jodie has a rectangular piece of wood with a width of 4 ft and length of 16 ft. She is cutting it to create two large tables of the exact same size. She cuts the length diagonally to create two trapezoids. The smaller side of each trapezoid that results from the cut is 6 ft. What is the length of the diagonal cut, c? Show your reasoning.

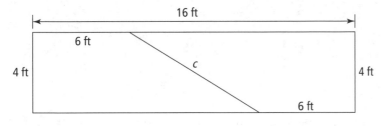

12. Tyrus is flying a kite. He lets out 155 ft of string, ties the string to a tent peg, and pounds the peg into the ground. He then measures the distance to the point directly below the kite. He finds this distance to be 85 ft. Assuming that the kite string is taut, how high is the kite? Show your reasoning.

Connect

13. Describe the error in the following simplification. Then, show the correct simplification.

$$\sqrt{16b} + \sqrt{4b} = \sqrt{20b}$$
$$= 2\sqrt{5b}$$

14. What radical expression could be added to $-3\sqrt{45} + 2\sqrt{12} + 3\sqrt{27} - 3\sqrt{20}$ to obtain a sum of $\sqrt{500} + \sqrt{300}$?

15. Use the relationship between the sides of a 45°-45°-90° triangle to show that the area of an isosceles right triangle can be found using the formula $A = \dfrac{s^2}{4}$, where s is the length of the hypotenuse and A is the area in square units.

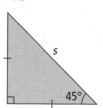

KEY IDEAS

Definitions		
Term	**Description**	**Examples**
Rationalize the denominator	• write an equivalent expression in which the denominator is a rational number	$\dfrac{3}{\sqrt{2}} = \dfrac{3(\sqrt{2})}{\sqrt{2}(\sqrt{2})}$ $= \dfrac{3\sqrt{2}}{2}$
Conjugates	• two binomial factors whose product is the difference of two squares • To find the conjugate of a binomial, reverse the sign of the second term in the binomial, creating the difference of two squares. The result is a rational number.	binomial: $4 - \sqrt{6}$ conjugate: $4 + \sqrt{6}$ Check: $(4 - \sqrt{6})(4 + \sqrt{6})$ $= 16 + 4\sqrt{6} - 4\sqrt{6} - 6$ $= 10$

Working With Radicals		
Action	**Strategies**	**Examples**
Rationalize the denominator when it contains a square root binomial	• The three steps to simplify an expression where the binomial in the denominator contains a radical are 1) find the conjugate of the denominator 2) multiply the numerator and denominator by the conjugate 3) simplify	• Simplify $\dfrac{3}{4 - \sqrt{6}}$. The conjugate of the denominator is $4 + \sqrt{6}$. $\dfrac{3}{4 - \sqrt{6}}\left(\dfrac{4 + \sqrt{6}}{4 + \sqrt{6}}\right)$ $= \dfrac{12 + 3\sqrt{6}}{16 + 4\sqrt{6} - 4\sqrt{6} - 6}$ $= \dfrac{12 + 3\sqrt{6}}{10}$
Multiply radicals with the same indices	• Multiply the coefficients and multiply the radicands: $(m\sqrt[k]{a})(n\sqrt[k]{b}) = mn\sqrt[k]{ab}$, where k is a natural number $m, n, a,$ and b are real numbers • If the index, k, is even, then $a \geq 0$ and $b \geq 0$. • When multiplying radicals with more than one term, use the distributive property and simplify.	• $(6\sqrt[4]{8})(3\sqrt[4]{5})$ $= (6)(3)\sqrt[4]{(8)(5)}$ $= 18\sqrt[4]{40}$ • $(6\sqrt[4]{8})(3\sqrt[4]{5 + x}), x \geq -5$ $= (6)(3)\left(\sqrt[4]{8(5 + x)}\right)$ $= 18\sqrt[4]{40 + 8x}$

Divide two radicals with the same indices	• Divide the coefficients and divide the radicands: $\dfrac{m\sqrt[k]{a}}{n\sqrt[k]{b}} = \dfrac{m}{n}\sqrt[k]{\dfrac{a}{b}}$, where k is a natural number m, n, a, and b are real numbers $n \neq 0, b \neq 0$ • If k is even, $a \geq 0, b > 0$.	$\dfrac{14\sqrt{6}}{2\sqrt{2}} = \left(\dfrac{14}{2}\right)\left(\dfrac{\sqrt{6}}{2}\right)$ $= 7\sqrt{3}$

Working Example 1: Multiply Radicals

Simplify.

a) $\left(3\sqrt{5}\right)\left(\sqrt{10}\right)$

b) $\left(4\sqrt{14x}\right)\left(2\sqrt{7x^3}\right)$, $x \geq 0$

c) $\sqrt{3}\left(-5\sqrt{10} + \sqrt{6}\right)$

d) $\left(5\sqrt{2x} + \sqrt{5}\right)\left(-4\sqrt{2x} + \sqrt{5x}\right)$, $x \geq 0$

e) $\left(7x\sqrt[3]{8xy^2}\right)\left(3\sqrt[3]{8x^2y^2}\right)$

Solution

a) The indices are the same, so the two can be multiplied.

$\left(3\sqrt{5}\right)\left(\sqrt{10}\right) = (\underline{\quad\quad})(\underline{\quad\quad})\sqrt{(\boxed{\quad})(\boxed{\quad})}$ Multiply the coefficients and multiply the radicands.

$= \underline{\quad\quad}\sqrt{50}$

$= (3)(5)\sqrt{\boxed{\quad}}$

$= 15\sqrt{2}$

b) $\left(4\sqrt{14x}\right)\left(2\sqrt{7x^3}\right) = (\underline{\quad\quad})(\underline{\quad\quad})\sqrt{(\boxed{\quad})(\boxed{\quad})}$

$= 8\sqrt{98x^4}$

$= 8(\underline{\quad\quad})(\underline{\quad\quad})\sqrt{2}$

$= \underline{\quad\quad}\sqrt{2}$

c) $\sqrt{3}\left(-5\sqrt{10} + \sqrt{6}\right) = \sqrt{3}(\underline{\quad\quad}) + \sqrt{3}(\underline{\quad\quad})$ Use the distributive property.

$= -5\sqrt{(\boxed{\quad})(\boxed{\quad})} + \sqrt{(\boxed{\quad})(\boxed{\quad})}$ Multiply the coefficients and the radicands.

$= -5\sqrt{30} + \sqrt{\boxed{\quad}}$

$= -5\sqrt{30} + \underline{\quad\quad}\sqrt{2}$

d) $(5\sqrt{2x} + \sqrt{5})(-4\sqrt{2x} + \sqrt{5x})$

$= \underline{\hspace{1cm}}(-4\sqrt{2x} + \sqrt{5x}) + \sqrt{5}\,(\boxed{\hspace{3cm}})$ Use the distributive property.

$= 5(-4)\sqrt{(2x)(2x)} + 5\sqrt{(2x)(5x)} + \left(-4\sqrt{(\boxed{\hspace{0.6cm}})(\boxed{\hspace{0.6cm}})}\right) + \sqrt{(\boxed{\hspace{0.6cm}})(\boxed{\hspace{0.6cm}})}$

$= -20(\underline{\hspace{1cm}}) + 5\underline{\hspace{1.5cm}}\sqrt{10} - 4\sqrt{10x} + 5\sqrt{\boxed{\hspace{0.6cm}}}$

$= -40x + 5x\sqrt{10} - 4\sqrt{10x} + 5\sqrt{x},\ x \geq 0$

e) $\left(7x\sqrt[3]{8xy^2}\right)\left(3\sqrt[3]{8x^2y^2}\right) = (\underline{\hspace{1.2cm}})(\underline{\hspace{1.2cm}})\sqrt[3]{(\boxed{\hspace{1.5cm}})(\boxed{\hspace{1.5cm}})}$

$= 21x\sqrt[3]{\boxed{\hspace{2cm}}}$ Group the perfect cube terms.

$= 21x\sqrt[3]{(4)^3 x^3 y^3(\boxed{\hspace{1.5cm}})}$ Simplify.

$= \underline{\hspace{1.5cm}}\sqrt[3]{y}$

Working Example 2: Divide Radicals

Simplify. Rationalize denominators where needed.

a) $\dfrac{\sqrt{15xy}}{\sqrt{5x}},\ x > 0,\ y \geq 0$ **b)** $\dfrac{8\sqrt{5}}{2\sqrt{3}}$

> Why are there restrictions on the variables in part a)?

c) $\dfrac{7}{5\sqrt{3} - \sqrt{2}}$ **d)** $\sqrt[3]{\dfrac{8k}{3}}$

> Why are there no restrictions on k in part d)?

Solution

a) $\dfrac{\sqrt{15xy}}{\sqrt{5x}} = \sqrt{\dfrac{15xy}{5x}}$ Divide the dividends.

$= \sqrt{\boxed{\hspace{0.8cm}}y},\ \text{where } x > 0,\ y \geq 0$

b) $\dfrac{8\sqrt{5}}{2\sqrt{3}} = \dfrac{\boxed{\hspace{0.6cm}}}{\boxed{\hspace{0.6cm}}}\sqrt{\dfrac{\boxed{\hspace{0.6cm}}}{\boxed{\hspace{0.6cm}}}}$ Divide the coefficients. Divide the dividends.

$= 4\sqrt{\dfrac{\boxed{\hspace{0.6cm}}}{\boxed{\hspace{0.6cm}}}}$

$= 4\dfrac{\sqrt{5}}{\sqrt{3}}\left(\dfrac{\sqrt{3}}{\sqrt{3}}\right)$ Rationalize the denominator.

$= \dfrac{4\sqrt{\boxed{\hspace{0.8cm}}}}{3}$ Simplify.

c) $\dfrac{7}{5\sqrt{3} - \sqrt{2}}$

Multiply the top and bottom by the conjugate of the denominator. What is the conjugate of $5\sqrt{3} - \sqrt{2}$? _____

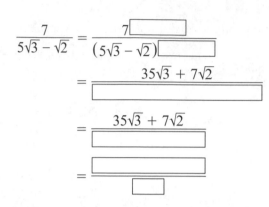

$$\dfrac{7}{5\sqrt{3} - \sqrt{2}} = \dfrac{7\boxed{}}{(5\sqrt{3} - \sqrt{2})\boxed{}}$$

$$= \dfrac{35\sqrt{3} + 7\sqrt{2}}{\boxed{}}$$

$$= \dfrac{35\sqrt{3} + 7\sqrt{2}}{\boxed{}}$$

$$= \boxed{}$$

> If the denominator was $\sqrt{3}$, you would rationalize the denominator by multiplying top and bottom by $\sqrt{3}$. In this case, why can't you multiply the numerator and denominator by $5\sqrt{3} - \sqrt{2}$? Try it.

d) $\sqrt[3]{\dfrac{8k}{3}} = \dfrac{\sqrt[3]{8k}}{\sqrt[3]{3}}$ Separate the radical into the quotient of two radicals.

$$= \dfrac{\boxed{}\sqrt[3]{k}}{\sqrt[3]{3}}$$ Simplify.

$$= \left(\dfrac{2\sqrt[3]{k}}{\sqrt[3]{3}}\right)\left(\dfrac{\boxed{}}{\boxed{}}\right)$$

$$= \dfrac{2\sqrt[3]{9k}}{\boxed{}}$$

> What would happen if you simply multiplied the numerator and denominator by $\sqrt[3]{3}$? Remember that you are multiplying by a value that allows you to get rid of the radical in the denominator.

📖 Compare these methods to those on pages 287–288 of *Pre-Calculus 11*.

Check Your Understanding

Practise

1. Multiply. Express as mixed radicals in simplest form.

   a) $(6\sqrt{3})(5\sqrt{2})$

   The product of the coefficients is _____. The product of the radicands is _____.

   $(6\sqrt{3})(5\sqrt{2}) =$ _____ $\sqrt{\boxed{}}$

   > Always check to see if you can simplify further. Can this term be simplified?

   b) $(4\sqrt{18a^2})(\sqrt{3a^2})$

   c) $(-5\sqrt{28x})(\sqrt{7x^3})$, where $x \geq 0$

   d) $(\sqrt[3]{81y^4})(\frac{1}{3}\sqrt[3]{9y^3})$

   📖 #1 uses the same concepts as #1 on page 289 of *Pre-Calculus 11*.

2. Multiply using the distributive property. Simplify.

   a) $2\sqrt{5}(\sqrt{6} + 2)$

   $= 2\sqrt{(\boxed{})(\boxed{})} +$ _____ $\sqrt{5}$

   $= 2\sqrt{\boxed{}} +$ _____ $\sqrt{5}$

   b) $\sqrt{3}(-5\sqrt{10} + \sqrt{6})$

   c) $\sqrt{14x}(3\sqrt{10} - \sqrt{2x})$, $x \geq 0$

   d) $\sqrt{21a}(5 - \sqrt{7a} + 2\sqrt{3})$, $a \geq 0$

   📖 #2 uses the same concepts as #2 on page 289 of *Pre-Calculus 11*.

3. Expand, using the distributive property. Simplify.

a) $(5 - 4\sqrt{3})(-2 + \sqrt{3})$

$= 5(-2 + \sqrt{3}) - 4\sqrt{3}(-2 + \sqrt{3})$

$= \underline{\hspace{1.5cm}} + \underline{\hspace{1.5cm}} \sqrt{\boxed{}} + \underline{\hspace{1.5cm}} \sqrt{\boxed{}} - \underline{\hspace{1.5cm}} \sqrt{\boxed{}}$

$= \underline{\hspace{1.5cm}} + \underline{\hspace{1.5cm}} \sqrt{\boxed{}}$

b) $(-2 - 3\sqrt{6})^2 = (-2 - 3\sqrt{6})(-2 - 3\sqrt{6})$

$= \underline{\hspace{4cm}}$

$= \underline{\hspace{4cm}}$

c) $(7 - 3\sqrt{5})(7 + 3\sqrt{5})$ **d)** $(\sqrt{7} - 4)(3\sqrt{3} + \sqrt{7} + 2)$

📖 #3 uses the same concepts as #4 on page 290 of *Pre-Calculus 11*.

---

4. Expand and simplify. State any restrictions on the values for the variables.

a) $(-3\sqrt{3k} + 4)(\sqrt{3k} - 5)$

$= \underline{\hspace{1.2cm}} \sqrt{\boxed{}} + \underline{\hspace{1.2cm}} \sqrt{\boxed{}} + \underline{\hspace{1.2cm}} \sqrt{\boxed{}} - \underline{\hspace{1.2cm}}$

$= \underline{\hspace{1.2cm}} + \underline{\hspace{1.2cm}} \sqrt{\boxed{}} - \underline{\hspace{1.2cm}}$, where $k \geq \underline{\hspace{1.2cm}}$

b) $(\sqrt{2} - 3\sqrt{5m})^2 = (\sqrt{2} - 3\sqrt{5m})(\sqrt{2} - 3\sqrt{5m})$

$= \underline{\hspace{3cm}}$

$= \underline{\hspace{3cm}}$, where $m \underline{\hspace{1.5cm}} 0$

c) $(5\sqrt{2x} + \sqrt{5})(-4\sqrt{2x} + \sqrt{5x})$ **d)** $\left(8\sqrt[3]{4y^2} - y\right)\left(\sqrt[3]{2y} + 5y\right)$

Since the index is 3, y can be $\underline{\hspace{3cm}}$.

📖 #4 uses the same concepts as #5 on page 290 of *Pre-Calculus 11*.

---

5. Divide. Rationalize the denominators, if necessary. Express each radical in simplest form.

a) $\dfrac{\sqrt{117}}{\sqrt{13}}$

b) $\dfrac{-5\sqrt{80}}{\sqrt{5}} =$ _____ $\sqrt{\dfrac{\Box}{\Box}}$

$=$ _____ $\sqrt{\Box}$

$=$ _____

c) $\dfrac{3\sqrt{28}}{4\sqrt{4}}$

d) $\dfrac{-3\sqrt{3a}}{4\sqrt{8a}}$, where $a > 0$

e) $\dfrac{\sqrt{15xy}}{\sqrt{10xy^3}}$, where $x > 0$ and $y > 0$

f) $\dfrac{3 - 3\sqrt{3a}}{4\sqrt{8a}}$, where $a > 0$

📖 #5 uses the same concepts as #6 and 8 on page 290 of *Pre-Calculus 11*.

6. Complete the table.

Binomial	Conjugate	Product of the Two Binomials
$4 + \sqrt{5}$		
$-5 - 3\sqrt{3}$		
$7\sqrt{5} + 4\sqrt{2}$		
$2\sqrt{z} - \sqrt{3}$, $z \geq 0$		

📖 #6 uses the same concepts as #9 on page 290 of *Pre-Calculus 11*.

7. Rationalize each denominator. Simplify.

a) $\dfrac{4}{\sqrt{2}-7} = \left(\dfrac{4}{\sqrt{2}-7}\right)\left(\dfrac{\sqrt{2}+7}{\sqrt{2}+7}\right)$

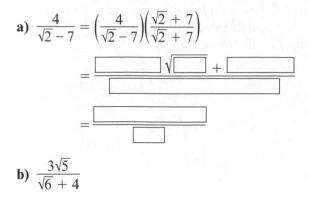

$= \dfrac{\boxed{}\sqrt{\boxed{}} + \boxed{}}{\boxed{}}$

$= \dfrac{\boxed{}}{\boxed{}}$

b) $\dfrac{3\sqrt{5}}{\sqrt{6}+4}$

c) $\dfrac{\sqrt{5}+2\sqrt{2}}{4-5\sqrt{5}}$

d) $\dfrac{9}{4-\sqrt{x}}$, where $x \geq 0$ and $x \neq 16$

📖 #7 uses the same concepts as #11 on page 290 of *Pre-Calculus 11*.

Apply

8. Express the volume of the right rectangular prism in simplest radical form.

$6\sqrt{2} - 2\sqrt{3}$

$\sqrt{10}$

$6\sqrt{2} + 2\sqrt{3}$

9. The lateral surface area of a cone can be found using the formula $LSA = \pi r \sqrt{r^2 + h^2}$, where r is the radius of the base and h is the height of the cone. Find the lateral surface area of the cone in the diagram. Write the answer in simplest radical form containing π.

> Lateral surface area, *LSA*, is the entire surface area, excluding the area of the base.

12 m

8 m

10. Find the area of the each of the following polygons. Express the answers in simplest radical form. Be sure to include units in your answers.

a)

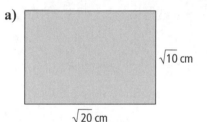

$\sqrt{10}$ cm

$\sqrt{20}$ cm

b)

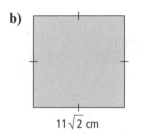

$11\sqrt{2}$ cm

c) a right triangle with legs of $6\sqrt{3}$ cm and $4\sqrt{2}$ cm

11. Tineka simplified the following expression. Identify and explain any errors. Then, correct the errors and state the correct solution.

$$(3\sqrt{2} - \sqrt{5})^2 = (3\sqrt{2})^2 - (\sqrt{5})^2$$
$$= 9(2) - 5$$
$$= 18 - 5$$
$$= 13$$

12. Without the use of technology, arrange the following expressions in ascending order.

$$\sqrt{7}(\sqrt{7} + 2), (\sqrt{7} + 2)(\sqrt{7} - 2), (2 - \sqrt{7})^2, (\sqrt{7} + 2)^2$$

13. To find the radius of a right cylinder, you can use the formula $r = \sqrt{\dfrac{V}{\pi h}}$, where r is the radius, V is the volume in cubic units, and h is the height. A grain silo is a right cylinder. It has a height of 14 m and a volume of 224 m³. Find the radius of the silo. Express the answer rounded to the nearest hundredth of a metre.

14. Anthony simplified the expression $\left(\dfrac{\sqrt{m}-2}{6-\sqrt{m}}\right)$ as shown. Identify any errors he made, including the restriction he has identified. Show the correct simplification and restriction(s) on the variable.

$$\left(\dfrac{\sqrt{m}-2}{6-\sqrt{m}}\right) = \left(\dfrac{\sqrt{m}-2}{6-\sqrt{m}}\right)\left(\dfrac{6+\sqrt{m}}{6+\sqrt{m}}\right)$$

$$= \dfrac{6\sqrt{m}-12+m}{6-m}$$

$$= 6\sqrt{m}-2, \text{ where } m > 0$$

Connect

15. State three conditions that must be true for a radical expression to be in simplest form.

16. Is the following statement true or false? Explain.

$$\left(\sqrt{-8}\right)\left(\sqrt{-2}\right) = 4$$

Chapter 5 Skills Organizer A

Complete the missing information in the chart for the topics in Section 5.1 and 5.2.

Entire Radical	Mixed Radical	Like Radical
An entire radical is…	A mixed radical is …	Like radicals are…
Example:	Example:	Example:

Strategy for converting entire radical to mixed radical:	Strategy for converting mixed radical to entire radical:

Comparing and Ordering Radicals	When radicals have the same index, I…	Example:
	If they are radicals, I…	Example:
	If they have the same radicand, I…	Example:

Multiplying Radicals	Dividing Radicals
If radicals have the same indices, I can multiply them by…	If radicals have the same indices, I can divide them by…
Example:	Example:

Radicals in Simplest Form	Conjugate
A radical is in simplest form if: 1) 2) 3)	A conjugate is: I use a conjugate to… Example:

KEY IDEAS

Solving a radical equation is similar to solving a linear or quadratic equation, as shown in the table.

Working With Radicals		
	Strategies	**Example**
Isolate one of the radical terms	• Perform the same mathematical operation on each side of the equation to isolate a radical term.	$\sqrt{4x} - 7 = 13,\ x > 0$ $\sqrt{4x} - 7 + 7 = 13 + 7$ $\sqrt{4x} = 20$
Eliminate a root	• For a square root, raise both sides of the equation to the exponent 2. • For a cube root, raise both sides of the equation to the exponent 3.	• $\sqrt{4x} = 20$ $(\sqrt{4x})^2 = (20)^2$ $4x = 400$ $x = 100$ • $\sqrt[3]{4x} = 20$ $(\sqrt[3]{4x})^3 = (20)^3$ $4x = 8000$ $x = 2000$
Check the answer or root	• Substitute the calculated value into the original equation to check.	Substitute $x = 100$. <table><tr><td>Left Side</td><td>Right Side</td></tr><tr><td>$\sqrt{4x} - 7$ $= \sqrt{4(\mathbf{100})} - 7$ $= \sqrt{400} - 7$ $= 20 - 7$ $= 13$</td><td>13</td></tr></table>
Extraneous root	• Check for a solution, or root, that does not satisfy the restrictions on the variable or does not make sense in the context of the problem.	• For $\sqrt{x}$, a root of $x = -3$ does not meet the restrictions because x must be greater than or equal to zero. • For an area problem, $A = -4$ does not make sense because you cannot have a negative area.

Working Example 1: Solve an Equation With One Radical Term

a) Solve $\sqrt{y-1} + 7 = 13$.

b) State the restrictions on y so the radical is a real number.

c) Verify the solution.

> If this equation was $x + 7 = 13$, how would you solve it?

Solution

a) Isolate the radical term.

$$\sqrt{y-1} + 7 = 13$$

$$\sqrt{y-1} + 7 - \underline{\hspace{1cm}} = 13 - \underline{\hspace{1cm}}$$

$$\sqrt{y-1} = \underline{\hspace{1cm}}$$

Raise both sides of the equation to the exponent 2.

$$\left(\sqrt{y-1}\right)^2 = 6^2$$

$$\underline{\hspace{1.5cm}} = \underline{\hspace{1.5cm}}$$

Solve for y.

$$y - 1 + \underline{\hspace{1.5cm}} = 36 + \underline{\hspace{1.5cm}}$$

$$y = \underline{\hspace{1.5cm}}$$

b) The radicand, $y - 1$, must be greater than or equal to zero for the radical to be a real number. So, for $y - 1 \geq 0$, $y \geq \underline{\hspace{1.5cm}}$.

c) The solution is 37, which satisfies the restriction. To check this solution, substitute 37 into the original equation.

Left Side	Right Side
$\sqrt{y-1} + 7$	13
$= \sqrt{37 - 1} + 7$	
$= \sqrt{36} + 7$	
$= 6 + 7$	
$= 13$	

Left Side = Right Side, so the solution $y = 37$ is correct.

Working Example 2: Radical Equation With an Extraneous Root

a) Solve the equation $m = \sqrt{2 - m}$.

b) Check the solution for extraneous roots.

> Remember that an extraneous root is one that does not fit the restrictions, or does not make sense in the context of the question.

c) State the restrictions on the variable so that the equation involves real numbers.

Solution

a) Raise both sides of the equation to the exponent 2.

$$m = \sqrt{2 - m}$$

$$m^2 = (\sqrt{2 - m})^2$$

$$m^2 = \underline{\hspace{2cm}}$$

Set the quadratic equation equal to 0 by subtracting the binomial from the right side.

$$m^2 + \underline{\hspace{1.5cm}} - \underline{\hspace{1.5cm}} = 2 - m + m - \underline{\hspace{1.5cm}}$$

$$m^2 + \underline{\hspace{1.5cm}} - \underline{\hspace{1.5cm}} = 0$$

Solve the quadratic equation by either factoring or using the quadratic formula.

Method 1: Use Factoring

$$m^2 + m - 2 = 0$$

$$(\underline{\hspace{1.5cm}})(\underline{\hspace{1.5cm}}) = 0$$

Use the zero product property by setting each factor equal to zero.

$$m + 2 = 0 \qquad\qquad m - 1 = 0$$

$$m = \underline{\hspace{1.5cm}} \qquad\qquad m = \underline{\hspace{1.5cm}}$$

So, $m = \underline{\hspace{1.5cm}}$ and $\underline{\hspace{1.5cm}}$.

Method 2: Use the Quadratic Formula

$$m^2 + m - 2 = 0$$

> What is the coefficient of a variable that does not have a number in front of it?

$$a = \underline{\hspace{1.5cm}} \qquad b = \underline{\hspace{1.5cm}} \qquad c = \underline{\hspace{1.5cm}}$$

Substitute into the quadratic formula, $m = \dfrac{-b \pm \sqrt{b^2 - 4ac}}{2a}$.

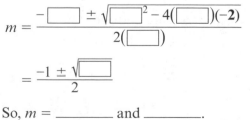

$$m = \frac{-\boxed{} \pm \sqrt{\boxed{}^2 - 4(\boxed{})(-2)}}{2(\boxed{})}$$

> When multiplying, do not forget about the negative sign that precedes 4 in the term "$-4ac$." What is $-4(-2)$?

$$= \frac{-1 \pm \sqrt{\boxed{}}}{2}$$

So, $m = \underline{\hspace{1.5cm}}$ and $\underline{\hspace{1.5cm}}$.

b) Check the two solutions by substituting into the original equation: $m = \sqrt{2-m}$.

For $m = 1$:

Left Side	Right Side
m	$\sqrt{2-m}$
1	$= \sqrt{2-\mathbf{1}}$
1	$=$ _____

Left Side _____ Right Side
(= or ≠)

For $m = -2$:

Left Side	Right Side
m	$\sqrt{2-m}$
−2	$= \sqrt{2-(\mathbf{-2})}$
−2	$=$ _____

Left Side _____ Right Side
(= or ≠)

Therefore, the solution is $m =$ _____. The value $m = -2$ is _____.

c) The radicand $2 - m$ must be positive for the radical equation to have a real value.

$$2 - m \geq 0$$
$$2 - m + m \geq 0 + m$$
$$2 \geq m$$

Written another way, m _____ 2. So, the value of m must be less than or equal to 2 for the value of the radical equation to be a real number. The solution $m = 1$ satisfies this condition.

Working Example 3: Solve an Equation With Two Radicals

Solve the radical equation $\sqrt{2x + 5} = 2\sqrt{2x} + 1$, $x \geq 0$. Check your solution.

Solution

$$\sqrt{2x + 5} = 2\sqrt{2x} + 1$$

Square both sides.

$$(\sqrt{2x + 5})^2 = (2\sqrt{2x} + 1)^2$$

$$\underline{\hspace{2cm}} = (\underline{\hspace{1.5cm}})(\underline{\hspace{1.5cm}})$$

$$2x + 5 = 4(2x) + \underline{\hspace{1.5cm}} + 1$$

$$2x + 5 = 8x + 4\sqrt{2x} + 1$$

> When squaring a binomial, a trinomial is formed.

$$2x + 5 - 8x - 1 = 8x - 8x + 4\sqrt{2x} + 1 - 1 \qquad \text{Isolate the remaining radical.}$$

$$-6x + 4 = 4\sqrt{2x}$$

$$(-6x + 4)^2 = (4\sqrt{2x})^2 \qquad \text{Square both sides.}$$

$$(\underline{\hspace{1.5cm}})(\underline{\hspace{1.5cm}}) = (\underline{\hspace{1.5cm}})(\underline{\hspace{1.5cm}})$$

$$36x^2 - \underline{\hspace{1.5cm}} + 16 = 32x \qquad \text{Simplify.}$$

Set the quadratic equal to zero.

$$36x^2 - 48x - \underline{\hspace{1.5cm}} + 16 = 32x - \underline{\hspace{1.5cm}}$$

$$36x^2 - 80x + 16 = 0$$

$$\underline{\hspace{1.5cm}}(9x^2 - 20x + \underline{\hspace{1.5cm}}) = 0 \qquad \text{Remove common factor.}$$

$$4(9x - \underline{\hspace{1.5cm}})(x - \underline{\hspace{1.5cm}}) = 0 \qquad \text{Factor.}$$

Using the zero property, set each factor equal to zero and solve.

$$9x - 2 = 0 \qquad\qquad\qquad x - 2 = 0$$

$$9x = \underline{\hspace{1.5cm}} \qquad\qquad\qquad x = \underline{\hspace{1.5cm}}$$

$$x = \underline{\hspace{1.5cm}}$$

Check $x = \dfrac{2}{9}$ and $x = 2$ by substituting into the original equation: $\sqrt{2x + 5} = 2\sqrt{2x + 1}$.

For $x = \dfrac{2}{9}$:

Left Side	Right Side
$\sqrt{2x + 5}$	$2\sqrt{2x} + 1$
$= \sqrt{2\left(\dfrac{2}{9}\right) + 5}$	$= \sqrt[2]{2\left(\dfrac{2}{9}\right)} + 1$
$= \underline{\hspace{1.5cm}}$	$= \sqrt[2]{\dfrac{4}{9}} + 1$
$= \underline{\hspace{1cm}}$	$= \underline{\hspace{1.5cm}}$
$= \dfrac{7}{3}$	$= \underline{\hspace{1cm}}$

Left Side _____ Right Side

(= or ≠)

For $x = 2$:

Left Side	Right Side
$\sqrt{2x + 5}$	$2\sqrt{2x} + 1$
$= \sqrt{2(2) + 5}$	$= \sqrt{2(2)} + 1$
$= \underline{\hspace{1.5cm}}$	$= \underline{\hspace{1.5cm}}$
$= \underline{\hspace{1.5cm}}$	$= \underline{\hspace{1.5cm}}$
$= \underline{\hspace{1.5cm}}$	$= \underline{\hspace{1.5cm}}$

Left Side _____ Right Side

(= or ≠)

Therefore, $x = \dfrac{2}{9}$ is a solution, but $x = 2$ is an extraneous root.

See pages 297–298 of *Pre-Calculus 11* for similar examples.

Check Your Understanding

Practise

1. Square each expression.

   a) $4x - 5$

   $$(4x - 5)^2 = (\underline{\hspace{1.5cm}})(\underline{\hspace{1.5cm}})$$

   $$= \underline{\hspace{1.5cm}}$$

   b) $\sqrt{7y}$, $y \geq 0$

   c) $\sqrt{2x - 3}$, $x \geq \dfrac{3}{2}$

   d) $6\sqrt{9m}$, $m \geq 0$

   $$(6\sqrt{9m})^2 = (6\sqrt{9m})(6\sqrt{9m})$$

   $$= \underline{\hspace{1.5cm}} (9m)$$

   $$= \underline{\hspace{1.5cm}}$$

   e) $3\sqrt{n} - 8$, $n \geq 0$

📖 #1 uses the same concepts as #1 on page 300 of *Pre-Calculus 11*.

---

2. Mitchell obtained $x = 6$ and $x = 2$ as the solutions to the radical equation $3 = x + \sqrt{2x - 3}$. Do you agree with Mitchell's solutions? Show your reasoning.

   For $x = \underline{\hspace{1.5cm}}$:

Left Side	Right Side

   For $x = \underline{\hspace{1.5cm}}$:

Left Side	Right Side

   Left Side $\underline{\hspace{1.5cm}}$ Right Side
   ($=$ or $\neq$)

   Left Side $\underline{\hspace{1.5cm}}$ Right Side
   ($=$ or $\neq$)

   Therefore, $\underline{\hspace{8cm}}$.

📖 #2 uses the same concepts as #5 on page 300 of *Pre-Calculus 11*.

---

3. Solve. State any restrictions and check for extraneous roots.

a) $\sqrt{x-2} = 9$

Square both sides.

Solve for x.

Verify.

b) $10 = \dfrac{\sqrt{m}}{10}$

c) $-8 + \sqrt{5a-5} = -3$

d) $p = \sqrt{2-p}$

e) $-n + \sqrt{6n+19} = 2$

f) $\sqrt{7c-54} - c = -6$

📖 #3 uses the same concepts as #3, 4, and 6 on page 300 of *Pre-Calculus 11*.

4. Solve. State any restriction on variables.

    a) $\sqrt{9x^2 + 4} = 3x + 2$ **b)** $\sqrt{2x^2 - 9} = 3 - x$

    c) $\sqrt{x}\left(\sqrt{x - 7}\right) = 12$

📖 #4 uses the same concepts as #7 and 8 on page 301 of *Pre-Calculus 11*.

---

5. Solve the following equation with two radicals. Check for extraneous roots.

    a) $\sqrt{3n} = \sqrt{4n - 1}$ **b)** $\sqrt{\dfrac{x}{10}} = \sqrt{3x - 58}$

    Square both sides.

    Solve for *n*.

    Verify.

    c) $\sqrt{2y + 3} = 1 + \sqrt{y + 1}$ **d)** $\sqrt{c + 7} + \sqrt{2c - 3} = 4$

📖 #5 uses the same concepts as #9 and 10 on page 301 of *Pre-Calculus 11*.

Apply

6. Examine the following steps that Su Ling used to solve the equation $4 + \sqrt{-3m + 10} = m$. Is her work correct? If not, solve correctly. Show your reasoning.

$$4 + \sqrt{-3m + 10} = m$$

$$\sqrt{-3m + 10} = m - 4$$

$$(\sqrt{-3m + 10})^2 = (m - 4)^2$$

$$-3m + 10 = m^2 - 16$$

$$0 = m^2 + 3m - 26$$

Substitute a, b, and c into the quadratic formula and solve.

$$a = 1, b = 3, c = 26$$

$$m = \frac{-b \pm \sqrt{b^2 - 4ac}}{2a}$$

$$m = \frac{-3 \pm \sqrt{3^2 - 4(1)(-26)}}{2(1)}$$

$$m = \frac{-3 \pm \sqrt{113}}{2}$$

📖 #6 uses the same concepts as #12 on page 301 of *Pre-Calculus 11*.

7. The kinetic energy, E_k, in joules, of a moving object can be expressed as $E_k = \frac{1}{2}mv^2$, where m is the mass, in kilograms, and v is the speed at which the body is moving, in metres per second.

   a) If the kinetic energy of a car with a mass of 1000 kg is 189 000 J, determine the car's speed to the nearest hundredth of a metre per second.

   b) State the speed of the object to the nearest kilometre per hour.

8. The speed, V, in feet per second of outflow of a liquid from an orifice is given by the formula $V = 8\sqrt{h}$, where h is the height, in feet, of the liquid above the opening. How high, to the nearest hundredth of a foot, is a liquid above an orifice if the velocity of outflow is 50 ft/s?

9. Strings of certain musical instruments are under tension. When they are plucked or struck, the speed of the wave of the string can be calculated using the formula $V = \sqrt{\dfrac{FL}{M}}$, where

   - V represents the speed of a wave on a string in metres per second
   - F represents the force of the tension in newtons
   - M represents the mass per unit length in kilograms
   - L represents the unit length in metres

   If a wave travels through a string with a mass of 0.2 kg at a speed of 9 m/s, it is stretched by 10.6 N. Use the formula to find the length of the string to the nearest thousandth of a metre.

10. The surface area of a cone (SA) with slant height (h) and radius of base (r) can be found using the formula $SA = \pi r^2 + \pi rh$. Find the radius of the base of the cone shown here.

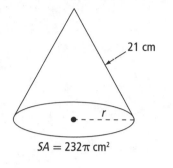

21 cm

r

$SA = 232\pi$ cm^2

Connect

11. Why does $a^2 - b^2 \neq (a - b)^2$?

   a) Explain algebraically.

   b) Explain by substituting values for a and b.

   c) Are there any values for a and b for which the two sides of the equation are equal? Explain.

12. Sandra was absent for the lesson on solving radical equations. Your teacher has asked you to help her catch up. Explain, step by step, the procedure for solving the equation $\sqrt{4n + 8} - 3 = n$.

13. a) Show that there is no solution to the equation $\sqrt{2a + 9} - \sqrt{a - 4} = 0$.

b) State an example of another radical equation that has no solution. Show why it has no solution.

5.1 Working With Radicals, pages 188–198

1. Convert each entire radical to a mixed radical in simplest form. State any restrictions on the variable(s).

   a) $\sqrt{288}$

   b) $\sqrt{128c^2}$

   c) $\sqrt{24a^4b^3}$

   d) $\sqrt[3]{250x^3y^5}$

2. Convert each mixed radical to an entire radical. State any restriction on the variable(s).

   a) 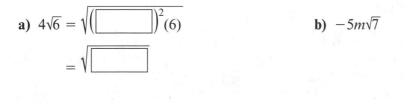 $4\sqrt{6} = \sqrt{\left(\boxed{}\right)^2(6)}$

   $= \sqrt{\boxed{}}$

   b) $-5m\sqrt{7}$

   c) $3y\sqrt[3]{2y^2}$

   d) $-2x\sqrt[4]{6xy^3}$

3. Simplify. State any restrictions on the values for the variables.

a) $3\sqrt{6} - 4\sqrt{6} =$ _____ $\sqrt{6}$

b) $-\sqrt{45} + 2\sqrt{5} - \sqrt{20}$

c) $-3\sqrt{18} + 3\sqrt{8x} - \sqrt{32x^3}$

d) $2\sqrt[3]{6x^2y} - \sqrt[3]{48x^2y}$

4. Put the following values in ascending order: $3\sqrt{30}$, $\sqrt{250}$, 16, $4\sqrt{15}$.

5. A wire is pulled taut between two posts. A weight is placed in the middle of the wire, which pulls the wire down at its centre by 2 ft. How long is the wire after the weight is place on it? Write the answer in simplest radical form.

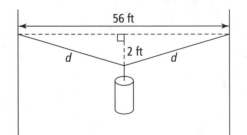

5.2 Multiplying and Dividing Radical Expressions, pages 199–209

6. Multiply. Express each product in simplest form. State any restrictions on the values for the variables.

a) $(\sqrt{6})(\sqrt{14})$

b) $(\sqrt{3x^2})(2\sqrt{3x^4})$

$$= \underline{\qquad} \sqrt{(\boxed{})(\boxed{})}$$

$$= \underline{\qquad}, \ x \underline{\qquad} 0$$

c) $(-10y\sqrt{5})(4\sqrt{50})$

d) $(5 - 4\sqrt{3})(3 + 3\sqrt{3})$

e) $(\sqrt{2} - 3\sqrt{5r})^2$

f) $(3 - \sqrt{2x})(3 + \sqrt{2x})$

7. Rationalize each denominator. State any restrictions on the values for the variable(s).

a) $\dfrac{4}{\sqrt{5}} = \left(\dfrac{4}{\sqrt{5}}\right)\left(\dfrac{\boxed{}}{\boxed{}}\right)$

$$= \underline{\qquad\qquad}$$

b) $\dfrac{-\sqrt{2}}{8\sqrt{3}}$

c) $\dfrac{3}{\sqrt{5} + 4}$

d) $\dfrac{3 + 4\sqrt{3}}{\sqrt{2} + 2\sqrt{5}}$

e) $\dfrac{\sqrt{15xy}}{\sqrt{10xy^3}}$

f) $\dfrac{3n^2 + \sqrt{2n^2}}{\sqrt{10n}}$

8. Write the conjugate of each expression.

   a) $\sqrt{3k} - 5$

   b) $-3\sqrt{2} - 4\sqrt{7}$

9. For the given right triangle, express the following in simplest radical form.

   a) the perimeter

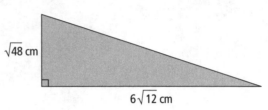

√48 cm

6√12 cm

   b) the area

5.3 Radical Equations, pages 211–222

10. Solve each radical equation. State any restrictions on the values for the variable(s).

   a) $-8 + \sqrt{5a - 5} = -3,\ a \geq$ _____

   $\sqrt{5a - 5} =$ _____

   $(\sqrt{5a - 5})^2 = ($ _____ $)^2$

   _____ $=$ _____

   $5a =$ _____

   $a =$ _____

   b) $\sqrt{2n - 88} = \sqrt{\dfrac{n}{6}}$

   c) $b - 6 = \sqrt{18 - 3b}$

   d) $\sqrt{x + 4} - \sqrt{x - 4} = 2$

11. Two adjacent sides of a parallelogram have the measures $\sqrt{14n - 45}$ cm and $2n$ cm. Determine the actual lengths of the two sides if the perimeter of the parallelogram is 54 cm.

12. The Japanese game called Chu Shogi uses a square board. The board is covered with smaller squares that are alternating black and white. Each of these squares is 3 cm by 3 cm. If the diagonal of the square playing board is $\sqrt{2592}$ cm, how many small squares are on the board?

Complete the organizer for the concepts in Section 5.3, Radical Equations.

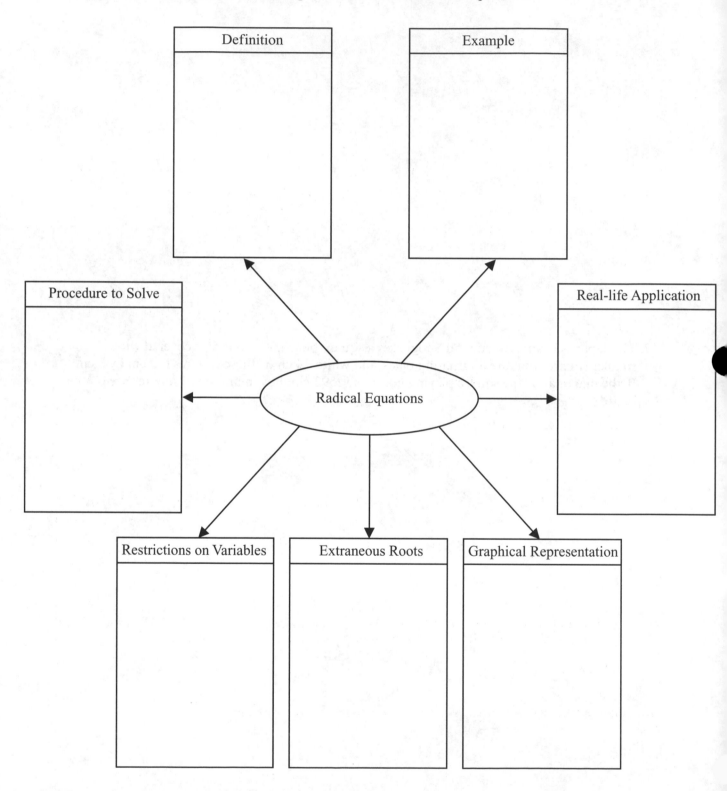

Definition

Example

Procedure to Solve

Real-life Application

Radical Equations

Restrictions on Variables

Extraneous Roots

Graphical Representation

Chapter 6 Rational Expressions and Equations

6.1 Rational Expressions

《 KEY IDEAS 》

- A rational number is a ratio of integers, $\frac{a}{b}$, $b \neq 0$. For example, $\frac{22}{7}, \frac{-2}{3}, \frac{15}{10}, 7, 0$.

- A rational expression is a ratio of polynomials, $\frac{p}{q}$, $q \neq 0$.

  For example, $\frac{x-3}{x^2+4}, \frac{x^2+7x+6}{x^2-36}, \frac{2}{4x+8}, \frac{3xy}{x-y^2}$.

- The value for a variable in a rational expression can be any real value except for non-permissible values. Non-permissible values are values of the variable(s) that make the denominator of a rational expression equal to zero.

  For example, in the rational expression $\frac{x^2+7x+6}{x^2-36}$, $x \neq \pm 6$. The non-permissible values are 6 and −6, since $x^2-36 = (x+6)(x-6)$, and dividing by zero is undefined.

- Like fractions, rational expressions can be simplified to lowest terms. To simplify a rational expression,
  - fully factor the numerator and denominator
  - determine any non-permissible values
  - divide the numerator and the denominator by all identical factors

- Use these properties when working with rational expressions:
  - Any number divided by itself is 1.
    For example, $\frac{14}{14} = 1$.
  - Any polynomial divided by itself is 1 (except for the non-permissible values of the variable).
    For example, $\frac{x^2-2x+1}{x^2-2x+1} = 1$, $x \neq 1$
  - Any number divided by its opposite is −1.
    For example, $\frac{29}{-29} = -1$.
  - Any polynomial divided by its opposite is also −1 (except for the non-permissible values of the variable).
    The opposite of polynomial $a - b$ is $b - a$ because $-1(a-b) = -a + b$, or $b - a$.
    For example, $\frac{x-5}{5-x} = -1$, $x \neq 5$.

Working Example 1: Determine Non-Permissible Values

For each rational expression, determine all non-permissible values.

a) $\dfrac{1}{2x-3}$

b) $\dfrac{1}{x^2-5x+6}$

c) $\dfrac{x^2-9x+14}{x^2-25}$

Solution

Non-permissible values occur because dividing by zero is not allowed (undefined). To find the non-permissible values, set the denominator equal to zero and solve for the variable(s).

a) In the rational expression $\dfrac{1}{2x-3}$, the denominator is _____.

$2x - 3 = 0$

$2x =$ _____

$x =$ _____

Therefore, the non-permissible value of x is _____. Write this as $x \neq$ _____.

b) In the rational expression $\dfrac{1}{x^2-5x+6}$, the denominator is _____.

Determine the roots, or zeros, of the quadratic expression in the denominator to determine the non-permissible values.

$$x^2 - 5x + 6 = 0$$

$$(\underline{\hspace{3cm}})(\underline{\hspace{3cm}}) = 0$$

$\underline{\hspace{3cm}} = 0$ or $\underline{\hspace{3cm}} = 0$

$x =$ _____ $x =$ _____

Therefore, the non-permissible values of x are _____ and _____.

Write this as $x \neq$ _____, _____.

c) In the rational expression $\dfrac{x^2-9x+14}{x^2-25}$, the denominator is _____.

Ignore the numerator when finding non-permissible values.

$$x^2 - 25 = 0$$

$$(\underline{\hspace{3cm}})(\underline{\hspace{3cm}}) = 0$$

$\underline{\hspace{3cm}} = 0$ or $\underline{\hspace{3cm}} = 0$

$x =$ _____ $x =$ _____

Therefore, the non-permissible values of x are _____ and _____.

Write this as $x \neq \pm$ _____.

Working Example 2: Simplify a Rational Expression

Simplify each rational expression. State the non-permissible values.

a) $\dfrac{\frac{4}{3}\pi r^3}{4\pi r^2}$

b) $\dfrac{x^2 - 1}{x^2 + 3x + 2}$

c) $\dfrac{2x^3 - 4x^2 - 30x}{4x^2 - 20}$

Solution

a) $\dfrac{\frac{4}{3}\pi r^3}{4\pi r^2}$

> π is a constant, not a variable.

Determine the non-permissible values.

$r =$ _____

Express the rational expression in simplest form.

> Look for common factors in the numerator and the denominator.

$\dfrac{\frac{4}{3}\pi r^3}{4\pi r^2} = \dfrac{\cancel{4\pi r^2}\left(\frac{1}{3}\right)r}{\cancel{4\pi r^2}}$

$\qquad = \underline{\hspace{1.5cm}},\ r \neq 0$

b) $\dfrac{x^2 - 1}{x^2 + 3x + 2}$

Factor the numerator and denominator.

$\dfrac{x^2 - 1}{x^2 + 3x + 2} = \dfrac{(\boxed{})(\boxed{})}{(x + 1)(x + 2)}$

Determine the non-permissible values.

_____ $= 0$ or _____ $= 0$

$x =$ _____ $x =$ _____

The non-permissible values are $x =$ _____, _____.

Simplify the expression.

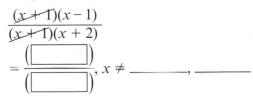

$\dfrac{\cancel{(x + 1)}(x - 1)}{\cancel{(x + 1)}(x + 2)}$

$= \dfrac{(\boxed{})}{(\boxed{})},\ x \neq$ _____, _____

c) $\dfrac{2x^3 - 4x^2 - 30x}{4x^2 - 20x}$

Factor the numerator and denominator.

$\dfrac{2x^3 - 4x^2 - 30x}{4x^2 - 20x} = \dfrac{\boxed{}}{4x(x - 5)}$

> Check for common factors first!

Determine the non-permissible values.

$\underline{\hspace{4cm}} = 0 \qquad$ or $\qquad \underline{\hspace{4cm}} = 0$

$\qquad\qquad x = \underline{\hspace{2cm}} \qquad\qquad\qquad\qquad\qquad x = \underline{\hspace{2cm}}$

The non-permissible values are $x = \underline{\hspace{1.5cm}}, \underline{\hspace{1.5cm}}$.

Simplify the expression.

$\dfrac{2x \cancel{(x - 5)}(x + 3)}{2\,4x \cancel{(x - 5)}}$

$= \dfrac{\left(\boxed{}\right)}{2}, x \neq \underline{\hspace{1.5cm}}, \underline{\hspace{1.5cm}}$

Working Example 3: Rational Expressions With Pairs of Non-Permissible Values

For the rational expression $\dfrac{(w + 1)(h - 8)}{w - 4h}$, determine all non-permissible values.

Solution

To find the non-permissible values, set the denominator equal to zero and solve for one variable.

$w - 4h = 0$

$\qquad w = \underline{\hspace{2cm}}$

The value of one variable depends on the value of the other variable. Non-permissible values will come in pairs. For example,

When $h = 1$, $w = 4$. When $h = 5$, $w = \underline{\hspace{2cm}}$.

When $h = 8.25$, $w = \underline{\hspace{2cm}}$.

The non-permissible values of w are $4h$. Write this as $w \neq \underline{\hspace{2cm}}$.

Working Example 4: Recognize Additive Inverses (Opposites)

Simplify each rational expression. State the non-permissible values.

a) $\dfrac{x^2 - 81}{9 - x}$

b) $\dfrac{12 - 3x}{x^2 + x - 20}$

Solution

a) Factor the numerator and denominator.

$\dfrac{x^2 - 81}{9 - x} = \dfrac{(\boxed{})(\boxed{})}{9 - x}$

> Look for identical factors to help simplify the answer.

Determine the non-permissible values of x.

$9 - x = 0$

$x = \underline{}$

The non-permissible value is $x = \underline{}$.
To simplify, cancel factors common to the numerator and the denominator.

$\dfrac{(x - 9)(x + 9)}{9 - x}$

Simplify.

$\dfrac{(\cancel{x - 9})(x + 9)}{-1(\cancel{x - 9})} = \dfrac{(x + 9)}{-1}$

$= -(x + 9), \; x \neq 9$

> $x - 9$ and $9 - x$ are opposites.
> $(9 - x) = -1(-9 + x)$
> $\quad\quad = -1(x - 9)$

b) Factor the numerator and denominator. Look for common factors first.

$\dfrac{12 - 3x}{x^2 + x - 20} = \dfrac{\boxed{}}{(x + 5)(x - 4)}$

Determine the non-permissible values of x.

$\underline{} = 0 \quad\quad$ or $\quad\quad \underline{} = 0$

$x = \underline{} \quad\quad\quad\quad\quad\quad\quad x = \underline{}$

The non-permissible values are $x = \underline{}, \underline{}$.

Simplify to express the fraction in lowest terms.

$\dfrac{3(4 - x)}{(x + 5)(x - 4)}$

> Look for identical factors and opposite factors.

In the expression $\dfrac{3(4 - x)}{(x + 5)(x - 4)}$, the pair of opposites is $\underline{}$ and $\underline{}$.

Cancel the opposites to simplify.

$\dfrac{3(\cancel{4 - x})}{(x + 5)(-1)(\cancel{x - 4})} = \dfrac{3}{-(x + 5)}, \; x \neq -5, 4$

> Why did the factor (-1) appear in the denominator?

📖 This method is a shortcut that relies on factoring out -1 from one of the pair of opposites. See pages 314–315 of *Pre-Calculus 11*.

Check Your Understanding

Practise

1. For each rational expression, determine all non-permissible values of the variable(s).

a) $\dfrac{1}{x+4}$

The denominator is _____.

b) $\dfrac{1}{6x-3}$

The denominator is _____.

$x \neq$ _____

$x \neq$ _____

c) $\dfrac{1}{x(x-1)}$

d) $\dfrac{1}{(x+2)(3x-2)}$

$x \neq$ _____, _____

$x \neq$ _____, _____

e) $\dfrac{1}{x^2+3x}$

Factor the denominator. Then, determine the non-permissible values.

f) $\dfrac{1}{x^2+4x-21}$

$x \neq$ _____, _____

$x \neq$ _____, _____

g) $\dfrac{6x+3}{5x-10x^2}$

The numerator is not needed when finding non-permissible values.

h) $\dfrac{x-200}{x^2-100}$

$x \neq$ _____, _____

$x \neq$ _____, _____

2. Simplify each rational expression. State any non-permissible values for the variables.

a) $\dfrac{4x(x + 1)}{2(x + 1)}$

b) $\dfrac{6x^2(2x - 3)}{2x(2x - 3)}$

> Determine the non-permissible values before simplifying.

c) $\dfrac{(x - 7)(x + 4)}{(x + 4)(x + 7)}$

d) $\dfrac{x(2x + 7)(x + 6)}{x^2(x + 6)}$

3. Simplify each rational expression. State any non-permissible values for the variables.

a) $\dfrac{8x^2y^3}{12y^2}$

b) $\dfrac{\pi r^2}{2\pi rh}$

c) $\dfrac{10x^2 + 70x}{5x^2 + 5x}$

> Factor fully.
> Remember to look for common factors first.

d) $\dfrac{a^2b - ab^3}{5ab + 25a^2b}$

📖 Also try #6 and 8 on page 318 of *Pre-Calculus 11*.

4. Simplify and state the non-permissible values for the variables.

a) $\dfrac{x^2 - 25}{x^2 + 5x - 50}$

> Factor first. Then, determine non-permissible values before simplifying.

b) $\dfrac{x^2 + 5x - 6}{x^2 + 6x}$

c) $\dfrac{2x^2 - 4x - 70}{4x - 28}$

> Look for common factors first.

d) $\dfrac{6x^2 + 18x + 12}{3x + 3}$

e) $\dfrac{a^2 - a - 2}{a^2 + 5a - 14}$

f) $\dfrac{z^2 + 9z + 18}{z^2 - 3z - 18}$

g) $\dfrac{2x^2 - 11x - 6}{x^2 - 5x - 6}$

h) $\dfrac{3x^2 - 8x - 3}{3x^2 - 15x + 18}$

5. State the opposite of each binomial.

What is the result when a binomial is divided by its opposite?

a) $x - 1$

The opposite of $x - 1$ is _____. So, $\dfrac{(x - 1)}{\left(\boxed{}\right)} =$ _____, $x \neq 1$.

b) $2 - x$

c) $2a - b$

d) $-5x - 2$

6. Simplify each rational expression. State any non-permissible values for the variables.

a) $\dfrac{3a(a - 7)}{(7 + a)(7 - a)}$

b) $\dfrac{x^2 - 81}{18x - 2x^2}$

c) $\dfrac{-12x + 4x^2}{x^2 - 6x + 9}$

d) $\dfrac{a^2 - 2ab}{4b^2 - a^2}$

📖 This question will help you with #25 on page 320 of *Pre-Calculus 11*.

Apply

7. A rectangular box has length x cm. Its width is 2 cm shorter than its length. Its height is 4 cm shorter than its length.

   a) Determine an expression, in lowest terms, for the ratio of the surface area to the volume of the box.

   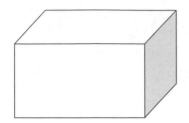

   length: _____   width: _____   height: _____

   Write expressions for the surface area and the volume of the box.

   $SA =$ _____

   $V =$ _____

   $\dfrac{SA}{V} = \dfrac{\rule{8cm}{0pt}}{\rule{8cm}{0pt}}$

   b) What are the non-permissible values of the variable x? What meaning do the non-permissible values have in the context of the problem? Are there any further restrictions on the variable that result from the context rather than the algebra?

📖 For more application questions, see pages 318–319 of *Pre-Calculus 11*.

8. In manufacturing, you often need to know the ratio of the surface area to the volume of a container. Determine the ratio of surface area to volume of a cylinder with radius r and height h. Simplify this ratio and give any non-permissible values of the variables.

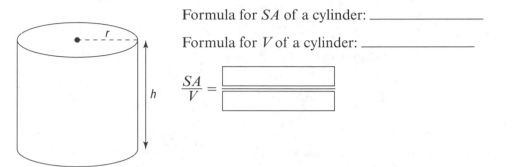

Formula for SA of a cylinder: _____

Formula for V of a cylinder: _____

$$\frac{SA}{V} = \frac{\boxed{}}{\boxed{}}$$

9. Consider the quadratic formula $x = \dfrac{-b \pm \sqrt{b^2 - 4ac}}{2a}$.

a) Does the quadratic formula contain a rational expression? Why or why not?

b) What are the non-permissible values of the denominator? What meaning do the non-permissible values have in the context of solving quadratic equations?

10. a) State the non-permissible values for $\dfrac{1}{x^2 - 4x + 3}$.

b) Create a rational expression in which $x \neq 2, 3$.

c) Simplify and state the non-permissible values for $\dfrac{x^2 - 5x - 24}{x + 3}$.

d) Create a rational expression that is equivalent to $(x - 8)$ in which $x \neq -1$.

Connect

11. Is the following work correct? Explain.

$$\frac{x + 10}{10} = \frac{x + \cancel{10}}{\cancel{10}}$$
$$= x$$

<< **KEY IDEAS** >>

- A rational expression is a ratio of polynomials, $\frac{p}{q}$, $q \neq 0$.

  For example, $\frac{x+3}{x+7}$, $\frac{x^2+3x+2}{x^2-4}$, $\frac{6.5}{3.6x+9.1}$, $\frac{3x+y}{x-y}$.

- Like fractions, rational expressions can be multiplied and divided.
  - The product is the result of multiplying.
  - The quotient is the result of dividing.
  - Always express the product or quotient in simplest form.

- To multiply two rational expressions,
  - factor each numerator and denominator
  - determine any non-permissible values
  - multiply the numerators together and the denominators together
  - simplify factors (not terms) common to both the numerator and the denominator
    For example,

Correct	Incorrect
$\dfrac{\cancel{(x+4)}(x-1)}{3x\cancel{(x+4)}} = \dfrac{x-1}{3x}$	$\dfrac{\cancel{x}-1}{3\cancel{x}} = \dfrac{-1}{3}$

- To divide one rational expression by another rational expression, multiply the first by the reciprocal of the second. Then, proceed as for multiplication.

$$\frac{A}{B} \div \frac{C}{D} = \frac{\frac{A}{B}}{\frac{C}{D}}$$

$$= \frac{A}{B} \times \frac{D}{C}$$

- The non-permissible values in a division question arise every time you divide. In the example above, there are two kinds of division. Expressions B and D are in the denominator of the original expression. A division sign ($\div$) tells you to divide by expression C. Therefore, B, D, and C must all be considered when determining non-permissible values for the variable(s).

  For example, in

$$\frac{A}{B} \div \frac{C}{D} = \frac{\frac{A}{B}}{\frac{C}{D}}$$

  the non-permissible values are $B \neq 0$, $D \neq 0$, and $C \neq 0$.

Working Example 1: Multiply Rational Numbers and Rational Expressions

Determine each product. Identify any non-permissible values of the variable.

a) $\dfrac{5}{9} \times \dfrac{3}{10}$

b) $\dfrac{x+1}{x^2-5x+6} \times \dfrac{x-2}{x^2+5x+4}$

Solution

a) Factor the numerator and denominator.

$\dfrac{5}{9} \times \dfrac{3}{10} = \dfrac{5}{3(3)} \times \dfrac{2}{2(5)}$

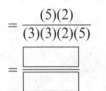 Write each factor as a product of prime numbers.

There are no variables, so there are no non-permissible values.
Multiply the numerators together and the denominators together.
To simplify, cancel factors common to both the numerator and the denominator.

$= \dfrac{(5)(2)}{(3)(3)(2)(5)}$

$= \dfrac{\boxed{}}{\boxed{}}$

Remember that identical factors cancel to 1.

b) Factor the numerator and denominator. Look for binomial factors.

$\dfrac{x+1}{x^2-5x+6} \times \dfrac{x-2}{x^2+5x+4}$

$= \dfrac{(x+1)}{(x-3)\left(\boxed{}\right)} \times \dfrac{(x-2)}{(x+4)\left(\boxed{}\right)}$

Identify any non-permissible values.

$x - 3 = 0$ $\underline{\hspace{2cm}} = 0$

$x = \underline{\hspace{2cm}}$ $x = \underline{\hspace{2cm}}$

$x + 4 = 0$ $\underline{\hspace{2cm}} = 0$

$x = \underline{\hspace{2cm}}$ $x = \underline{\hspace{2cm}}$

The non-permissible values are $x = \underline{\hspace{1.5cm}}, \underline{\hspace{1.5cm}}, \underline{\hspace{1.5cm}},$ and $\underline{\hspace{1.5cm}}$.

Multiply the numerators together and the denominators together.

To simplify, cancel factors common to both the numerator and the denominator.

$= \dfrac{(x+1)(x-2)}{(x-3)\left(\boxed{}\right)(x+4)\left(\boxed{}\right)}$

$= \dfrac{\boxed{}}{\boxed{}}, \; x \neq -4, -1, 2, 3$

Remember that the quotient of identical factors is 1.
If all the factors in the numerator cancel, the numerator is 1.

Working Example 2: Identify Non-Permissible Values

State the non-permissible values of the variable(s).

$$\frac{ab^2}{c^2d} \div \frac{(e-2)(f+1)}{g(h-6)}$$

Solution

Identify (circle or highlight) all forms of division in the expression.

The denominators are _____ and _____.

Also divide by _____ (the numerator of the second expression).

Set each of the relevant factors equal to zero to determine the non-permissible values.

$c^2 = 0$ $d =$ _____

$c =$ _____

$e - 2 = 0$ $f + 1 = 0$

$e =$ _____ $f =$ _____

$g =$ _____ $h - 6 = 0$

$h =$ _____

The non-permissible values are $c =$ _____, $d =$ _____, $e =$ _____,

$f =$ _____, $g =$ _____, and $h =$ _____.

Working Example 3: Divide Rational Numbers and Rational Expressions

Determine each quotient. Identify any non-permissible values of the variable.

a) $\frac{3}{4} \div \frac{9}{2}$

b) $\frac{x+3}{x-3} \div \frac{x}{4x-12}$

c) $\frac{x-7}{x+4} \div \frac{x^2-2x-15}{x^2-x-20}$

Solution

a) To divide, multiply by the reciprocal.

$$\frac{3}{4} \div \frac{9}{2} = \frac{3}{4} \times \frac{2}{9}$$

$$= \frac{3}{(2)(2)} \times \frac{2}{(3)(3)}$$

$$= \frac{\boxed{}}{\boxed{}}$$

b) Factor each numerator and denominator fully.

$$\frac{x+3}{x-3} \div \frac{x}{4x-12} = \frac{x+3}{x-3} \div \frac{x}{4(x-3)}$$

Determine the non-permissible values.

The denominators are _____ and _____.

Also divide by _____.

The non-permissible values are _____ and _____.

To divide, multiply by the reciprocal.

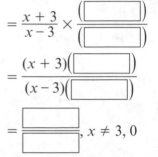

$$= \frac{x+3}{x-3} \times \frac{\left(\boxed{}\right)}{\left(\boxed{}\right)}$$

$$= \frac{(x+3)\left(\boxed{}\right)}{(x-3)\left(\boxed{}\right)}$$

$$= \frac{\boxed{}}{\boxed{}}, \; x \neq 3, 0$$

c) Factor each numerator and denominator fully. Then, determine the non-permissible values.

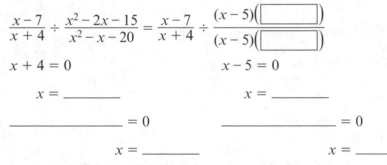

$$\frac{x-7}{x+4} \div \frac{x^2-2x-15}{x^2-x-20} = \frac{x-7}{x+4} \div \frac{(x-5)\left(\boxed{}\right)}{(x-5)\left(\boxed{}\right)}$$

$$x+4=0 \qquad\qquad\qquad x-5=0$$

$$x = \underline{} \qquad\qquad\qquad x = \underline{}$$

$$\underline{} = 0 \qquad\qquad \underline{} = 0$$

$$x = \underline{} \qquad\qquad\qquad x = \underline{}$$

To divide, multiply by the reciprocal.

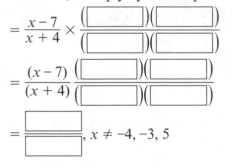

$$= \frac{x-7}{x+4} \times \frac{\left(\boxed{}\right)\left(\boxed{}\right)}{\left(\boxed{}\right)\left(\boxed{}\right)}$$

$$= \frac{(x-7)}{(x+4)} \frac{\left(\boxed{}\right)\left(\boxed{}\right)}{\left(\boxed{}\right)\left(\boxed{}\right)}$$

$$= \frac{\boxed{}}{\boxed{}}, \; x \neq -4, -3, 5$$

Check Your Understanding

Practise

1. What are the non-permissible value(s) for the variable(s) in each product?

a) $\dfrac{1}{x-2} \times \dfrac{3}{x-4}$

$x \neq$ _____, _____

b) $\dfrac{\pi r^2}{2\pi r} \times \dfrac{\pi r h}{r+h}$

$r \neq$ _____, _____

c) $\dfrac{x^2 + 3x + 2}{x^2 - 1} \times \dfrac{1}{3x+2}$

d) $\dfrac{y-8}{y^2 + 7x + 6} \times \dfrac{y+4}{y^2 + 16y + 60}$

2. Write the reciprocal of each rational expression.

a) $\dfrac{3}{7x}$

b) $\dfrac{2x-7}{x+4}$

c) $\dfrac{x^2 + 2x + 1}{6x - 3}$

d) $49 - x^2$

3. Determine the non-permissible value(s) of the variable for each quotient.

a) $\dfrac{l+1}{4l} \div \dfrac{(w-2)^2}{6w}$

The denominators are _____ and _____.

Also divide by _____ (the numerator of the second expression).

The non-permissible values are _____.

b) $\dfrac{x-1}{x^2 - 4} \div \dfrac{2x-3}{x+5}$

The denominators are _____ and _____.

Also divide by _____ (the numerator of the second expression).

The non-permissible values are _____.

4. Write each product in simplest form. Determine all non-permissible values of the variable(s).

a) $\dfrac{3x^3}{y^2} \times \dfrac{y^3}{6x}$

b) $\dfrac{5x^2}{x-3} \times \dfrac{x-3}{10x}$

> Always identify the non-permissible values before simplifying.

c) $\dfrac{x-6}{x+2} \times \dfrac{x+6}{x-6}$

d) $\dfrac{x+1}{x-2} \times \dfrac{x^2+x-6}{x-4}$

> Put brackets around each binomial factor.

e) $\dfrac{2x-8}{x+3} \times \dfrac{x^2+4x+3}{x-4}$

f) $\dfrac{x^2+6x-40}{x^2-100} \times \dfrac{10x-x^2}{x^2+x-20}$

📖 Also try #2 on page 327 of *Pre-Calculus 11*.

5. Write each quotient in simplest form. State any non-permissible values for the variables.

a) $\dfrac{x + 2}{4x - 5} \div \dfrac{2x + 4}{4x - 5}$

Factor the numerators and denominators.

Multiply by the reciprocal.

Determine the non-permissible values of x.

Multiply.

Simplify.

b) $\dfrac{a^2b}{c - 1} \div \dfrac{bc - b}{a}$

c) $\dfrac{x^2 + 8x + 12}{x^2 - 15x + 56} \div \dfrac{x - 7}{3x + 6}$

d) $\dfrac{x^2 - 3x - 18}{x^2 + 6x + 9} \div \dfrac{x^2 + 3x + 2}{x^2 + 8x + 15}$

📖 Also try #4 and 8 on page 327 of *Pre-Calculus 11*.

6. Simplify and state the non-permissible values for the variable.

a) $\dfrac{x^2 + 16x + 64}{x^2 - 4x} \times \dfrac{x - 4}{x + 8}$

Factor the numerators and denominators.

Determine the non-permissible values of x.

Multiply.

Simplify.

b) $\dfrac{x^2 - 17x + 72}{x^2 - 4x + 3} \times \dfrac{9 - x^2}{x^2 - 6x - 27}$

c) $\dfrac{x + 11}{2x} \div \dfrac{121 - x^2}{x^2 + 4x}$

Factor the numerators and denominators.

Multiply by the reciprocal.

Determine the non-permissible values of x.

Multiply.

Simplify.

d) $\dfrac{x^2 - 5x - 50}{144 - 24x + x^2} \div \dfrac{5x + 25}{x^2 - 20x + 96}$

Apply

7. Simplify the following expressions. Identify any non-permissible values of the variable.

a) $\dfrac{4x + 20}{x + 6} \times \dfrac{x - 4}{x^2 - 25} \div \dfrac{2x - 8}{x + 6}$

Factor the numerators and denominators.

Multiply by the reciprocal.

Determine the non-permissible values of x.

Multiply.

Simplify.

b) $\dfrac{x^2 + 2x + 1}{2x + 1} \div \dfrac{x^2 - 3x}{x + 10} \times \dfrac{2x^2 - 5x - 3}{x^2 + x}$

c) $\dfrac{9x - x^3}{10x - 10} \div \dfrac{x^2 - 11x + 24}{3x^2 - 4x + 1} \div \dfrac{45x + 5x^2}{x - 8}$

8. There is at least one error in Jaime's solution. Circle the error(s).

   Complete the question correctly in the space provided.

Jaime's Solution	Correct Solution
$\dfrac{x^2 + \cancel{4x + 4}}{\cancel{4x + 4}} \times \dfrac{x + 1}{x + 2}$	$\dfrac{x^2 + 4x + 4}{4x + 4} \times \dfrac{x + 1}{x + 2}$
$= \dfrac{x^2\,(x + 1)}{x + 2}$	$=$
$= \dfrac{x^3 + 1}{x + 2},\ x \neq -1, -2$	

9. There is at least one error in Kelly's solution. Circle the error(s).

   Complete the question correctly in the space provided.

Kelly's Solution	Correct Solution
$\dfrac{x - 4}{x + 6} \div \dfrac{2x + 6}{2x - 8}$	$\dfrac{x - 4}{x + 6} \div \dfrac{2x + 6}{2x - 8}$
$= \dfrac{\cancel{x - 4}}{x + 6} \div \dfrac{2(x + 3)}{2(\cancel{x - 4})}$	$=$
$= \dfrac{x + 3}{x + 6},\ x \neq -6, 4$	

10. A sphere is contained in a rectangular box such that the sides of the sphere are touching the sides of the box. What fraction of the volume of the box does the sphere occupy? Model the situation using a quotient of rational expressions, and then solve.

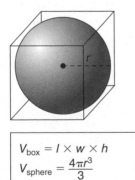

$$V_{box} = l \times w \times h$$
$$V_{sphere} = \dfrac{4\pi r^3}{3}$$

📖 See pages 328–329 of *Pre-Calculus 11* for more application questions.

Connect

11. Students are given the following expression to simplify: $\dfrac{2x-7}{x+6} \times \dfrac{x^2+3x-18}{x-5}$

Heather begins her solution by factoring the quadratic, as follows:

$$\dfrac{2x-7}{x+6} \times \dfrac{x^2+3x-18}{x-5} = \dfrac{2x-7}{x+6} \times \dfrac{(\boxed{})(\boxed{})}{x-5}$$

$$=$$

Shervin remembers that simplifying rational expressions is like simplifying rational numbers. He multiplies the numerators and the denominators first, and then looks for common factors.

For example, $\dfrac{10}{3} \times \dfrac{6}{5} = \dfrac{60}{15} = 4$.

He decides to try the same process with rational expressions. He begins his solution by using the distributive law to multiply the numerators and denominators together, as follows:

$$\dfrac{2x-7}{x+6} \times \dfrac{x^2+3x-18}{x-5} = \dfrac{2x^3-7x^2+6x^2-36x-21x+126}{x^2-5x+6x-30}$$

$$=$$

Complete Heather's and Shervin's solutions. Whose solution is more efficient? Why?

KEY IDEAS

- To add (or subtract) rational expressions,
  - factor each denominator if necessary
  - express all rational expressions with a common denominator
  - add (or subtract) the numerators; the denominator does not change

- In mathematics, you often group like things together, but keep unlike things separate. For example, group together like terms $(2x + 5x = 7x)$ but keep unlike terms separate $(2x + 5y = 2x + 5y)$.

  - The same idea holds for fractions (rational numbers). Fractions with the same denominator are alike, and you can group them together.

  $$\frac{5}{12} + \frac{2}{12} = \frac{5 + 2}{12} = \frac{7}{12}$$

  > Add (or subtract) the numerators. The denominator does not change.

  - Similarly, rational expressions with the same denominator are alike, and you can group them together.

  $$\frac{5x}{x + 12} + \frac{2x - 3}{x + 12} = \frac{5x + (2x - 3)}{x + 12}$$

  > Add (or subtract) the numerators. The denominator does not change.

  $$= \frac{7x - 3}{x + 12}$$

- If rational expressions have different denominators, rewrite them as equivalent expressions with the least common denominator (LCD):

  - Factor each denominator. Start with the factors from the first denominator, and then include any factors from the second (and subsequent) denominator that are not already represented.

  $$\frac{A}{(B)(C)} + \frac{E}{(C)(D)}$$

  $$LCD = (B)(C)(D)$$

  - Multiply the numerator and denominator of each rational expression by whichever factor of the LCD is missing (outside the circle) from the original denominator.

  $$\frac{A}{(B)(C)} + \frac{E}{(C)(D)} = \frac{A(D)}{(B)(C)(D)} + \frac{E(B)}{(C)(D)(B)}$$

  $$= \frac{AD + EB}{BCD}$$

Working Example 1: Add or Subtract Rational Expressions With Common Denominators

Simplify and identify any non-permissible values of the variable.

a) $\dfrac{2x + 4}{x^2 - 9} + \dfrac{7x - 10}{x^2 - 9}$

b) $\dfrac{10a + 5}{ab} - \dfrac{3a - 2}{ab}$

Solution

a) Both expressions have the same denominator, so add the numerators.

$$\dfrac{2x + 4}{x^2 - 9} + \dfrac{7x - 10}{x^2 - 9} = \dfrac{\left(\boxed{}\right) + \left(\boxed{}\right)}{x^2 - 9}$$

> Add the numerators. The denominator does not change.

$$= \dfrac{\boxed{}}{x^2 - 9}, \ x \neq \underline{\hspace{1cm}}$$

b) Both expressions have the same denominator, so subtract the numerators.

$$\dfrac{10a + 5}{ab} - \dfrac{3a - 2}{ab} = \dfrac{\left(\boxed{}\right) - \left(\boxed{}\right)}{ab}$$

> Subtract the numerators. The denominator does not change.

$$= \dfrac{\boxed{}}{\boxed{}}, \ a \neq \underline{\hspace{1cm}}, \ b \neq \underline{\hspace{1cm}}$$

> Be careful! You are subtracting −2.

Working Example 2: Determine the Least Common Denominator

Identify the least common denominator for each group of rational expressions.

a) $\dfrac{1}{2x}, \dfrac{1}{3x}, \dfrac{1}{y}$

b) $\dfrac{1}{x + 5}, \dfrac{1}{(x + 5)(x - 4)}, \dfrac{1}{(x - 4)(x + 7)}$

c) $\dfrac{1}{x^2 + 6x + 9}, \dfrac{1}{x^2 + 8x + 15}$

Solution

a) The denominators are _____, _____, and _____.

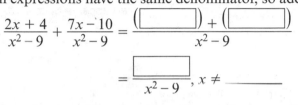

$\text{LCD} = (2)(x)(3)(y) = \underline{\hspace{2cm}}$

b) $\dfrac{1}{x + 5}, \dfrac{1}{(x + 5)(x - 4)}, \dfrac{1}{(x - 4)(x + 7)}$

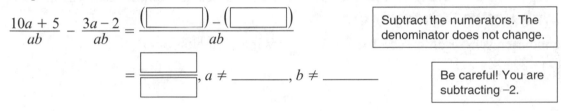

$\text{LCD} = (x + 5)(\underline{\hspace{2cm}})(\underline{\hspace{2cm}})$

c) $\dfrac{1}{x^2 + 6x + 9}, \dfrac{1}{x^2 + 8x + 15}$

First, factor each denominator. Then, make a diagram.

$x^2 + 6x + 9 = ($\underline{\hspace{3cm}}$)($\underline{\hspace{3cm}}$)$

$x^2 + 8x + 15 = ($\underline{\hspace{3cm}}$)($\underline{\hspace{3cm}}$)$

Denominator 1   Denominator 2

> The factor $(x + 3)$ appears twice in the first denominator. Make sure it appears twice in the LCD.

LCD = $($\underline{\hspace{2.5cm}}$)($\underline{\hspace{2.5cm}}$)($\underline{\hspace{2.5cm}}$)$

Working Example 3: Add and Subtract Rational Expressions With Unlike Denominators

Find each sum or difference. Express your answers in simplest form.

a) $\dfrac{x - 15}{x(x + 1)} + \dfrac{x - 4}{x + 1}, x \neq -1, 0$ **b)** $\dfrac{6x}{x - 5} - \dfrac{240}{x^2 - 2x - 15}, x \neq -3, 5$

Solution

a) $\dfrac{x - 15}{x(x + 1)} + \dfrac{x - 4}{x + 1}$

The two expressions have unlike denominators.

Determine the LCD: \underline{\hspace{5cm}}

The first expression already contains all the factors of the LCD.

The second expression is missing the factor \underline{\hspace{3cm}}.

Multiply the numerator and denominator of the second expression by the missing factor.

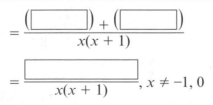

$$\dfrac{x - 15}{x(x + 1)} + \dfrac{x - 4}{x + 1} = \dfrac{x - 15}{x(x + 1)} + \dfrac{(x - 4)}{(x + 1)} \times \dfrac{(\boxed{})}{(\boxed{})}$$

$$= \dfrac{x - 15}{x(x + 1)} + \dfrac{\boxed{}}{x(x + 1)}$$

Now both expressions have a common denominator.

$$= \dfrac{(\boxed{}) + (\boxed{})}{x(x + 1)}$$

$$= \dfrac{\boxed{}}{x(x + 1)}, x \neq -1, 0$$

Simplify the numerator by collecting like terms. If possible, factor the result.
Check that the result cannot be simplified further.

b) The two expressions have unlike denominators. Factor.

$$\frac{6x}{x-5} - \frac{240}{x^2 - 2x - 15} = \frac{6x}{x-5} - \frac{240}{(\boxed{})(\boxed{})}$$

Determine the LCD: _____

Multiply the numerator and denominator of the first expression by the missing factor. Simplify the numerator of the first expression.

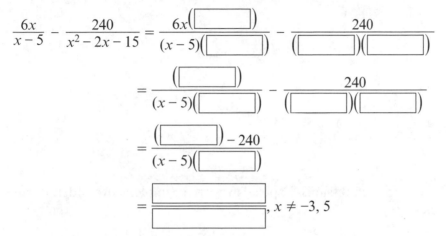

$$\frac{6x}{x-5} - \frac{240}{x^2 - 2x - 15} = \frac{6x(\boxed{})}{(x-5)(\boxed{})} - \frac{240}{(\boxed{})(\boxed{})}$$

$$= \frac{(\boxed{})}{(x-5)(\boxed{})} - \frac{240}{(\boxed{})(\boxed{})}$$

$$= \frac{(\boxed{}) - 240}{(x-5)(\boxed{})}$$

$$= \frac{\boxed{}}{\boxed{}}, x \neq -3, 5$$

Simplify the numerator by collecting like terms. If possible, factor the result. Check if the result can be further simplified.

Check Your Understanding

Practise

1. Add. Express answers in simplest form. Identify any non-permissible values.

   a) $\dfrac{7x + 1}{4x} + \dfrac{3x - 4}{4x}$

   b) $\dfrac{x^2 + 1}{x - 8} + \dfrac{2x + 1}{x - 8}$

2. Subtract the following rational expressions. Express answers in simplest form. Identify any non-permissible values.

   a) $\dfrac{4x - 8}{x^2} - \dfrac{x + 1}{x^2}$

   b) $\dfrac{x^2 + 6x}{x^2 - 25} - \dfrac{4x - 1}{x^2 - 25}$

   c) $\dfrac{x^2 - 1}{x + 9} - \dfrac{8 - 8x}{x + 9}$

   d) $\dfrac{x^2 + 3x - 20}{6 - x} - \dfrac{3x + 16}{6 - x}$

3. Determine the least common denominator (LCD) of the following pairs of rational expressions. Leave your answers in factored form. Be sure to put binomial factors in brackets.

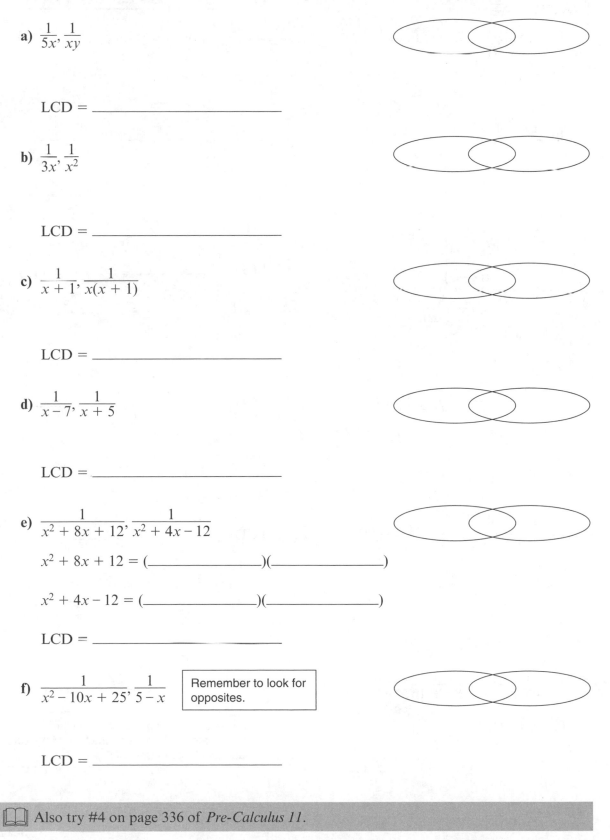

a) $\dfrac{1}{5x}, \dfrac{1}{xy}$

LCD = _____

b) $\dfrac{1}{3x}, \dfrac{1}{x^2}$

LCD = _____

c) $\dfrac{1}{x+1}, \dfrac{1}{x(x+1)}$

LCD = _____

d) $\dfrac{1}{x-7}, \dfrac{1}{x+5}$

LCD = _____

e) $\dfrac{1}{x^2+8x+12}, \dfrac{1}{x^2+4x-12}$

$x^2 + 8x + 12 = ($_____$)($_____$)$

$x^2 + 4x - 12 = ($_____$)($_____$)$

LCD = _____

f) $\dfrac{1}{x^2-10x+25}, \dfrac{1}{5-x}$ | Remember to look for opposites.

LCD = _____

📖 Also try #4 on page 336 of *Pre-Calculus 11*.

4. Find the sum or difference, as indicated. State any non-permissible values of the variable(s).

a) $\dfrac{1}{6x} + \dfrac{1}{xy}$

LCD = _____

b) $\dfrac{1}{7x} - \dfrac{1}{x^2}$

LCD = _____

c) $\dfrac{1}{x - 3} + \dfrac{1}{x(x - 3)}$

LCD = _____

d) $\dfrac{1}{x + 7} - \dfrac{1}{(x - 8)(x + 7)}$

LCD = _____

e) $\dfrac{1}{x^2 + 6x + 8} + \dfrac{1}{x^2 + x - 12}$

LCD = _____

f) $\dfrac{1}{4 - x} - \dfrac{1}{x^2 - 8x + 16}$

LCD = _____

> The factor $(x - 4)$ appears twice in the denominator of the second fraction. Make sure it appears twice in the LCD.

5. Determine the sum. Express your answers in simplest form. List the non-permissible values of the variable.

a) $\dfrac{a}{a+7} + \dfrac{2}{a+5}$

LCD = _____

b) $\dfrac{6x-19}{x^2-3x-4} + \dfrac{x-5}{x-4}$

LCD = _____

6. Determine the difference. Express your answers in simplest form. List the non-permissible values of the variable.

a) $\dfrac{3x}{x-9} - \dfrac{2x}{x-12}$

LCD = _____

b) $\dfrac{2x+2}{x^2+4x-12} - \dfrac{x+1}{x^2-4}$

LCD = _____

Apply

7. At Nathan's Deli in New York City, there is an annual hot-dog eating contest. Contestants have 12 min to consume as many hot dogs as they can. Suppose you can eat an average of n hot dogs per minute.

a) Write an expression for the number of minutes it would take to eat 5 hot dogs.

> Remember to state the non-permissible values.

b) Suppose that, after you have eaten 5 hot dogs, your average rate of consumption slows down by 1 hot dog per minute. Write an expression for the number of minutes it would take to eat the next 5 hot dogs.

c) Using the information from above, write a sum of rational expressions (in simplest form) representing the number of minutes it would take to eat 10 hot dogs.

8. Suppose that you are competing in the 10-km race at the Vancouver Sun Run.

   a) For the first 8 km, you run at an average rate of y km/h. Write an expression for the number of *minutes* it would take to run 8 km.

   b) After 8 km, you get tired. You run 5 km/h slower for the rest of the race. Write an expression for the number of *minutes* it takes to run the final 2 km of the race.

   c) Using the information from above, write a sum of rational expressions (in simplest form) representing the number of minutes it takes you to complete the race.

📖 See pages 337–340 of *Pre-Calculus 11* for more application questions.

9. Simplify the following expressions. List any non-permissible values for x.

a) $\dfrac{x + 1}{x - 2} + \dfrac{x^2 + 4x - 5}{x^2 + 5x - 14} \times \dfrac{x^2 + 4x - 21}{x - 1}$

> Do multiplication and division before addition and subtraction.

b) $\dfrac{x^2 - 3x - 18}{x^2 + 10x} \div \dfrac{x^2 - 13x + 42}{x^2 + 3x - 70} - \dfrac{x + 5}{2x + 3}$

Connect

10. Describe how to determine the least common denominator (LCD) of two rational expressions. Create an example to help you illustrate your explanation.

KEY IDEAS

- A rational equation is an equation that contains at least one rational expression. You can use rational equations to solve problems in which an unknown value is in the denominator. For example, $x + \frac{4}{x} = 4$ is a rational equation.

- To solve a rational equation,
  - factor all denominators (if necessary) and determine the least common denominator (LCD)
  - identify any non-permissible values of the variable (from the LCD)
  - multiply all terms on both sides of the equation by the LCD, and then simplify
  - solve for the variable
  - check that the solution(s) are permissible, and that they make sense in the given context
  - verify that any remaining solutions are correct in the original equation

In the example given above, the LCD is x. The non-permissible value is $x = 0$.

Multiply each term on both sides of the equation by x, and then simplify.

$$x + \frac{4}{x} = 4$$
$$x\left(x + \frac{4}{x}\right) = x(4)$$
$$x(x) + x\left(\frac{4}{x}\right) = 4x$$
$$x^2 + 4 = 4x$$

Collect all terms of the quadratic on the same side of the equation to solve for x.

$$x^2 - 4x + 4 = 0$$
$$(x - 2)(x - 2) = 0$$

Set each factor equal to 0 and solve for x: $x - 2 = 0$

$$x = 2$$

This value is permitted (recall that $x \neq 0$).

Verify in the original equation.

Left Side	Right Side
$x + \frac{4}{x}$	4
$= 2 + \frac{4}{2}$	
$= 2 + 2$	
$= 4$	

Left Side = Right Side

Therefore, $x = 2$ is a solution.

Working Example 1: Solve a Rational Equation

a) Solve the equation.

$$\frac{x^2 + 25}{x - 7} + \frac{x + 5}{2} = \frac{2x^2 - 12x - 9}{2x - 14}$$

b) Verify your solution(s).

Solution

a) Factor the numerators and denominators.

The least common denominator (LCD) is _____.

The non-permissible value is $x =$ _____.

Multiply each term on both sides of the equation by the LCD, and then simplify.

$$(\underline{})\left(\frac{x^2 + 25}{x - 7}\right) + (\underline{})\left(\frac{x + 5}{2}\right) = (\underline{})\left(\frac{2x^2 - 12x - 9}{2(x - 7)}\right)$$

$$(\underline{})(x^2 + 25) + (\underline{})(x + 5) = 2x^2 - 12x - 9$$

Collect all terms of the quadratic on the same side of the equation to solve for x.
Set each factor equal to zero and solve for x:

$(\underline{}) = 0 \quad$ or $\quad (\underline{}) = 0$

$\qquad x = \qquad\qquad\qquad\qquad x =$

b) For $x = -4$:

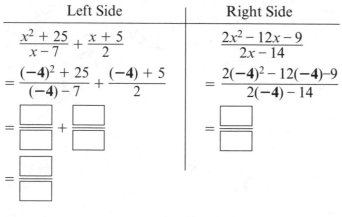

Left Side	Right Side
$\dfrac{x^2 + 25}{x - 7} + \dfrac{x + 5}{2}$	$\dfrac{2x^2 - 12x - 9}{2x - 14}$
$= \dfrac{(-4)^2 + 25}{(-4) - 7} + \dfrac{(-4) + 5}{2}$	$= \dfrac{2(-4)^2 - 12(-4) - 9}{2(-4) - 14}$

Therefore, $x = -4$ _____ a solution.
_____(*is* or *is not*)

For $x = -6$:

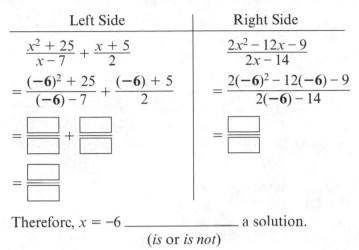

Left Side	Right Side
$\dfrac{x^2 + 25}{x - 7} + \dfrac{x + 5}{2}$	$\dfrac{2x^2 - 12x - 9}{2x - 14}$
$= \dfrac{(-6)^2 + 25}{(-6) - 7} + \dfrac{(-6) + 5}{2}$	$= \dfrac{2(-6)^2 - 12(-6) - 9}{2(-6) - 14}$
$= \dfrac{\boxed{}}{\boxed{}} + \dfrac{\boxed{}}{\boxed{}}$	$= \dfrac{\boxed{}}{\boxed{}}$
$= \dfrac{\boxed{}}{\boxed{}}$	

Therefore, $x = -6$ _____ a solution.

(*is* or *is not*)

Working Example 2: Solve a Rational Equation With an Extraneous Root

Solve the equation and verify your solution(s) in the original equation.

$$\frac{5x}{x - 4} + 2 = \frac{3x + 8}{x - 4}$$

Solution

The least common denominator (LCD) is _____. The non-permissible value is $x =$ _____.

Multiply each term on both sides of the equation by the LCD. Then, simplify and solve for x.

$$(\text{\_\_\_\_\_})\left(\frac{5x}{x - 4}\right) + (\text{\_\_\_\_\_})(2) = (\text{\_\_\_\_\_})\left(\frac{3x + 8}{x - 4}\right)$$

However, from the original equation, $x \neq 4$.
Therefore, there is no solution to the rational equation.

Working Example 3: Sharing a Task

Andrea and Phary are sharing a bag of popcorn at the movies.
• By himself, Phary can eat the whole bag of popcorn in 20 min.
• Andrea takes 25 min to eat the whole bag.

If they both eat popcorn at their usual rates, how quickly will they eat the popcorn?

Solution

Let x represent the time, in minutes, it takes Andrea and Phary together to eat the popcorn. Organize the information in a table.

	Time to Eat Popcorn (min)	Fraction of Popcorn Eaten in 1 min	Fraction of Popcorn Eaten in x min
Andrea (A)	25	$\frac{1}{25}$	$\frac{x}{25}$
Phary (P)			
Together	x	$\frac{1}{x}$	$x\left(\frac{1}{x}\right) = 1$

(fraction A eats) + (fraction P eats) = total

$$\frac{x}{25} \quad + \quad \frac{\boxed{}}{\boxed{}} \quad = \quad 1$$

The answer should lie somewhere between half of Andrea's time and half of Phary's time. Is this the case? Explain your answer.

Working Example 4: Create and Solve a Rational Model

A group of friends go on a 3-h bike ride together. They ride 15 km with the wind at their backs, and then 15 km straight into the wind. The wind adds or subtracts 3 km/h from their speed. What is the average speed of the group of friends with no wind?

Solution

Let x represent the average biking speed with no wind, in kilometres per hour.
Then the average speed with the wind at their backs is $(x + 3)$ km/h, and the average speed riding into the wind is $(x - 3)$ km/h.

	Distance, d (km)	Speed, s (km/h)	Time, t $t = \dfrac{d}{s}$
With wind	15	$x + 3$	$\dfrac{15}{x + 3}$
Against wind			
Total			3

(time biking with wind) + (time biking against wind) = (total time)

$$\frac{15}{x + 3} \quad + \quad \boxed{} \quad = \quad 3$$

Use the quadratic equation to solve for x.

$a =$ _____ , $b =$ _____ , $c =$ _____

$$x = \frac{-b \pm \sqrt{b^2 - 4ac}}{2a}$$

> Does either solution for x match any of the non-permissible values?
> Do both solutions for x make sense in the context of the problem?

Therefore, the average biking speed with no wind is _____ km/h.

Check Your Understanding

Practise

1. Use the least common denominator to eliminate the fractions from each equation. Do not solve.

   a) $\dfrac{7}{4x} + \dfrac{3}{4x} = 5x - 3$

   The least common denominator (LCD) is _____.

   The non-permissible value is $x =$ _____.

   $(\underline{\hspace{1cm}})\left(\dfrac{7}{4x}\right) + (\underline{\hspace{1cm}})\left(\dfrac{3}{4x}\right) = (\underline{\hspace{1cm}})\left(\dfrac{5x-3}{1}\right)$

   b) $\dfrac{x+1}{x-8} + \dfrac{2x+1}{x+2} = \dfrac{-7}{(x-8)(x+2)}$

   The LCD is _____.

   The non-permissible values are _____.

   c) $\dfrac{21-5x}{x-3} = \dfrac{x}{x^2-3x} - \dfrac{x-2}{2x}$

   The LCD is _____.

   The non-permissible values are _____.

Also try #1 on page 348 of *Pre-Calculus 11*.

2. Solve and verify each rational equation. Identify any non-permissible values.

a) $\frac{x}{3} + \frac{3}{x} = 2$

The LCD is _____.

The non-permissible value is

_____.

$(\text{\_\_\_\_\_})\frac{x}{3} + (\text{\_\_\_\_\_})\frac{3}{x}$

$= (\text{\_\_\_\_\_})2$

This value is _____.

       (*permitted* or *not permitted*)

Verify: For $x =$ _____:

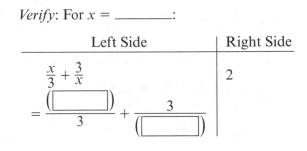

Left Side	Right Side
$\frac{x}{3} + \frac{3}{x}$	2

Therefore, $x =$ _____ a correct solution.

      (*is* or *is not*)

b) $\frac{2x}{x+1} - \frac{5}{x-1} = \frac{x^2 - 17}{x^2 - 1}$

The LCD is _____.

The non-permissible values are

_____.

These values are _____.

       (*permitted* or *not permitted*)

Verify first value: For $x =$ _____:

Left Side	Right Side

Therefore, $x =$ _____ a correct solution.

      (*is* or *is not*)

Verify second value: For $x =$ _____:

Left Side	Right Side

Therefore, $x =$ _____

_____ a correct solution.

    (*is* or *is not*)

3. Solve and verify each rational equation. Identify any non-permissible values.

a) $\dfrac{x-24}{x^2-8x} - \dfrac{5-x}{x-8} = \dfrac{2x+3}{x}$

    The LCD is _____.

    The non-permissible values are

    _____.

Verify permitted value: For $x =$ _____:

Left Side	Right Side

    The value $x =$ _____ is permitted

    but the value $x =$ _____ is not permitted.

Therefore, $x =$ _____

_____ a correct solution.
        (*is* or *is not*)

b) $\dfrac{4x-1}{3x} - \dfrac{x-7}{x-5} = \dfrac{8x-10}{3x^2-15x}$

    The LCD is _____.

    The non-permissible values are

    _____.

Verify permissible value(s): For $x =$ _____:

Left Side	Right Side

Are any of the values non-permissible?

Therefore, $x =$ _____

_____ a correct solution.
        (*is* or *is not*)

📖 Also try #2 to #4 on page 348 of *Pre-Calculus 11*.

Apply

4. Rico and Phania shovel the walkway together. Rico, working alone, can complete the task in 10 min. Phania, working alone, can complete the task in 15 min. How long will it take them to complete the task together?

	Time to Shovel (min)	Fraction Shovelled in 1 min	Fraction Shovelled in x min
Rico (R)			
Phania (P)			
Together (R)			

5. Charlie and Rose share a garden. Charlie can weed the garden, working alone, in 90 min. Rose can finish the task in 75 min. If they work together, how long will it take them to weed the garden?

Define your variable and write an equation to model the situation. Use the table to help you organize the information.

6. The distance from Calgary to Red Deer is approximately 140 km. Some friends leave Calgary at noon, drive to Red Deer, have a half-hour break, and then return to Calgary. They arrive at 3:15 p.m. Traffic is busier on the return trip, so their average speed is 10 km/h slower than on the outbound trip. What is the average speed of the round trip?

How much time in total do the friends spend driving? What is this as a decimal?

Is your answer reasonable in the context of the question? How do you know?

7. Marieke and Kate canoe 8 km up a river (against the current) and 8 km back (with the current). The total paddling time is 2.5 h. If the speed of the current is 2.6 km/h, what is Marieke and Kate's average speed in still water? How much time does it take them to paddle upstream (against the current)?

When travelling with the current, will the speed be faster or slower?

8. Two consecutive integers are represented by n and $n + 1$. The sum of the reciprocals of the integers is $-\dfrac{43}{462}$. Find the integers.

9. Two consecutive even integers are represented by n and $n + 2$.
The sum of the reciprocals of the integers is $\dfrac{29}{420}$. Find the integers.

See pages 348–351 of *Pre-Calculus 11* for more practice questions that involve modelling situations using rational equations.

Connect

10. You have worked on a number of word problems in this chapter. Summarize the kinds of situations that you can model using rational equations. Compare these situations with the other kinds of models (linear, quadratic, etc.) that you have used previously in this course.

Chapter 6 Review

6.1 Rational Expressions, pages 229–240

1. Simplify the following rational expressions. State any non-permissible values of the variable(s).

   a) $\dfrac{x^2 - 10x + 25}{x^2 - 11x + 30}$

   b) $\dfrac{3x^2 + 15x + 12}{3x^2 + 12x}$

2. Can the expression $\dfrac{-x + 7}{(x - 7)(x + 7)}$ be simplified further? Explain.

6.2 Multiplying and Dividing Rational Expressions, pages 241–251

3. Determine the product. Express your answer in simplest form. State the non-permissible values.

   $$\dfrac{10x^2 - 5x}{x^2 - x - 42} \times \dfrac{x^2 - 11x + 28}{60x - 15x^2}$$

4. Write an expression for tan θ based on the information in the diagram below. Simplify the expression and state any non-permissible values.

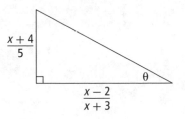

6.3 Adding and Subtracting Rational Expressions, pages 252–262

5. Determine the least common denominator (LCD) for the following set of rational expressions. Leave your answer in factored form.

$$\frac{x+7}{4x}, \frac{8x}{x^2-36}, \frac{1}{x^2+6x}$$

6. Determine each difference. Express each answer in simplest form. State the non-permissible values of the variable.

a) $\dfrac{2x^2 - 7x}{x^2 - 100} - \dfrac{x^2 - 2x + 10}{x^2 - 100}$

b) $\dfrac{2x - 3}{x^2 + 5x} - \dfrac{x + 9}{x^2 + 4x - 5}$

6.4 Rational Equations, pages 263–273

7. Emily can shovel the driveway in 25 min. It takes her younger brother Steve 40 min. If they work together to shovel the driveway, how quickly will they finish?

	Time to Shovel (min)	Fraction of Work Done in 1 min	Fraction of Work Done in t min
Emily			
Steve			
Together			

Chapter 6 Skills Organizer

Make note of some of the key details and things to remember about the processes you have learned in this unit. Use your class notes, textbook, or questions from this workbook to help you choose examples (or create your own). Some information is provided below to help you get started.

Process	Example	Things to Remember
Simplifying rational expressions		– cancel entire factors only – binomial factors in brackets – watch for opposites $(a - b) = -1(b - a)$
Determining non-permissible values		
Multiplying rational expressions		
Dividing rational expressions		
Finding a common denominator for rational expressions		
Adding rational expressions		
Subtracting rational expressions		
Solving rational equations		
Solving word problems with rational equations		

Chapter 7 Absolute Value and Reciprocal Functions

7.1 Absolute Value

- Absolute value represents the distance from zero on a number line, regardless of the direction.

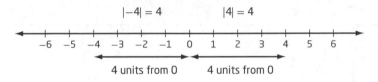

- Vertical bars around a number or expression represent its absolute value: $|-24|$, $|3 - 12|$.

- Absolute value is always zero or positive.
  - The absolute value of a positive number is positive: $|9| = 9$
  - The absolute value of a negative number is positive: $|-2| = 2$
  - The absolute value of zero is zero: $|0| = 0$

Working Example 1: Determine the Absolute Value of a Number

Evaluate.

a) $|25|$

b) $|-8|$

Solution

a) $|25| = 25$
    By definition, $|a| = a$, for $a \geq$ _____.

b) $|-8| = -(-8)$
        $= 8$
    By definition, $|a| = -a$, for $a <$ _____.

📖 See page 360 of *Pre-Calculus 11* for more examples.

Working Example 2: Compare and Order Absolute Values

Write the following real numbers in order from least to greatest.

$|-10.1|, \left|\dfrac{-21}{2}\right|, -9.8, |10|, -10, |-9.9|, \left|-9\dfrac{7}{8}\right|, -9$

Solution

Evaluate each number and express it in decimal form.

$|-10.1| = \underline{\hspace{2cm}}$ $\left|\dfrac{-21}{2}\right| = 10.\underline{\hspace{2cm}}$

$-9.8 = -9.8$ $|10| = \underline{\hspace{2cm}}$

$-10 = -10$ $|-9.9| = \underline{\hspace{2cm}}$

$\left|-9\dfrac{7}{8}\right| = 9.\underline{\hspace{2cm}}$ $-9 = \underline{\hspace{2cm}}$

Arrange the numbers in order: $-10, \underline{\hspace{2cm}}, -9, 9.875, \underline{\hspace{2cm}}, 10, 10.1, \underline{\hspace{2cm}}$

Show the original numbers in order: $-10, -9.8, \underline{\hspace{2cm}}, \left|-9\dfrac{7}{8}\right|, \underline{\hspace{2cm}}, 10, \underline{\hspace{2cm}}, \underline{\hspace{2cm}}$

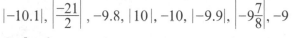 This question is similar to Example 2 on page 361 of *Pre-Calculus 11*.

Working Example 3: Evaluate Absolute Value Expressions

Evaluate.

a) $|5 - 6|$ **b)** $|2| - |3(-4)|$ **c)** $\left|5(-2)^2 + 7(-3) - 15\right|$

Solution

a) $|5 - 6| = |\underline{\hspace{2cm}}|$ Evaluate the expression inside the absolute value symbol.

$= \underline{\hspace{2cm}}$ Evaluate.

Therefore, $|5 - 6| = \underline{\hspace{2cm}}$.

b) $|2| - |3(-4)| = |2| - |\underline{\hspace{2cm}}|$ Evaluate the expressions inside the absolute value symbol.

$= \underline{\hspace{2cm}} - \underline{\hspace{2cm}}$ Evaluate the absolute values.

$= \underline{\hspace{2cm}}$ Subtract.

Therefore, $|2| - |3(-4)| = \underline{\hspace{3cm}}$.

c) $\left|5(-2)^2 + 7(-3) - 15\right| = |5(\underline{\hspace{2cm}}) + 7(-3) - 15|$ Evaluate the power.

$= |\underline{\hspace{2cm}}|$ Simplify the expression inside the absolute value symbol.

$= \underline{\hspace{2cm}}$ Evaluate.

Therefore, $\left|5(-2)^2 + 7(-3) - 15\right| = \underline{\hspace{2cm}}$.

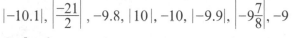 This question is similar to Example 3 on page 361 of *Pre-Calculus 11*.

Check Your Understanding

Practise

1. Evaluate

   a) $\left|\dfrac{-5}{6}\right|$

   b) $\left|-1\dfrac{1}{4}\right|$

   c) $|0.8|$

   d) $|12|$

   e) $|-1.2|$

   f) $|0|$

2. Order the numbers from greatest to least.

   $|-2.5|, \left|\dfrac{-15}{7}\right|, -2, -2\dfrac{6}{9}, |-2.09|, 2\dfrac{3}{5}$

   Determine each absolute value. Then, express each number in decimal form.

   Order the decimal numbers from greatest to least.

   _____

   Show the original numbers in order from greatest to least.

   _____

3. Given point A and the distance from A to B, show and label point B.

   a)

   distance of 6 units

   b)

   distance of 5 units

   c)

   distance of 4 units

   📖 This question is similar to #5 on page 363 of *Pre-Calculus 11*.

4. Evaluate each expression.

a) $|1.2 - 1.5|$

$= |\underline{\hspace{2cm}}|$ Evaluate the expression inside the absolute value symbol.

$= \underline{\hspace{2cm}}$ Evaluate.

b) $|-11| - |-19|$

$= \underline{\hspace{2cm}} - \underline{\hspace{2cm}}$

$= \underline{\hspace{2cm}}$

c) $|-11 - (-19)|$

$= |\underline{\hspace{2cm}}|$

$= \underline{\hspace{2cm}}$

d) $-4\left|\dfrac{1}{2} - \dfrac{3}{4}\right|$ Evaluate the expression inside the absolute value symbol.

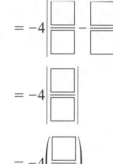

$= -4\left|\dfrac{\square}{\square} - \dfrac{\square}{\square}\right|$ Find a common denominator.

$= -4\left|\dfrac{\square}{\square}\right|$ Subtract the fractions.

$= -4\left(\dfrac{\square}{\square}\right)$ Evaluate the absolute value.

$= \underline{\hspace{2cm}}$ Multiply.

e) $|1.2 - 1.5|^2$

$= |\underline{\hspace{2cm}}|^2$ Evaluate the expression inside the absolute value symbol.

$= (\underline{\hspace{2cm}})^2$ Evaluate the absolute value.

$= \underline{\hspace{2cm}}$ Square the result.

f) $|-4 + 3^2| - |8 - (-10)| + |9 - 16| + |-10|$

$= \underline{\hspace{2cm}} - \underline{\hspace{2cm}} + \underline{\hspace{2cm}} + \underline{\hspace{2cm}}$

$= \underline{\hspace{2cm}} + \underline{\hspace{2cm}} + \underline{\hspace{2cm}}$

$= \underline{\hspace{2cm}}$

📖 This question is similar to #6 on page 363 of *Pre-Calculus 11*.

Apply

5. The surface of Great Slave Lake is 156 m above sea level.
   At the deepest point, the bottom of the lake is 458 m below sea level.

   a) Use absolute value symbols to write a statement to determine the depth of the lake.

   b) What is the depth of the lake?

   The depth of the lake is _____.

6. The melting point of mercury is −39 °C. Its boiling point is 357 °C.

   a) Use absolute value symbols to write a statement to determine the number of degrees between the boiling point and the melting point.

   b) How many degrees is it?

   The number of degrees is _____.

7. Use the wind chill chart to answer the following questions.

Wind Speed (km/h)	Air Temperature (°C)		
	−15	−20	−25
15	−23	−29	−35
20	−24	−31	−37
25	−25	−32	−38
30	−26	−33	−39
35	−27	−33	−40
40	−27	−34	−41

a) The air temperature is −15 °C. The wind gusts from 15 km/h to 40 km/h. Use an absolute value expression to determine the change in wind chill temperature for the two wind speeds.

b) The air temperature is −25 °C. Use an absolute value expression to determine the change in wind speed that would change a wind chill reading of −35 °C to −40 °C.

8. A stock opened Monday's trading at $25.98/share. On Tuesday, the stock's value dropped by $2.31/share. On Wednesday, it dropped by $0.75/share, and on Thursday it rose by $1.15/share. On Friday the stock closed trading at $26.83/share.

a) Write a statement using absolute value symbols to show its change in value from Monday's opening to Friday's closing.

b) What was the change?

Connect

9. The formula for the distance between two points (x_1, y_1) and (x_2, y_2) on a Cartesian plane is $d = \sqrt{(x_2 - x_1)^2 + (y_2 - y_1)^2}$.

How does the formula above compare to the following formula: $d = \sqrt{|x_2 - x_1|^2 + |y_2 - y_1|^2}$?

Differences: _____

Similarities: _____

10. The number of strokes an expert golfer should take to play a hole is called "par" for the hole. The first table shows golf terms related to the number of strokes above or below par. The second table shows par values for the first nine holes for the Victoria golf course in Edmonton's River Valley.

Golf Term	Number of Strokes Above or Below Par
Double bogey	+2
Bogey	+1
Par	0
Birdie	−1
Eagle	−2

Par	Holes
4	1, 2, 6, 8, 9
3	3, 7
5	4, 5

a) Write two problems that each use absolute value symbols and the information in the tables.

b) Solve each problem.

KEY IDEAS

- An absolute value function is a function that involves the absolute value of a variable. The graphs show some functions and their related absolute value functions.

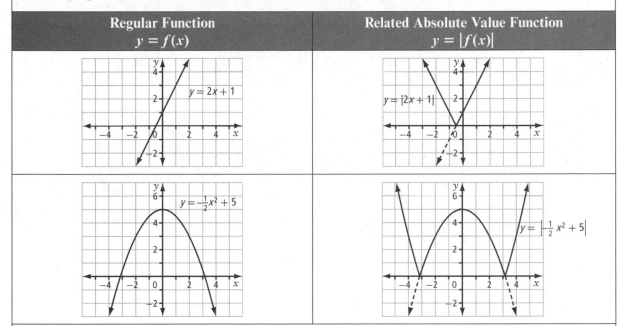

Regular Function $y = f(x)$	Related Absolute Value Function $y = |f(x)|$

- To graph an absolute value function:
  - Make a table of values, and then graph the function.
  - Use $y = f(x)$ and $y = -f(x)$ to sketch the function.
    For $y = -f(x)$, all negative y-values are reflected in the x-axis.

- To analyse an absolute value function graphically:
  - First, graph the function.
  - Then, identify the characteristics of the graph, such as the x-intercept, y-intercept, minimum values, and domain and range.

- You can write any absolute value function, $y = |f(x)|$, as a piecewise function:

$$y = \begin{cases} f(x), & \text{if } f(x) \geq 0 \\ -f(x), & \text{if } f(x) < 0 \end{cases}$$

> A piecewise function is made up of "pieces" of different functions. Each piece of the function has its own specific domain.

- The domain of an absolute function, $y = |f(x)|$, is the same as the domain of $y = f(x)$.

- The range of an absolute function, $y = |f(x)|$, depends on the range of $f(x)$. For an absolute linear or absolute quadratic function, the range will usually, but not always, be $\{y \mid y \geq 0, y \in \mathbb{R}\}$.

- An invariant point is a point that remains unchanged when a transformation is applied to it.

Working Example 1: Graph an Absolute Value Function of the Form $y = |ax + b|$

Consider the absolute value function $y = |3x - 1|$.

a) Determine the y-intercept and x-intercept.

b) Sketch the graph.

c) State the domain and range.

d) Express as a piecewise function.

Solution

a) The y-intercept occurs where the graph crosses the y-axis. The x-value at the y-intercept

is _____.

Substitute, and solve for y.

$y = |3x - 1|$

$y = |3(\underline{\hspace{1cm}}) - 1|$

$y = |\underline{\hspace{1cm}}|$

$y = \underline{\hspace{1cm}}$

The y-intercept occurs at $(0, \underline{\hspace{1cm}})$.

The x-intercept occurs where the graph crosses the _____.

The y-value at the x-intercept is 0.

To determine the x-intercept,

let $y = \underline{\hspace{1cm}}$ and solve for x.

$y = |3x - 1|$

$\underline{\hspace{1cm}} = 3x - 1$

$\underline{\hspace{1cm}} = 3x$

$\underline{\hspace{1cm}} = x$

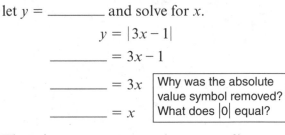

Why was the absolute value symbol removed? What does $|0|$ equal?

The x-intercept occurs at $(\underline{\hspace{1cm}}, 0)$.

b) Method 1: Sketch Using a Table of Values

Complete the table:

x	$y = |3x - 1|$
0	
	0
2	
	8
−1	
−2	
−3	

Graph the function.

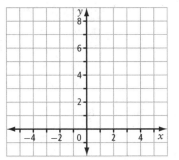

Method 2: Sketch Using the Graph of $y = 3x - 1$

Sketch the graph of $y = 3x - 1$, which is a line with

a slope of _____ and a y-intercept of _____.

Use the x-intercept from part a): (_____, 0).

Reflect all the points below the x-axis in the x-axis.
Use red to show the parts of the graph that represent $y = |3x - 1|$.

c) Any real number can be substituted for x into the function $y = |3x - 1|$.

Therefore, the domain is $\{x \mid x \in$ _____$\}$.

For all values of x, $|3x - 1| \geq 0$, or $y \geq$ _____.

Therefore, the range is $\{y \mid y \geq$ _____$, y \in$ _____$\}$.

d) The V-shaped graph of the absolute function $y = |3x - 1|$ is composed of two separate linear functions, each with its own domain.

When $x \geq \frac{1}{3}$, the graph of $y = |3x - 1|$ is the graph of $y =$ _____.

When $x < \frac{1}{3}$, the graph of $y = |3x - 1|$ is the graph of $y = 3x - 1$ reflected in the ____-axis.

The equation of the reflected graph is $y = -(3x - 1)$ or $y = -3x$_____.

As a piecewise function, the function is $y = \begin{cases} 3x - 1, \text{ if } x \geq \text{_____} \\ -(\text{_____}), \text{ if } x < \frac{1}{3} \end{cases}$

Working Example 2: Graph an Absolute Value Function of the Form $f(x) = |ax^2 + bx + c|$

Consider the absolute value function $y = |x^2 - 3x - 4|$.

a) Determine the y-intercept and x-intercept.

b) Graph the function.

c) Determine the domain and range.

d) Express as a piecewise function.

Solution

a) Determine the y-intercept by substituting $x = \underline{\qquad}$ in the function and solving for y.

$f(x) = |x^2 - 3x - 4|$

$f(x) = |(\underline{\qquad})^2 - 3(\underline{\qquad}) - 4|$

$f(x) = |\underline{\qquad\qquad\qquad}|$

$f(x) = \underline{\qquad}$

The y-intercept occurs at $(0, \underline{\qquad})$.

Determine the x-intercept by substituting $y = \underline{\qquad}$ into the function and solving for x.

$y = |x^2 - 3x - 4|$

$\underline{\qquad} = |x^2 - 3x - 4|$

$\underline{\qquad} = x^2 - 3x - 4$

$\underline{\qquad} = (x - 4)(\underline{\qquad})$

$x - 4 = 0 \quad$ or $\quad \underline{\qquad} = 0$

$x = \underline{\qquad} \qquad x = \underline{\qquad}$

The x-intercepts occur at $(\underline{\qquad}, 0)$ and $(\underline{\qquad}, 0)$.

b) Use the graph of $y = f(x)$ to graph $y = |f(x)|$.

Complete the square to convert the function $y = x^2 - 3x - 4$ to vertex form, $y = a(x - h)^2 + k$.

$y = \left[x^2 - 3x + \left(\frac{3}{2}\right)^2\right] - 4 + \underline{\qquad}$

$y = (x \underline{\qquad\qquad})^2 - \underline{\qquad}$

Since $h = \underline{\qquad}$ and $k = \underline{\qquad}$, the coordinates of the vertex are $(\underline{\qquad}, \underline{\qquad})$.

Since $a > 0$, the parabola opens $\underline{\qquad\qquad\qquad\qquad}$.
$\qquad\qquad\qquad\qquad$ (*upward* or *downward*)

Sketch the graph of $y = x^2 - 3x - 4$.

Reflect in the x-axis the part of the graph of $y = x^2 - 3x - 4$ that lies below the x-axis.

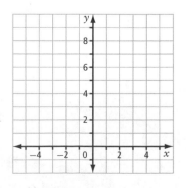

c) Any real number can be substituted for x into the function $y = |x^2 - 3x - 4|$.

The domain is $\{x \mid x$ _____ $\}$.

The range is all non-negative values of y,

$\{y \mid y \geq$ _____ $, y \in$ _____ $\}$.

d) The graph of $y = |x^2 - 3x - 4|$ consists of two separate quadratic functions. Use the x-intercepts to identify the specific domain for each function.

- When $x < -1$ and $x > 4$, the graph of $y = |x^2 - 3x - 4|$ is the graph of $y = x^2 - 3x - 4$;

  – opens _____
               (upward or *downward)*

  – vertex at (_____, -6.25)

  – y-intercept at (0, _____)

  – x-intercepts at (_____, 0) and (_____, 0)

- When $-1 \leq x \leq 4$, the graph of $y = |x^2 - 3x - 4|$ is the graph of $y = x^2 - 3x - 4$ reflected in the _____-axis. The equation of the reflected graph is $y = -(x^2 - 3x - 4)$ or $y =$ _____:

  – opens _____
               (upward or *downward)*

  – vertex at (1.5, _____)

  – y-intercept at (0, _____)

  – x-intercepts at (_____, 0) and (_____, 0)

The function $y = |x^2 - 3x - 4|$ can be written as a piecewise function:

$$y = \begin{cases} x^2 - 3x - 4, & \text{if } x \leq \text{_____ or } x \geq \text{_____} \\ -(x^2 - 3x - 4), & \text{if } -1 < x < \text{_____} \end{cases}$$

📖 This question is similar to Example 2 on pages 372–374 of *Pre-Calculus 11*.

Check Your Understanding

Practise

1. Given the values for $y = f(x)$, complete each table for $y = |f(x)|$.

a)

x	$y = f(x)$	$y = |f(x)|$
−4	0	
−2	−6	
0	−12	
2	−14	

b)

x	$y = f(x)$	$y = |f(x)|$
−2	7	
−1	4	
0	1	
1	−2	
2	−5	

2. In the table, the first column is a point on the graph of $y = f(x)$. Complete the second column for the corresponding point on $y = |f(x)|$.

$f(x)$	$|f(x)|$
(−1, −10)	
(0, −6)	
(1, −2)	
(2, 2)	

Questions 1 and 2 are similar to #1 and 2 on page 375 of *Pre-Calculus 11*.

3. Given each graph of $y = f(x)$, sketch the graph of $y = |f(x)|$ on the same grid.

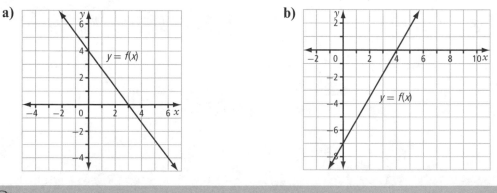

a)

b)

This question is similar to #5 on page 376 of *Pre-Calculus 11*.

4. Given each graph of $y = f(x)$, sketch the graph of $y = |f(x)|$ on the same grid.

a)

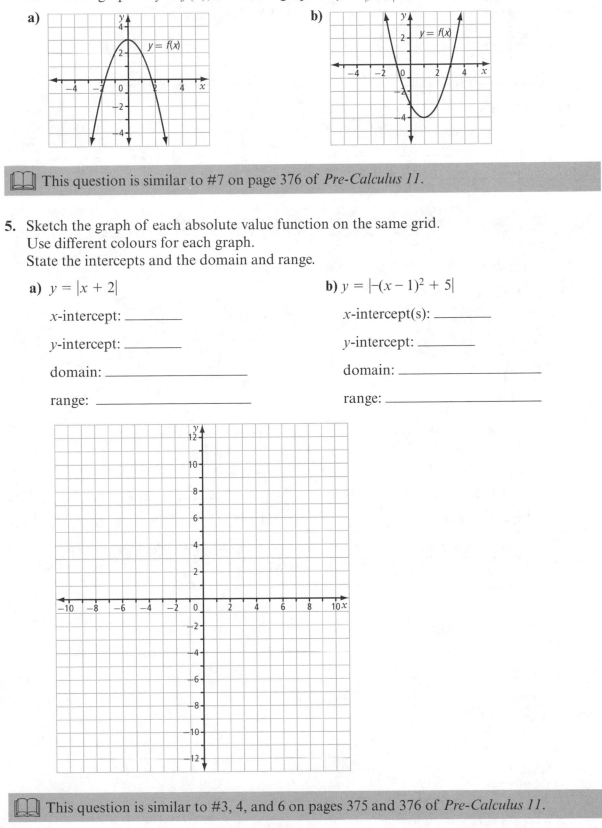

b)

This question is similar to #7 on page 376 of *Pre-Calculus 11*.

5. Sketch the graph of each absolute value function on the same grid.
Use different colours for each graph.
State the intercepts and the domain and range.

a) $y = |x + 2|$

x-intercept: _____

y-intercept: _____

domain: _____

range: _____

b) $y = |-(x - 1)^2 + 5|$

x-intercept(s): _____

y-intercept: _____

domain: _____

range: _____

This question is similar to #3, 4, and 6 on pages 375 and 376 of *Pre-Calculus 11*.

6. Write the piecewise function that represents each graph.

a)

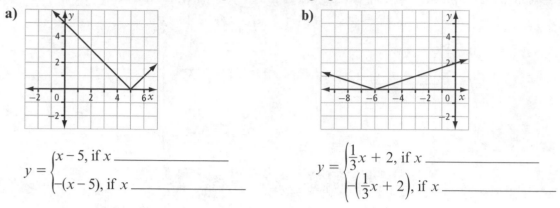

$$y = \begin{cases} x - 5, \text{ if } x \underline{\hspace{2cm}} \\ -(x - 5), \text{ if } x \underline{\hspace{2cm}} \end{cases}$$

b)

$$y = \begin{cases} \frac{1}{3}x + 2, \text{ if } x \underline{\hspace{2cm}} \\ -\left(\frac{1}{3}x + 2\right), \text{ if } x \underline{\hspace{2cm}} \end{cases}$$

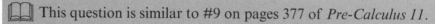

📖 This question is similar to #9 on pages 377 of *Pre-Calculus 11*.

7. Write the piecewise function that represents each graph.

a)

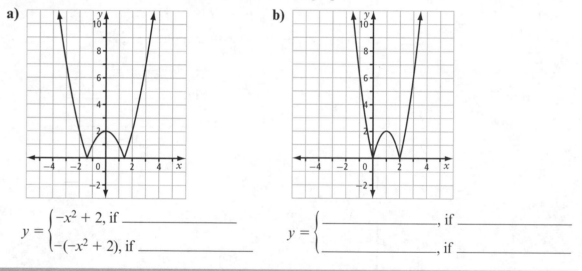

$$y = \begin{cases} -x^2 + 2, \text{ if } \underline{\hspace{2cm}} \\ -(-x^2 + 2), \text{ if } \underline{\hspace{2cm}} \end{cases}$$

b)

$$y = \begin{cases} \underline{\hspace{2cm}}, \text{ if } \underline{\hspace{2cm}} \\ \underline{\hspace{2cm}}, \text{ if } \underline{\hspace{2cm}} \end{cases}$$

📖 This question is similar to #10 on page 377 of *Pre-Calculus 11*.

Apply

8. Consider the function $f(x) = \left| \frac{1}{2}x - 6 \right|$.

   a) Complete the table of values.

x	$y = \left\lvert \frac{1}{2}x - 6 \right\rvert$
0	
	0
2	
4	
	3
−2	
−6	

   b) Sketch the graph of the function.

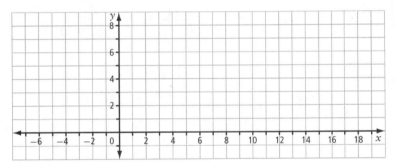

   c) Determine the domain and range.

   domain: $\{x \mid$ _____ $\}$

   range: $\{y \mid$ _____ $\}$

   d) Express as a piecewise function.

   $y = \begin{cases} \frac{1}{2}x - 6, & \text{if } x \underline{\hspace{3cm}} \\ \underline{\hspace{3cm}}, & \text{if } x < 12 \end{cases}$

📖 This question is similar to #12 on page 377 of *Pre-Calculus 11*.

9. Consider the function $f(x) = |x^2 + 4x - 3|$.

   a) Express the function in vertex form, $y = |a(x - p)^2 + q|$.

   b) What are the coordinates of the vertex?

   _____

   Where are the intercepts?

   x-intercepts: (_____, 0) and (_____,0)

   y-intercept: (0, _____)

   c) Sketch the graph on the grid.

   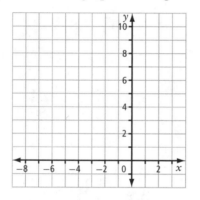

   d) Determine the domain and range.

   domain: $\{x \mid$ _____$\}$

   range: $\{y \mid$ _____$\}$

   e) Express as a piecewise function.

   $$y = \begin{cases} x^2 + 4x - 3, \text{ if } x \leq \underline{\hspace{1cm}} \text{ or } x \geq \underline{\hspace{1cm}} \\ -(x^2 + 4x - 3), \text{ if } \underline{\hspace{1cm}} < x < \underline{\hspace{1cm}} \end{cases}$$

   📖 This question is similar to #13 on page 377 of *Pre-Calculus 11*.

10. Consider these three functions:

$$f(x) = x^2 - 2x + 6 \qquad g(x) = |x^2 - 2x + 6| \qquad h(x) = |-(x^2 - 2x + 6)|$$

a) For what values of x is $f(x) < 0$? _____

For what values of x is $g(x) < 0$? _____

For what values of x is $h(x) < 0$? _____

b) Without graphing, predict how the graphs of the three functions compare.

c) Check your prediction using technology. Sketch the display shown on your graphing calculator below.

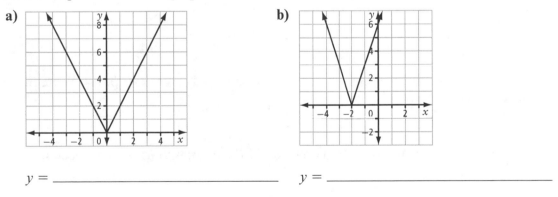

11. State an equation for each graph below.

a)

$y =$ _____

b)

$y =$ _____

Connect

12. a) Does $|2 - x| = |x - 2|$ for all real values of x? Explain.

b) Does $|x^2| = x^2$ for all real values of x? Explain.

13. The amount of profit that a cell phone company makes is given by the equation $y = -x^2 + 150x - 2600$, where y is the profit in dollars and x is the number of phones sold.

a) Graph the function.

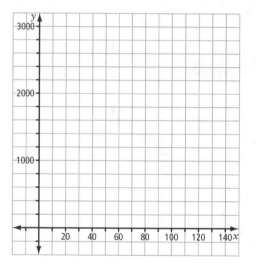

b) Use absolute value to change the function to show only a positive profit. Write the new function with absolute value symbols.

c) Between $x = 20$ and $x = 130$, what is the maximum profit that can be reached?

d) Is there a maximum profit for $x \in R$?

Explain. _____

7.3 Absolute Value Equations

> ### KEY IDEAS

- An absolute value equation includes the absolute value of an expression involving a variable. For example, $|x + 2| = 6$.

- To solve an absolute value equation by graphing:
  - Graph the left side and the right side of the equation on the same set of axes.
  - The point(s) of intersection are the solution(s).

For example, to solve $|x + 2| = 6$ by graphing, graph $y = |x + 2|$ and $y = 6$ and identify the points of intersection.

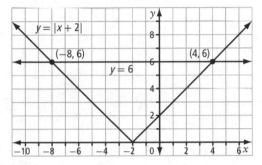

The solutions are $x = -8$ and $x = 4$.

- To solve an absolute value equation algebraically,
  - consider two separate cases:
    Case 1: The expression inside the absolute value symbol is greater than or equal to 0.
    Case 2: The expression inside the absolute value symbol is less than 0.
  - the roots in each case are the solutions
  - there may be extraneous roots that need to be identified and rejected

For example, to solve $|x + 2| = 6$, consider the cases $x + 2 \geq 0$ and $x + 2 < 0$:

Case 1	**Case 2**
When $x + 2 \geq 0$:	When $x + 2 < 0$:
$x + 2 = 6$	$-(x + 2) = 6$
$x = 4$	$-x - 2 = 6$
	$x = -8$

- Verify solutions by substituting into the original equation.

- Since, by definition, absolute value is greater than or equal to zero, there can be no solution if $|f(x)| = a$, where $a < 0$.

Working Example 1: Solve an Absolute Value Equation

Solve $|x + 3| = 8$.

Solution

Method 1: Use Algebra

Use the definition of absolute value to determine the cases.

$$|x + 3| = \begin{cases} x + 3, \text{ if } x \geq -3 \\ -(x + 3), \text{ if } x < -3 \end{cases}$$

Case 1: $x + 3 \geq 0$

$x + 3 = 8$

$x = \underline{\hspace{1.5cm}}$

The value $\underline{\hspace{1cm}}$ satisfies the condition $x \geq -3$.

Case 2: $x + 3 < 0$

$-(x + 3) = 8$

$-x - 3 = 8$

$-x = \underline{\hspace{1.5cm}}$

$x = \underline{\hspace{1.5cm}}$

The value $\underline{\hspace{1cm}}$ satisfies the condition $x < -3$.

Verify the solution algebraically by substitution.

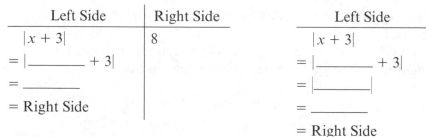

For $x = 5$:

Left Side	Right Side
$\lvert x + 3\rvert$	8
$= \lvert \underline{\hspace{1cm}} + 3\rvert$	
$= \underline{\hspace{1cm}}$	
$= $ Right Side	

For $x = -11$:

Left Side	Right Side
$\lvert x + 3\rvert$	8
$= \lvert \underline{\hspace{1cm}} + 3\rvert$	
$= \lvert \underline{\hspace{1cm}} \rvert$	
$= \underline{\hspace{1cm}}$	
$= $ Right Side	

The solutions are $x = \underline{\hspace{1.5cm}}$ and $x = \underline{\hspace{1.5cm}}$.

Method 2: Use a Graph

Write the left side and right side as separate functions, $f(x) = |x + 3|$ and $g(x) = 8$.

Graph $f(x)$ and $g(x)$ on the same grid.

Determine where the functions intersect.

The graphs intersect at ($\underline{\hspace{1cm}}$, 8)

and ($\underline{\hspace{1cm}}$, $\underline{\hspace{1cm}}$).

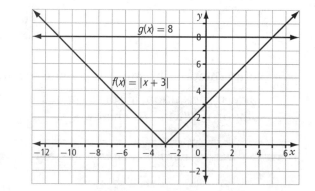

Thus, $x = \underline{\hspace{1cm}}$ and $x = \underline{\hspace{1cm}}$ are the solutions to the equation $|x + 3| = 8$.

Verify by using technology. Enter $f(x) = |x + 3|$ and $g(x) = 8$ into a graphing calculator. Use the intersect feature to determine the points of intersection.

📖 This question is similar to Example 1 on pages 382–383 of *Pre-Calculus 11*.

Working Example 2: Solve an Absolute Value Equation With an Extraneous Solution

Solve $|3x + 2| = 4x + 5$.

Solution

Determine the cases. Then, determine the restrictions on the domain.

$$|3x + 2| = \begin{cases} 3x + 2, \text{ if } x \geq \underline{\hspace{1.5cm}} \\ -(3x + 2), \text{ if } x < \underline{\hspace{1.5cm}} \end{cases}$$

Case 1: $3x + 2 \geq 0$
$3x + 2 = 4x + 5$

$x = \underline{\hspace{1.5cm}}$

The value $x = \underline{\hspace{1.5cm}}$ $\underline{\hspace{3cm}}$
(*does* or *does not*)

satisfy the condition $x \geq \underline{\hspace{1.5cm}}$.

Case 2: $3x + 2 < 0$
$-(3x + 2) = 4x + 5$

$x = \underline{\hspace{1.5cm}}$

The value $x = \underline{\hspace{1.5cm}}$ $\underline{\hspace{3cm}}$
(*does* or *does not*)

satisfy the condition $x < \underline{\hspace{1.5cm}}$.

Verify the solution algebraically by substitution.

For $x = \underline{\hspace{1.5cm}}$:

Left Side	Right Side

For $x = \underline{\hspace{1.5cm}}$:

Left Side	Right Side

Therefore, the solution is $x = \underline{\hspace{1.5cm}}$.

Working Example 3: Solve an Absolute Value Equation With No Solution

Solve $|5x + 1| + 7 = 3$.

Solution

Isolate the absolute value expression.
$|5x + 1| + 7 = 3$

$|5x + 1| = \underline{\hspace{1.5cm}}$

This statement is $\underline{\hspace{3cm}}$ true because of the definition of absolute value.
(*always* or *never*)

Since the absolute value of a number must be greater than or equal to $\underline{\hspace{1.5cm}}$, by inspection

this equation has $\underline{\hspace{1.5cm}}$ solution(s).

Working Example 4: Solve an Absolute Value Equation Involving a Quadratic Expression

Solve $|x^2 - 6x| = 8$.

Solution

Use the definition of absolute value to determine the cases.

$$|x^2 - 6x| = \begin{cases} x^2 - 6x, & \text{if } x \le 0 \text{ or } x \ge 6 \\ -(x^2 - 6x), & \text{if } \underline{\hspace{2cm}} < x < \underline{\hspace{2cm}} \end{cases}$$

Case 1: $x^2 - 6x \ge 0$

$$x^2 - 6x = 8$$

$$x^2 - 6x \underline{\hspace{2cm}} = 0 \qquad \text{Move all terms to one side, equal to zero.}$$

Use the quadratic formula.

$$x = \frac{-b \pm \sqrt{b^2 - 4ac}}{2a}, a = \underline{\hspace{1.5cm}}, b = \underline{\hspace{1.5cm}}, c = \underline{\hspace{1.5cm}}$$

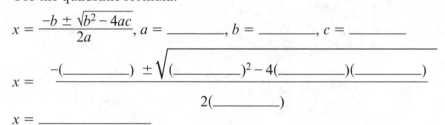

$$x = \underline{\hspace{3cm}}$$

Verify.

For $x = $ \underline{\hspace{3cm}}:

Left Side	Right Side

For $x = $ \underline{\hspace{3cm}}:

Left Side	Right Side

Case 2: $x^2 - 6x < 0$

$$-(x^2 - 6x) = 8$$

$$-x^2 \underline{\hspace{2cm}} = 8$$

$$-x^2 + 6x - 8 = 0 \qquad \text{Move all terms to one side, equal to zero.}$$

$$(\underline{\hspace{2.5cm}})(\underline{\hspace{2.5cm}}) = 0 \qquad \text{Factor.}$$

$$(\underline{\hspace{2cm}}) = 0 \quad \text{or} \quad (\underline{\hspace{2cm}}) = 0$$

$$x = \underline{\hspace{2.5cm}} \qquad \text{or} \qquad x = \underline{\hspace{2.5cm}}$$

Verify.

For $x =$ _____:

Left Side	Right Side

For $x =$ _____:

Left Side	Right Side

The solutions are $x =$ _____, $x =$ _____, $x =$ _____, and $x =$ _____.

Working Example 5: Solve an Absolute Value Equation Involving a Linear and a Quadratic Equation

Solve $\left| x^2 - 1 \right| = x$.

Solution

Use the definition of absolute value to determine the cases.

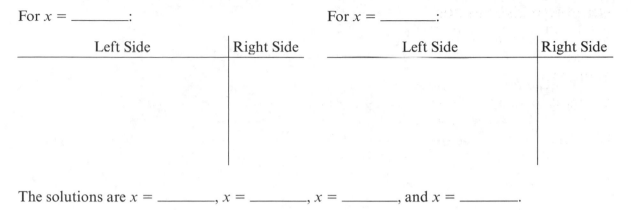

$$\left| x^2 - 1 \right| = \begin{cases} x^2 - 1, & \text{if } x \leq \rule{1cm}{0.4pt} \text{ or } x \geq \rule{1cm}{0.4pt} \\ -(x^2 - 1), & \text{if } \rule{1cm}{0.4pt} < x < \rule{1cm}{0.4pt} \end{cases}$$

Case 1: $x^2 - 1 \geq 0$

$$x^2 - 1 = x$$

x^2 _____ $= 0$ Move all terms to one side, equal to zero.

Use the quadratic formula to solve for x.

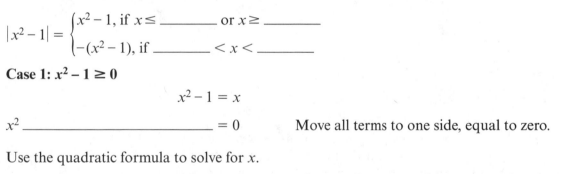

$$x = \frac{-b \pm \sqrt{b^2 - 4ac}}{2a}, \quad a = \rule{1cm}{0.4pt}, \quad b = \rule{1cm}{0.4pt}, \quad c = \rule{1cm}{0.4pt}$$

$$x = \frac{-(\rule{1cm}{0.4pt}) \pm \sqrt{(\rule{1.5cm}{0.4pt})^2 - 4(\rule{1.5cm}{0.4pt})(\rule{1cm}{0.4pt})}}{2(\rule{1cm}{0.4pt})}$$

$$x = \rule{3cm}{0.4pt}$$

Verify.

For $x =$ _____:

Left Side	Right Side

For $x =$ _____:

Left Side	Right Side

Case 2: $x^2 - 1 < 0$

$-(x^2 - 1) = x$

Set the equation equal to zero.

$-x^2$ _____ $= 0$ Move all terms to one side, equal to zero.

Use the quadratic formula to solve for x.

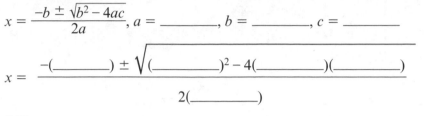

$x = \dfrac{-b \pm \sqrt{b^2 - 4ac}}{2a}$, $a =$ _____, $b =$ _____, $c =$ _____

$x = \dfrac{-(\underline{\hspace{1cm}}) \pm \sqrt{(\underline{\hspace{1cm}})^2 - 4(\underline{\hspace{1cm}})(\underline{\hspace{1cm}})}}{2(\underline{\hspace{1cm}})}$

$x =$ _____

Verify.

For $x =$ _____ :   For $x =$ _____ :

Left Side	Right Side		Left Side	Right Side

The solutions are $x =$ _____ and $x =$ _____.

The solutions can also be verified graphically by using technology.
Enter $f(x) = |x^2 - 1|$ and $g(x) = x$ into your graphing calculator.
Use the intersect function to read the solutions. (Note: The values may be given as decimal approximations).

   📖   This question is similar to Example 6 on pages 387–388 of *Pre-Calculus 11*.

Check Your Understanding

Practise

1. Use the number line to solve each equation geometrically.

```
  ←――+――+――+――+――+――+――+――+――+――+――+――+――+――+――+――+――+――+――+――+――+――+――+――+――→
   -12 -11 -10 -9  -8  -7  -6  -5  -4  -3  -2  -1   0   1   2   3   4   5   6   7   8   9  10  11  12
```

   a) $|x| = 11$

   b) $|x| - 6 = 0$

   c) $|x| + 8 = 10$

   d) $|x| - 2.5 = 7$

📖 This question is similar to #1 on page 389 of *Pre-Calculus 11*.

---

2. Solve each absolute value equation by graphing.

   a) $|-2 + x| = 5$

   b) $9 = |x + 3|$

   c) $|5 - x| = 8$

   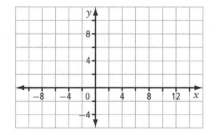

3. Solve each absolute value equation. Verify your solutions.

    a) $|3 + 7x| = 73$

        Case 1: $3 + 7x \geq 0$ **Case 2: $3 + 7x < 0$**

        $3 + 7x = 73$ $-(3 + 7x) = 73$

        Verify.

        For $x =$ _____: For $x =$ _____:

Left Side	Right Side

Left Side	Right Side

        The solutions are $x =$ _____ and $x =$ _____.

    b) $|x + 3| = -5$

        There is _____ solution because _____.

    c) $|-5x| + 4 = -11$

4. Solve each absolute value equation. Verify your solutions.

a) $\dfrac{|x + 4|}{10} = 1$

Case 1: $x + 4 \geq 0$ **Case 2:** $x + 4 < 0$

b) $|x^2 + x - 2| = x + 3$

Apply

5. A machine fills containers with 32 ounces of oatmeal. After the containers are filled, another machine weighs them. If the container's weight differs from the desired 32-ounce weight by more than 0.5 ounces, the container is rejected.

a) Write an absolute value equation that can be used to find the heaviest and lightest acceptable weights for the container.

b) Solve the equation.

6. Your supervisor allows you to clock-in for your 8 a.m. shift up to 15 min before and up to 15 min after.

   a) Write an absolute value equation that can be used to find the acceptable limits for your clock-in times.

   b) Solve the equation.

7. To fit correctly, the width of a machine part can vary no more than 0.01 mm from the ideal width of 2.5 mm.

   a) Write an absolute value equation to find the acceptable limits to the width in millimetres for this part.

   b) Solve the equation.

8. A technician measures an electric current that is 0.036 amperes with a possible error of $\pm$ 0.002 amperes.

   a) Write this current, i, as an absolute value equation that finds the limits to the current.

   b) Solve the equation.

9. A manufacturer has a tolerance of 0.35 lb for a bag of potting soil advertised as weighing 9.6 lb. Write and solve an absolute value equation that finds the limits to the weight of each bag.

10. A company is building a movie theatre. Based on similar movie theatres, an analyst tells the company that its earnings per day are based on the solution to the equation $y = |-x^2 + 48x - 512|$, where y is thousands of dollars and x is the number of movie screens.

   a) If the company can build between 16 and 32 movie screens, what is the number of screens within this range that will give the maximum profit?

   b) What is the amount of profit?

11. Is the following absolute value equation solved correctly? Explain. If it is not correct, solve it correctly.

   $4 - 9|-6 - x| = -15$

   $-5|-6 - x| = -15$

   $|-6 - x| = 3$

   Case 1: $-6 - x \geq 0$ **Case 2: $-6 - x < 0$**

   $-6 - x = 3$ $6 + x = 3$

   $x = 9$ $x = -3$

Connect

12. A lab worker observes a mouse walking through a straight tunnel. When the mouse moves forward, a positive number is recorded. When it moves backward, a negative number is recorded. The worker records that the mouse has walked a, b, and c feet.

a) Does the equation $d = |a + b + c|$ represent the total distance, d, the mouse walked in feet? If no, explain why not. If yes, replace a, b, and c with values to verify.

b) Use your answer to part a) to determine if $|a + b + c| = |a| + |b| + |c|$.

13. Twin babies have masses of m_1 and m_2 grams. Their mother wants to know how many grams separate the masses of the two babies.

a) Write an equation for this difference, d, in such a way that the result will always be positive no matter which baby is heavier.

b) Write an application problem that would use absolute values as part of the solution.

c) Write an equation and solve your problem.

14. a) Explain without solving why the equation $|4x + 7| + 8 = 2$ has no solution.

b) Write an absolute value equation that has no solution. Explain why it has no solution.

KEY IDEAS

- For any function $f(x)$, the reciprocal function is $\frac{1}{f(x)}$.

  The reciprocal function is not defined when the denominator is 0, so $f(x) \neq 0$.

  For example, if $f(x) = x$, then $\frac{1}{f(x)} = \frac{1}{x}$, $x \neq 0$.

- Use these guidelines when graphing $y = \frac{1}{f(x)}$ given the graph of $y = f(x)$.

  – An asymptote is a straight line that the graph approaches, but never touches.

  – The general equation of a vertical asymptote is $x = a$, where a is a non-permissible value of $\frac{1}{f(x)}$.

  – As $|f(x)|$ gets very large, the absolute value of the reciprocal function, $\left|\frac{1}{f(x)}\right|$, approaches zero.

    This means the graph will approach the x-axis, but not meet the x-axis.

    The x-axis, defined by the equation $y = 0$, is a horizontal asymptote.

  – An invariant point does not change when a transformation is applied.

  – For a reciprocal function, invariant points occur when $f(x) = 1$ and when $f(x) = -1$.

  > Why is this true?
  > What is the reciprocal of 1?
  > What is the reciprocal of –1?

  – To find the x-values of the invariant points, solve the equations $f(x) = \pm 1$.

  – If a point (x, y) satisfies the function $y = f(x)$, then the point $\left(x, \frac{1}{y}\right)$ satisfies the reciprocal function.

  – As the value of x approaches a non-permissible value, the absolute value of the reciprocal function, $\left|\frac{1}{f(x)}\right|$, gets very large.

Working Example 1: Compare the Graphs of a Function and Its Reciprocal

a) Sketch the graphs of $y = f(x)$ and its reciprocal function, $y = \dfrac{1}{f(x)}$, where $f(x) = 2x$.

b) State how the functions are related.

Solution

a) Complete the table of values for $y = 2x$ and $y = \dfrac{1}{2x}$.

x	$y = 2x$	$y = \dfrac{1}{2x}$
-4	-8	$-\dfrac{1}{8}$
-3		
-2		
-1		
$-\dfrac{1}{2}$		
$-\dfrac{1}{4}$		
$-\dfrac{1}{6}$		
0	0	Undefined
$\dfrac{1}{6}$		
$\dfrac{1}{4}$		
$\dfrac{1}{2}$		
1		
2		
3		
4		

- What is the product of each pair of numbers in columns 2 and 3?
- What happens to the values of $\dfrac{1}{f(x)}$ as the values of x increase?
- What happens to the values of $\dfrac{1}{f(x)}$ as the values of x get closer to zero?
- Why is the value of $\dfrac{1}{f(x)}$ undefined for $x = 0$?

Graph each function.

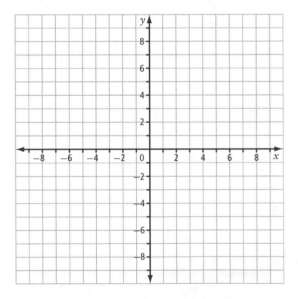

b) The function $y = 2x$ is a function of degree _____.

The vertical asymptote is defined by the non-permissible value of x.

The equation of the vertical asymptote is $x =$ _____.

The equation of the horizontal asymptote is $y =$ _____.

Complete the following table.

Characteristic	$y = 2x$	$y = \dfrac{1}{2x}$
Domain		
Range		
Asymptotes		
Can $x = 0$?		
Can $y = 0$?		
What happens to the value of y as x increases in value?		
What happens to the value of y as x decreases in value?		
Invariant point(s)		

Working Example 2: Graph the Reciprocal of a Linear Function

Consider the function $f(x) = 2x + 1$.

a) What is the reciprocal function of $f(x)$?

b) Determine the equation of the vertical asymptote for $y = \dfrac{1}{f(x)}$.

c) Graph the function $f(x)$ and its reciprocal function, $y = \dfrac{1}{f(x)}$.

Solution

a) If $f(x) = 2x + 1$, the reciprocal of $y = f(x)$ is $y =$ _____.

b) The vertical asymptote(s) occurs at any non-permissible values of $y = \dfrac{1}{2x + 1}$.

Determine the non-permissible value(s).

The non-permissible value is $x =$ _____.

The equation of the vertical asymptote is $x =$ _____.

c) Method 1: Use Pencil and Paper

To graph $y = 2x + 1$, use the slope and y-intercept.

The slope is _____ and the y-intercept is _____.

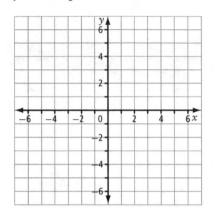

Complete the table to help sketch the graph of $y = \dfrac{1}{2x + 1}$.

Characteristic	$y = 2x + 1$	$y = \dfrac{1}{2x + 1}$
x-intercept	(_____, 0)	None
Asymptotes	None	$x =$ _____ $y =$ _____
Invariant points	(_____, 1) and (_____, −1)	
As x increases in value. y _____ in value.		

Add the graph of $y = \dfrac{1}{f(x)}$ to the grid.

Method 2: Use Technology

Graph the function using a graphing calculator. Enter $y = 2x + 1$ and $y = \dfrac{1}{2x + 1}$.

What window settings allow you to see both branches of the graph?

_____

Sketch the display shown on your calculator below.

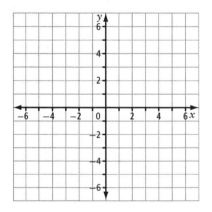

Use the table feature of the calculator and the graph to complete the table below.

Characteristic	$y = 2x + 1$	$y = \dfrac{1}{2x + 1}$
x-intercept	(_____, 0)	None
Asymptotes	None	$x =$ _____ $y =$ _____
Invariant points	(_____, 1) and (_____, −1)	
As x increases in value. y _____ in value.		

Working Example 3: Graph the Reciprocal of a Quadratic Equation

Consider the function $f(x) = x^2 - 1$.

a) What is the reciprocal function of $y = f(x)$?

b) Determine the non-permissible values of x for $y = \dfrac{1}{f(x)}$.

c) State the equation(s) of the vertical asymptote(s) of $y = \dfrac{1}{f(x)}$.

d) Determine the x-intercept(s) and y-intercept of $y = \dfrac{1}{f(x)}$.

e) Graph $y = f(x)$ and $y = \dfrac{1}{f(x)}$.

Solution

a) If $f(x) = x^2 - 1$, the reciprocal of $y = f(x)$ is $y = $ _____.

b) The reciprocal function, $y = \dfrac{1}{f(x)}$, is not defined when $f(x) = $ _____.

Determine the non-permissible values.

The non-permissible values are $x = $ _____ and $x = $ _____.

c) The vertical asymptotes are located at the non-permissible values of x.

The equations of the vertical asymptotes are $x = $ _____ and $x = $ _____.

d) At the x-intercept(s), the y-coordinate is _____.

There are no x-values for which $y = $ _____, so there are _____ x-intercepts.

At the y-intercept(s), the x-coordinate is _____.

$$y = \frac{1}{x^2 + 1}$$

$$y = \underline{\hspace{2cm}}$$

$$(\underline{\hspace{1.5cm}})^2 - 1$$

$$y = \underline{\hspace{1.5cm}}$$

The y-intercept is located at $(0,$ _____ $)$.

e) Method 1: Use Pencil and Paper

For $f(x) = x^2 - 1$, the coordinates of the vertex are (0, _____).

The x-intercepts are at (_____, 0) and (_____, 0).

Use this information to graph $y = x^2 - 1$.

To graph $y = \dfrac{1}{f(x)}$:

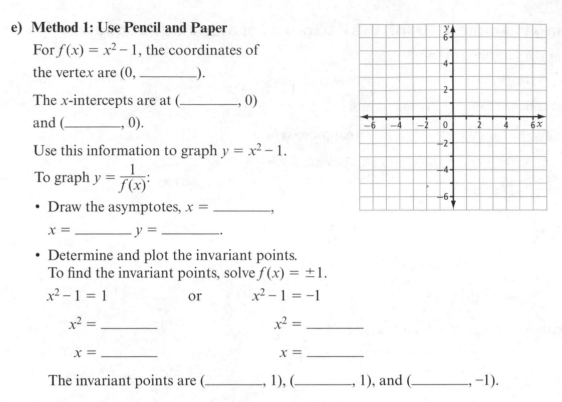

• Draw the asymptotes, $x =$ _____,

  $x =$ _____ $y =$ _____.

• Determine and plot the invariant points.
  To find the invariant points, solve $f(x) = \pm 1$.

  $x^2 - 1 = 1$ or $x^2 - 1 = -1$

  $x^2 =$ _____ $x^2 =$ _____

  $x =$ _____ $x =$ _____

  The invariant points are (_____, 1), (_____, 1), and (_____, −1).

• Complete the following table and plot the points.

x	$y = x^2 - 1$	$y = \dfrac{1}{x^2 - 1}$
3	8	$\dfrac{1}{8}$
2		
1		Undefined
0		
−1		Undefined
−2	−3	
$\dfrac{1}{2}$		
$\dfrac{1}{3}$		
$\dfrac{1}{4}$		
$-\dfrac{1}{2}$		
$-\dfrac{1}{3}$		
$-\dfrac{1}{4}$		

Add the graph of $y = \dfrac{1}{f(x)}$ to the grid above.

Method 2: Use Technology

Enter the functions $y = x^2 - 1$ and $y = \dfrac{1}{x^2 - 1}$ into your graphing calculator.

What window settings allow you to see the vertex and the intercepts?

_____

Sketch the display on your calculator.

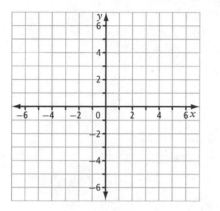

Working Example 4: Graph $y = f(x)$ Given the Graph of $y = \dfrac{1}{f(x)}$

The graph of a reciprocal function, $y = \dfrac{1}{ax + b}$, where $a \neq 0$ and $b \neq 0$, is shown.

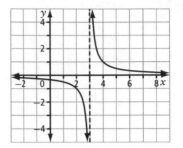

a) Sketch the graph of $y = f(x)$.

b) State the equation of $y = f(x)$ in the form $y = ax + b$.

Solution

a) $y = \dfrac{1}{f(x)}$ is of the form $y = \dfrac{1}{ax + b}$, so $f(x)$ is of the form $y = ax + b$.

This is a _____ function.
                         (*linear* or *quadratic*)

The graph of $y = \dfrac{1}{f(x)}$ has a vertical asymptote at $x =$ _____, so $f(x)$ has an x-intercept at (_____, 0).

The graph of $y = \dfrac{1}{f(x)}$ has invariant points at (_____, 1) and (_____, −1).

Plot the x-intercept and the invariant points. Draw a line through the points.

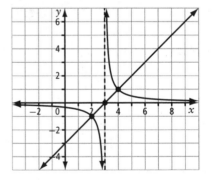

b) Method 1: Use the Slope and *y*-Intercept

Use the coordinates of the *x*-intercept and one of the invariant points from part a) to determine the slope.

$$m = \frac{y_2 - y_1}{x_2 - x_1}$$

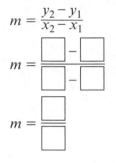

$$m = \underline{\hspace{1cm}}$$

From the graph, the *y*-intercept, *b*, is −3.

The equation for $y = f(x)$ in the form $y = mx + b$ is $y = $ _____.

Method 2: Use the *x*-Intercept

With an *x*-intercept of 3, the function $y = f(x)$ is based on a factor of $x - 3$. That is, $y = a(x - 3)$, where *a* is another factor of *y*.

To determine *a*, substitute the coordinates of an invariant point from part a) for *x* and *y*.

$$y = a(x - 3)$$

_____ $= a($_____ $- 3)$

_____ $=$ _____ a

_____ $= a$

The equation for $y = f(x)$ is $y = $ _____.

📖 This question is similar to Example 4 on pages 401–402 of *Pre-Calculus 11*.

Check Your Understanding

Practise

1. Complete the table with either the missing original function, $f(x)$, or its corresponding reciprocal function, $\frac{1}{f(x)}$.

$y = f(x)$	$y = \dfrac{1}{f(x)}$
$y = -x$	
	$y = \dfrac{1}{3x - 1}$
$y = x^2 - 4x + 4$	
	$y = \dfrac{1}{x^2}$
$y = \dfrac{1}{2}x$	

📖 This question is similar to #1 on page 403 of *Pre-Calculus 11*.

2. Write the equation(s) of the vertical asymptote(s) for each reciprocal function.

   a) $y = \dfrac{1}{x}$; $x =$ _____

   b) $y = \dfrac{1}{x + 5}$; $x =$ _____

   c) $y = \dfrac{1}{7x - 2}$; $x =$ _____

   d) $y = \dfrac{1}{x^2 - 16}$; $x =$ _____ and $x =$ _____

   e) $y = \dfrac{1}{x^2 + x - 6}$; $x =$ _____ and $x =$ _____

📖 This question is similar to #3 on page 404 of *Pre-Calculus 11*.

3. Complete the table with the reciprocal function and the invariant point(s)

$y = f(x)$	$y = \dfrac{1}{f(x)}$	Invariant Point(s)
$y = x - 8$		(_____, 1), (_____, −1)
$y = 3x - 4$		(_____, 1), (_____, −1)
$y = x^2 - 25$		(_____, 1), (_____, 1), (_____, −1), (_____, −1)
$y = x^2 - x - 29$		(_____, 1), (_____, 1), (_____, −1), (_____, −1)

4. For the following graphs, identify
   - the domain
   - the range
   - the equations of the vertical asymptotes

a)

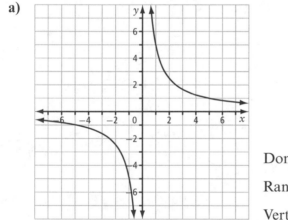

Domain: _____

Range: _____

Vertical asymptote: _____

b)

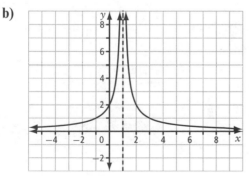

Domain: _____

Range: _____

Vertical asymptote: _____

5. For each graph of $y = f(x)$, sketch the graph of the reciprocal function, $y = \dfrac{1}{f(x)}$, on the same set of axes.

a)

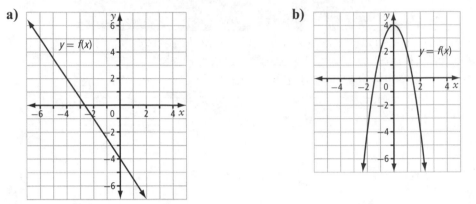

b)

This question is similar to #6 on page 404 of *Pre-Calculus 11*.

6. Sketch the graphs of $y = f(x)$ and $y = \dfrac{1}{f(x)}$ on the same set of axes below.

State the equations of the asymptotes, the invariant points, and the intercepts.

a) $f(x) = x + 3$ **b)** $f(x) = x^2 + x - 6$

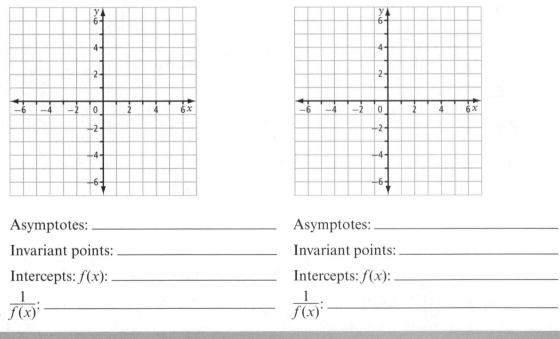

Asymptotes: _____   Asymptotes: _____

Invariant points: _____   Invariant points: _____

Intercepts: $f(x)$: _____   Intercepts: $f(x)$: _____

$\dfrac{1}{f(x)}$: _____ $\dfrac{1}{f(x)}$: _____

This question is similar to #7 and 8 on page 404 of *Pre-Calculus 11*.

Apply

7. Consider this graph of a reciprocal function, $y = \dfrac{1}{f(x)}$.

- On the same set of axes, sketch the graph of the original function, $y = f(x)$.
- Explain the steps you used to obtain the graph.
- State the original function, $f(x)$, showing how you obtained your answer.

a)

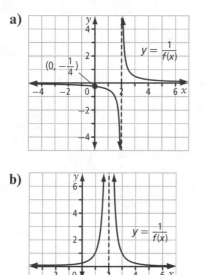

b)

This question is similar to #10 on page 406 of *Pre-Calculus 11*.

8. One factor that affects the speed, s, of a tsunami is the depth of the water the tsunami is travelling through. The speed of a particular tsunami, in kilometres per hour, multiplied by the reciprocal of the square root of the water depth, d, in kilometres, is equal to 365.

a) Write an equation to find the speed.

_____

b) Rewrite the formula to isolate d.

_____

c) Use the formula from part b) to find the depth of the water at each speed.

i) 800 km/h   ii) 580 km/h   iii) 190 km/h

9. Find and correct the errors in the following table:

Characteristic	$y = 2x + 5$	$y = \dfrac{1}{2x + 5}$
x-intercept	$-\dfrac{5}{2}$	$-\dfrac{2}{5}$
y-intercept	5	$\dfrac{1}{5}$
Invariant points	$\left(\dfrac{-5}{2}, 0\right)$, $(0, 5)$, and $\left(0, \dfrac{1}{5}\right)$	

10. Your height, h, above ground in metres and the distance, d, you can see to the horizon, in kilometres, are related to the constant 12.759 as follows: $\dfrac{d^2}{h} = 12.759$

a) Complete the table.

Height, h (m)	Distance, d (km)
2	
	12
40	
100	
	40

b) Sketch the graph.

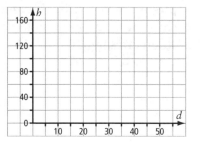

c) If you are at a height of 20 m, what distance can you see to the horizon?

d) If you see a boat on the ocean at a distance of 8 km, what is your viewing height?

Connect

11. Compare the function $f(x) = x^2 - 3$ to $|f(x)|$ and to $\dfrac{1}{f(x)}$ by completing the table below.

	$f(x) = x^2 - 3$	$g(x) = |x^2 - 3|$	$h(x) = \dfrac{1}{x^2 - 3}$
x-intercept(s)			
y-intercept(s)			
Domain			
Range			
Piecewise function			
Invariant points			
Asymptote(s)			

Check the accuracy of your answers by using technology. Enter the functions in your graphing calculator and use the trace function to verify your answers. Sketch the display shown on your calculator of all three functions on the grid below.

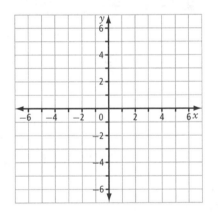

Chapter 7 Review

7.1 Absolute Value, pages 278–284

1. Evaluate.

   a) $|-17| =$ _____

   b) $-\left|-1\frac{1}{2}\right| =$ _____

   c) $|1.02| =$ _____

2. Arrange the numbers in order from greatest to least.

   $|-20.1|,\ -|20|,\ \left|\dfrac{41}{2}\right|,\ -20.2,\ \left|-19\dfrac{3}{4}\right|,\ -19.65$

3. Evaluate.

   a) $|0 - 18| =$ _____

   b) $-2|10.5| + |(-3)^3| =$ _____

   c) $|-20 + 3(-2)^2| =$ _____

4. Insert absolute value symbols to make each statement true.

   a) $9 - 12 + (-2)(4) = -5$

   b) $(1.3 - 3.3)^3 = 8$

   c) $8 - 11(12 - 15) = -25$

5. The deepest point in Lake Superior is 732 ft below sea level.
   The surface elevation is 600 ft above sea level.

   a) Write an absolute value statement to determine the maximum depth.

   b) What is the depth?

7.2 Absolute Value Functions, pages 285–296

6. Consider the functions $f(x) = 2x - 1$ and $g(x) = |2x - 1|$.

a) Complete the table.

x	$f(x)$	$g(x)$
−1		
0		
1		
2		
3		
4		

b) Sketch the graphs of $f(x)$ and $g(x)$.

c) Complete the table.

Characteristic	$f(x)$	$g(x)$
Domain		
Range		
x-intercepts		
y-intercepts		
Piecewise function	N/A	

7. Consider the functions $f(x) = -x^2 + 4$ and $g(x) = |-x^2 + 4|$.

   a) Complete the table.

x	$f(x)$	$g(x)$
-3		
-2		
-1		
0		
1		
2		
3		

   b) Sketch the graphs of $f(x)$ and $g(x)$.

   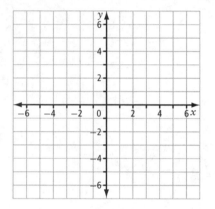

   c) Complete the table.

Characteristic	$f(x)$	$g(x)$
Domain		
Range		
x-intercepts		
y-intercepts		
Similarities		
Differences		
Piecewise function	N/A	

8. a) Without graphing, predict how the graphs of $f(x) = x^2 + 3x + 6$ and $g(x) = |x^2 + 3x + 6|$ are related.

b) Check your prediction by using technology. Sketch the graph(s) below.

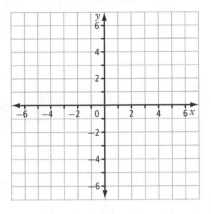

9. Write an absolute value function of the form $y = |ax + b|$ that has the following graph.

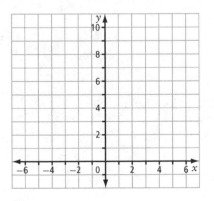

7.3 Absolute Value Equations, pages 297–308

10. Solve each absolute value equation by graphing.

a) $|-5x| + 4 = 9$

b) $|x^2 - 1| = 8$

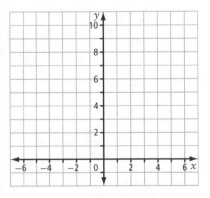

11. Solve each absolute value equation algebraically.

    a) $|2x + 10| = 14$

    b) $|3x - 6| = x + 4$

    c) $|x^2 - 8x + 12| = 20$

12. The adult dose of a medicine is 50 mg, but it is acceptable for the dose to vary by 0.5 mg.

    a) Write an absolute value equation to determine the limits of an acceptable dosage.

    b) What are the limits?

7.4 Reciprocal Functions, pages 309–323

13. For each graph of $y = f(x)$ below,

- Sketch the graph of the reciprocal function, $y = \dfrac{1}{f(x)}$, on the same grid.

- Find the equations of the asymptotes, invariant points, and intercepts.

a)

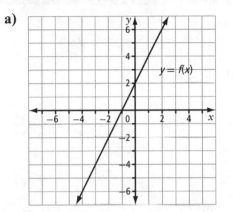

Asymptotes: _____

Invariant points: _____

x-intercept: _____; y-intercept: _____

b)

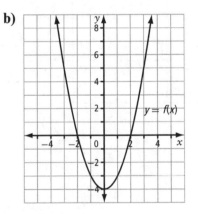

Asymptotes: _____

Invariant points: _____

x-intercept: _____; y-intercept: _____

14. Sketch the graphs of $y = f(x)$ and $y = \dfrac{1}{f(x)}$ on the same set of axes. Then, complete the table.

a) $f(x) = 3x + 4$

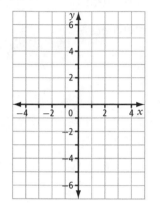

Characteristic	$f(x)$	$\dfrac{1}{f(x)}$
Asymptotes	N/A	
x-intercept		
y-intercept		
Invariant points		
Domain		
Range		

b) $f(x) = x^2 - x - 12$

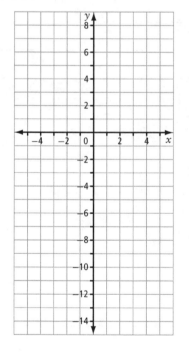

Characteristic	$f(x)$	$\dfrac{1}{f(x)}$
Asymptotes	N/A	
x-intercept		
y-intercept		
Invariant points		
Domain		
Range		

15. The resistance, R, in ohms in an electric circuit is equal to the power, P, in watts, multiplied by the reciprocal of the square of the current, I, in amperes.

   a) Write an equation to represent the relationship.

   b) What is the resistance, in ohms, for a circuit that uses 500 watts of power with a current of 2 amperes?

   c) The resistance in a circuit is 4 ohms. The same circuit uses 100 watts of power. Find the current in the circuit, in amperes.

   d) Find the power, in watts, when the current is 0.5 amperes and the resistance is 600 ohms.

Chapter 7 Skills Organizer

Complete the table for any function $y = f(x)$

Characteristic	$y = f(x)$	$y = |f(x)|$	$y = \dfrac{1}{f(x)}$
x-intercept(s)			
y-intercept(s)			
Domain			
Range			
Piecewise function			
Invariant points			
Asymptote(s)			

Chapter 8 Systems of Equations

8.1 Solving Systems of Equations Graphically

- A system of equations is two or more different equations involving the same variabes.

- Determining the solution to a system of equations means determining point(s) that are common to both equations. A common point is called a point of intersection.

- Graphing a linear equation and a quadratic equation can produce one of three possible scenarios:

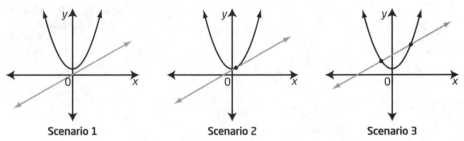

| Scenario 1 | Scenario 2 | Scenario 3 |

- In Scenario 1, the line and parabola do not intersect. There is no solution.

- In Scenario 2, the line and parabola intersect at one point. There is one solution.

- In Scenario 3, the line and parabola intersect at two different points. There are two solutions.

- Graphing two quadratic equations can produce one of four possible scenarios. In the scenario in which the quadratic equations are the same, there are an infinite number of solutions. The other three scenarios are illustrated:

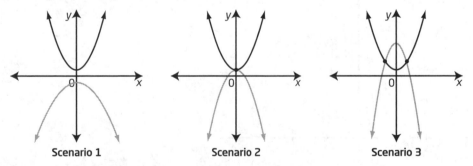

| Scenario 1 | Scenario 2 | Scenario 3 |

- In Scenario 1, the parabolas do not intersect. There is no solution.

- In Scenario 2, the parabolas intersect at one point. There is one solution.

- In Scenario 3, the parabolas intersect at two different points. There are two solutions.

- Once you have determined the point of intersection, remember to check the ordered pair in both of the original equations.

Working Example 1: Solve a System of Linear-Quadratic Equations Graphically

a) Solve the following system of equations graphically.

$$y + 3x^2 - 2x - 4 = 0$$
$$y + x + 2 = 0$$

b) Verify the solution.

Solution

a) Isolate y in the first equation. Perform the opposite operations to both sides of the equation to isolate y.

$$y + 3x^2 - 2x - 4 = 0$$

> Why do you have to perform inverse operations to both sides of the equation?

New equation: _____

Isolate y in the second equation.

$$y + x + 2 = 0$$

New equation: _____

Enter the equations into your graphing calculator. Use the intersect feature to determine the point(s) of intersection.

Sketch the graph of each equation and label the point(s) of intersection.

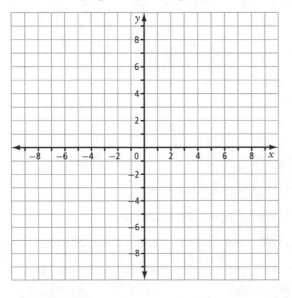

> How many points of intersection are there? How many solutions are there?

b) Verify your solution by substituting the first solution into both of the original equations.

Left Side	Right Side
$y + 3x^2 - 2x - 4$	0

Left Side	Right Side
$y + x + 2$	0

Why do you have to use the original equations to verify your solution(s)?

Verify your solution by substituting the second solution into both of the original equations.

Left Side	Right Side
$y + 3x^2 - 2x - 4$	0

Left Side	Right Side
$y + x + 2$	0

Working Example 2: Solve a System of Quadratic-Quadratic Equations Graphically

a) Solve the following system of equations graphically.

$$y - 3x^2 + 12x = 16$$
$$y + 4x^2 - 16x = -12$$

b) Verify the solution.

Solution

a) Isolate y in the first equation.

$$y - 3x^2 + 12x = 16$$

New equation: _____

Isolate y in the second equation.

$$y + 4x^2 - 16x = -12$$

New equation: _____

Enter the equations into your graphing calculator. Use the intersect feature to determine the point(s) of intersection.

Sketch the graph of each equation and label the point(s) of intersection.

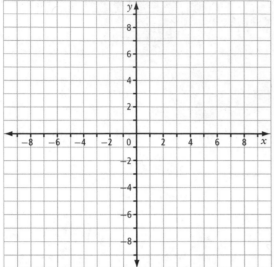

How many points of intersection are there? How many solutions are there?

b) Verify your solution by substituting the solution into both of the original equations.

Left Side	Right Side
$y - 3x^2 + 12x$	16

Left Side	Right Side
$y + 4x^2 - 16x$	−12

Working Example 3: Model a Situation Using a System of Equations

Two numbers have a sum of 17. The square of the first number plus 5 equals the second number. What are the two numbers?

Solution

Identify and define the unknowns in the scenario.

Let x represent the _____.   Let y represent the _____.

Using the variables as you have defined them, fill in the blanks to define the system of equations.

$\boxed{} + \boxed{} = 17$ The sum of the two numbers is 17.

$\boxed{}^2 + 5 = \boxed{}$ The square of the first number plus 5 equals the second number.

Isolate y in each equation.

Graph the system.

Interpret the point(s) of intersection.

The two numbers are _____ and _____.

> 📖 This example should help you complete #13 on page 437 of *Pre-Calculus 11*.

Check Your Understanding

Practise

1. Check to determine which point is a solution to the given equation.

Choose one point. Substitute the *x*-coordinate for *x* in the equation and the *y*-coordinate for *y* in the equation.

a) $y = 2x^2 + 5x - 3$; $(0, -3)$ or $(0, 3)$

$$y = 2x^2 + 5x - 3$$

_____ = 2_____^{2} + 5_____ − 3

_____ = 2_____ + _____ − 3

_____ = _____ + _____ − 3

_____ = _____ − 3

_____ = _____   **True   False**   (*circle one*)

$$y = 2x^2 + 5x - 3$$

_____ = 2_____^{2} + 5_____ − 3

_____ = 2_____ + _____ − 3

_____ = _____ + _____ − 3

_____ = _____ − 3

_____ = _____   **True   False**   (*circle one*)

b) $y + 3x^2 - 4x = 12$; $(-7, 19)$ or $(-1, 5)$

c) $2y - x^2 + 5x = 8$; $(3, 2)$ or $(-2, 11)$

2. What type of system of equations is represented in each graph? Give the solution(s) to each system.

a)

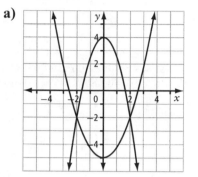

b)

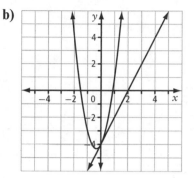

c)

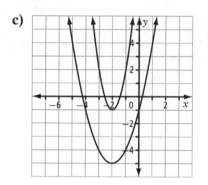

3. Solve each system by graphing. Verify your solutions.

a) $2y - x^2 - 4x + 6 = 0$
$y - x - 1 = 0$

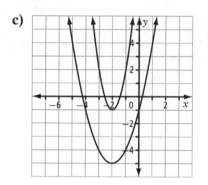

> Enter the equations into your graphing calculator. Use the intersect feature to determine the point(s) of intersection. Sketch a graph of the equations and label the point(s) of intersection.

Verify by substituting any solution(s) into each of the original equations.

There is/are _____ points of intersection.

The solutions are _____.

b) $y - 2x^2 + 4x - 5 = 0$
$y + x - 4 = 0$

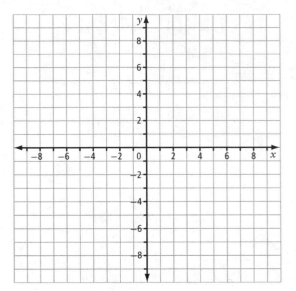

c) $y - 4x^2 - 7x + 5 = 0$
$10y - 32x + 90 = 0$

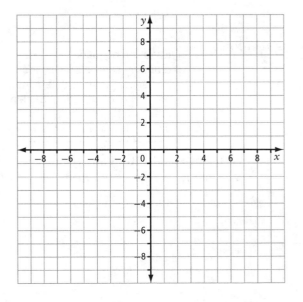

4. Solve each system by graphing. Verify your solutions.

a) $y + 4x^2 - x = 12$
$y - 3x^2 + 6x = -2$

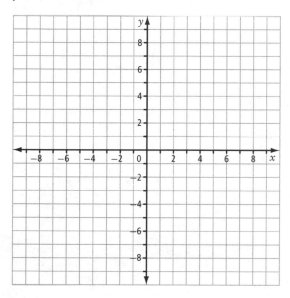

Verify by substituting any solution(s) into both of the original equations.

There are _____ points of intersection.

The solutions are _____.

b) $y - 3x^2 + 24 = 30$
$y + 2x^2 + 8x = -9$

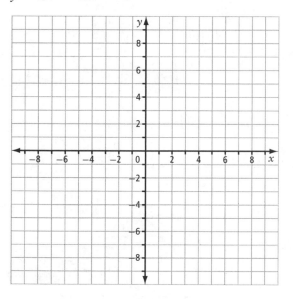

c) $y - x^2 + 6x = 13$
$y + 2x^2 - 12x = -14$

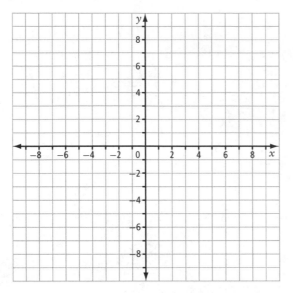

Apply

5. The graph of a quadratic function is shown.

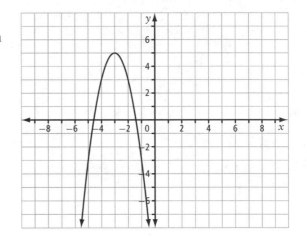

   a) Draw a line on the graph so that a system of equations with one solution is represented.

   b) Choose two points on the line and determine the equation of the line.

   First point: (_____, _____)

   Second point: (_____, _____)

   Determine the slope, m, of the line using the points you have selected.

   $$m = \frac{y_2 - y_1}{x_2 - x_1}$$

   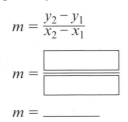

   $m = $ _____

   Use the slope-intercept form to determine the equation of the line.

   $y = mx + b$

   $y = $ _____ $x + $ _____

   > Recall that b is the y-intercept of the line. What is the y-intercept of the line you drew?

   c) Determine the solution to the system of equations you created.

6. The graph of a linear function is shown.

   a) Draw a parabola on the graph so that a system of equations with two solutions is represented.

   b) Determine the equation of the parabola.

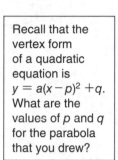

Recall that the vertex form of a quadratic equation is $y = a(x - p)^2 + q$. What are the values of p and q for the parabola that you drew?

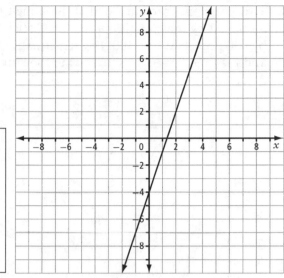

   c) Determine the solution(s) to the system of equations you created.

7. Two positive numbers have a difference of 17. When the square of the smaller number is added to that number, the result is 13 less than the larger number. What are the two numbers?

Let x represent the _____.　　Let y represent the _____.

Using the variables as you have defined them, fill in the blanks.

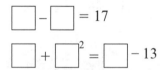

$\boxed{} - \boxed{} = 17$　　　　The difference of the two numbers is 17.

$\boxed{} + \boxed{}^2 = \boxed{} - 13$　　　The sum of the smaller number and its square is 13 less than the larger number.

   a) Solve the system graphically and interpret the solution(s).

   b) Is there a solution that cannot be used in this question? Explain.

8. Two projectiles are launched at the same time. The height of the first projectile is modelled by the equation $h = -5t^2 + 50t - 50$. The height of the second projectile is given by $h = -5t^2 + 100t - 300$. In each equation, h represents height above ground, in metres, and t is time, in seconds, following the launch. Graph the path of both projectiles. Then, determine and interpret the point(s) of intersection.

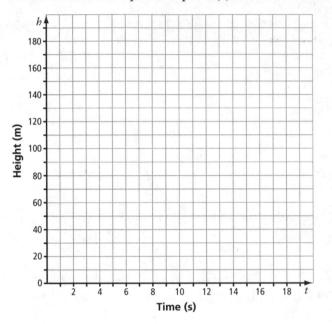

Connect

9. Without graphing, use your knowledge of linear and quadratic equations to determine whether each system has no solution, one solution, two solutions, or an infinite number of solutions. Explain how you know.

a) $y = x^2$
$y = x - 1$

b) $y = (x - 3)^2 - 1$
$y = x^2 - 6x + 8$

c) $y = -3(x + 2)^2 + 4$
$y = 3(x + 2)^2 + 4$

d) $y = \frac{1}{2}(x - 2)^2 + 4$
$y = (x - 2)^2 + 2$

>> **KEY IDEAS** >>

- Algebraically, solving a system of equations in two variables means determining values of any ordered pairs (x, y) that satisfy both of the equations in the system.

- To solve a linear-quadratic system of equations, you may use either a substitution method or an elimination method. Both methods will give you the same solution.

Example

$$y = x^2 - x - 6$$
$$y = x - 3$$

Method 1: Use Substitution

Since both equations equal y, they must equal each other. Substitute one expression for y into the other equation. Then, solve for x.

$$x^2 - x - 6 = x - 3$$
$$x^2 - 2x - 3 = 0$$
$$(x - 3)(x + 1) = 0$$

Set each factor equal to zero.

$$x - 3 = 0 \quad \text{or} \quad x + 1 = 0$$
$$x = 3 \qquad\qquad x = -1$$

Substitute these values into the original linear equation to determine the corresponding values of y.

When $x = 3$:   When $x = -1$:
$$y = x - 3 \qquad\quad y = x - 3$$
$$y = \mathbf{3} - 3 \qquad\quad y = \mathbf{-1} - 3$$
$$y = 0 \qquad\qquad\quad y = -4$$

The two solutions are $(3, 0)$ and $(-1, -4)$.

Method 2: Use Elimination

Since both equations equal y, the second equation can be subtracted from the first equation to eliminate y. Then, solve for x.

Align the terms with the same degree and subtract the second equation from the first.
$$y = x^2 - x - 6$$
$$y = x - 3$$
$$\overline{}$$
$$0 = x^2 - 2x - 3$$

Then, solve the equation $x^2 - 2x - 3 = 0$ by factoring, as in the substitution method at left, to obtain the two solutions, $(3, 0)$ and $(-1, -4)$.

- To solve a quadratic-quadratic system of equations, you may use a substitution method or an elimination method. When solving this type of system using elimination, you cannot eliminate x, so you should always eliminate y.

  Example
  $y = 4x^2 + 8x + 4$
  $y = 3x^2 - 2x - 5$

  Since both equations equal y, the second equation can be subtracted from the first equation to eliminate y.

  $y = 4x^2 + 8x + 4$
  $\underline{-y = -3x^2 + 2x + 5}$
  $0 = x^2 + 10x + 9$

  > Since both equations equal y, the substitution may also be used. Setting the quadratic expressions $4x^2 + 8x + 4$ and $3x^2 - 2x - 5$ equal to each other and then solving produces the same quadratic equation as the elimination method.

  To solve for x, factor $x^2 + 10x + 9$.
  $0 = (x + 9)(x + 1)$

  Set each factor equal to zero. Then, solve.
  $x + 9 = 0 \qquad$ or $\qquad x + 1 = 0$
  $\qquad x = -9 \qquad\qquad\qquad x = -1$

  Substitute these values into either of the original equations to determine the corresponding values of y.

  When $x = -9$:
  $y = 4x^2 + 8x + 4$
  $y = 4(-9)^2 + 8(-9) + 4$
  $y = 324 - 72 + 4$
  $y = 256$

  When $x = -1$:
  $y = 4x^2 + 8x + 4$
  $y = 4(-1)^2 + 8(-1) + 4$
  $y = 4 - 8 + 4$
  $y = 0$

  The two solutions are $(256, -9)$ and $(-1, 0)$.

- For both types of systems, remember to take the values you determine and substitute them back into the original equation to find the corresponding values of the other variable. You should always verify solutions by substituting into both of the original equations.

- To solve linear-quadratic and quadratic-quadratic systems, you must determine the solution to a quadratic equation. Remember that to solve a quadratic equation means to determine the x-intercepts of the graph of the corresponding quadratic function or the zeros of the function. This can be done by factoring and setting each factor equal to zero to solve for x. In the case of un-factorable quadratics, the quadratic formula can be used. Once you determine a value of x, substitute it into one of the original equations to determine the corresponding value of y.

Working Example 1: Solve a System of Linear-Quadratic Equations Algebraically

a) Solve the following system of equations algebraically.

$x^2 - x - y = 6$
$2x - y = 2$

b) Verify your solution.

Solution

a) Rewrite each equation so that y is isolated on one side of the equal sign.

$x^2 - x - y = 6$ $\longrightarrow$ $y = \boxed{}^2 - \boxed{} - \boxed{}$ ①

$2x - y = 2$ $\longrightarrow$ $y = \boxed{} - \boxed{}$ ②

Since each equation is equal to y, you can use either elimination or substitution.

Method 1: Use Elimination

You could eliminate _____ by _____ ② from ①. You would
            (x or y)
end up with a quadratic equation with only _____ variable.

Method 2: Use Substitution

You could substitute the expression for _____ from the first equation into the second equation.

Solve using either method.

State your solution(s) as ordered pair(s).

b) Verify both solutions in both of the original equations.

Working Example 2: Solve a System of Quadratic-Quadratic Equations Algebraically

a) Solve the following system of equations algebraically.

$$3x^2 - 24x - y = -52$$
$$-2x^2 - y + 16x - 28 = 0$$

b) Verify the solution(s) in the original equations.

Solution

a) Rewrite each equation so that y is isolated on one side of the equal sign.

$3x^2 - 24x - y = -52$ $\longrightarrow$ $y = \boxed{}^2 - \boxed{} + \boxed{}$ ①

$-2x^2 - y + 16x - 28 = 0$ $\longrightarrow$ $y = \boxed{}^2 + \boxed{} - \boxed{}$ ②

To solve this system using elimination, you could eliminate _____ by _____ ②
$\qquad\qquad\qquad\qquad\qquad\qquad\qquad\qquad$ (x or y)

from ①. You would end up with a quadratic equation with only _____ variable.

① − ②:

> Can you divide each term by a common factor to make the quadratic easier to work with?

Factor your quadratic:

> How many solutions are there?

b) Verify the solution(s) by substituting into both of the original equations.

Working Example 3: Model a Situation With a System of Equations

Two golfers are practising their swing at a driving range. Each hits a ball at the same time. The path of the first ball can be modelled by the equation $y + 27 = -5x^2 + 40x$. The path of the second ball can be modelled by the equation $y + 8x^2 = 40x$. In each equation, y is the height above ground, in metres, after x seconds. Determine and interpret the solution(s) to the system of equations.

Solution

Write each equation as a "$y =$" equation.

Eliminate y.

Solve the resulting equation for x.

> Why is there only one possible answer for x?

Use your value for x to determine the corresponding value for y.

State your answer as a point.

What does the solution mean in the context of the question?

Verify your solution in the original equations.

📖 See pages 443–446 of *Pre-Calculus 11* for more examples.

Check Your Understanding

Practise

1. Solve the following systems of linear-quadratic equations algebraically. Verify your solution(s).

   a) $x^2 - y - 2x = -2$
   $y - 2x = -2$

   Isolate y in each equation.

   Solve using elimination or substitution.

   State the point(s) of your solution.

   Check your solution(s) in both of the original equations.

   b) $x^2 - y = -1$
   $y - x = 1$

c) $3x - y = -5$
  $x^2 - y + 2x = 1$

d) $-2x^2 - y + 3x = -4$
  $2x - y + 3 = 0$

2. Solve the following systems of quadratic-quadratic equations algebraically, and verify your solution(s).

   a) $-4x^2 - y - 2x = -5$
   $3x^2 - 4y - 46x - 37 = 0$

   Isolate the y-term in each equation.

   > How can you make the y-values in each equation match?

   Solve using elimination.

   State the point(s) of your solution.

   Check your solution(s) in both of the original equations.

   b) $4x^2 - y + 8x = -2$
   $y + 2 = 4x^2 - 8x$

c) $2x^2 + 12x - y = -17$
    $y = -x^2 - x + 7$

d) $y = \frac{1}{2}x^2 - 4x + 12$
    $y = -2x^2 - 12x - 23$

This question should help you complete #4 on page 452 of *Pre-Calculus 11*.

Apply

3. Determine the values of m and n if $(3, 4)$ is a solution to the following system of equations.

$$mx^2 - y = 32$$
$$mx^2 - 5y = n$$

4. The perimeter of a parallelogram is 28 cm. Its area is $10y$ cm^2.

   a) Write a simplified equation for the parallelogram's perimeter.

   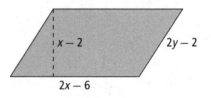

   b) Write a simplified equation for the parallelogram's area.

   c) Write a system of equations and solve the system for x and y.

   d) Interpret your solution.

5. You have two unknown integers. Double the larger number increased by triple the smaller number is 46. Squaring the larger number and increasing it by four times itself gives the same result as multiplying the smaller number by 20 and adding 5. What are the two integers?

Connect

6. A parabola has its vertex at $(3, -1)$ and passes through the point $(1, 7)$. A second parabola has its vertex at $(1, 4)$ and has y-intercept 3. What are the approximate coordinates of the point(s) at which these parabolas intersect?

8.1 Solving Systems of Equations Graphically, pages 333–344

1. Sketch graphs to show the possible solutions to each system of equations.

   a) linear-quadratic

   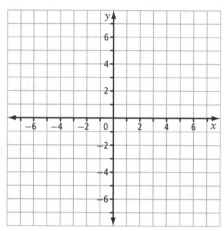

   b) quadratic-quadratic

   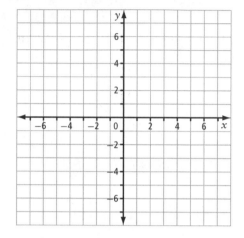

2. Solve each system of equations by graphing. Verify your solutions.

   a) $2y + 6x^2 + x - 8 = 0$
   $2y + x - 8 = 0$

   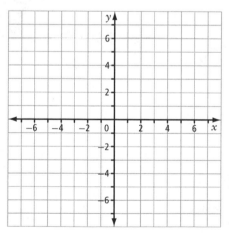

b) $y - x^2 + 2x + 4 = 0$
$y - 3x + 8 = 0$

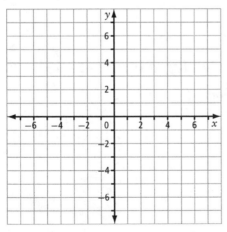

c) $y - 3x^2 - 12x = 6$
$y + 4x^2 + 16x = -15$

3. A model rocket is launched from a field. The height of the rocket, y, in feet above the ground, after x seconds is modelled by the equation $y = -16x^2 + 177x + 4$. From the 10th floor of a nearby building, a boy looks out a window when he hears the rocket fired. The boy's line of sight is given by the equation $y = 65x + 100$.

   a) Graph the path of the rocket and the boy's line of sight on the same set of axes.

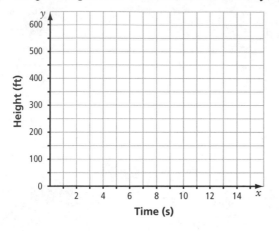

   b) Determine and interpret the point(s) of intersection.

8.2 Solving Systems of Equations Algebraically, pages 345–355

4. Solve each system algebraically. Verify your solutions.

   a) $4x^2 - y - 2x = -7$
   $-6x - y + 15 = 0$

b) $2x^2 - y + 16x + 29 = 0$
$-2x^2 - 16x - y = 35$

c) $3x^2 - y - 4x = -3$
$-2x^2 + 2x - y + 8 = 0$

5. Determine two whole numbers such that the first number increased by triple the second number is 24. If the first number is squared and decreased by five times itself, the result is 13 less than the second number.

6. Two players are throwing basketballs back and forth. Standing about 9 m apart and facing each other, each player throws a ball at the same time. In one exchange, the path of one basketball is represented by the equation $y = -x^2 + 12x - 28$. The path of the other ball is modelled by the equation $y = -x^2 + 4x + 2$. In each equation, x is the horizontal distance a ball travels, in metres, and y is the vertical distance it travels, also in metres. Determine the point(s) of intersection algebraically and interpret the solution.

Chapter 8 Skills Organizer

Complete the table for solving non-linear systems of equations.

Type of System	Possible Number of Solutions	How to Solve Graphically	How to Solve Algebraically
Linear-quadratic			
Quadratic-quadratic			

Chapter 9 Linear and Quadratic Inequalities

9.1 Linear Inequalities in Two Variables

- Recall that to graph a linear equation you can use one of two methods: solve for y or use the intercepts.

Method 1: Solve for y

- Isolate y on one side of the equation to express the equation in the form $y = mx + b$.

- Plot the y-intercept $(0, b)$. Use the slope and the y-intercept to determine another point.

- Draw a line passing through the y-intercept and the second point.

Method 2: Use the Intercepts

- Determine the x-intercept by letting $y = 0$ in the equation and solving for x. The x-intercept will be the point $(x, 0)$.

- Determine the y-intercept by letting $x = 0$ in the equation and solving for y. The y-intercept will be the point $(0, y)$.

- Plot the two intercepts and draw a line passing through them.

To graph and solve a linear inequality in two variables, isolate y in the inequality.

- Graph the linear equation (boundary) using one of the two methods described above.

- Determine whether the boundary line is solid or dashed:

  – A solid line means that points on the line are part of the solution region. Use a solid line if the inequality involves $\leq$ or $\geq$.

  – A dashed line means that points on the line are *not* part of the solution region. Use a dashed line if the inequality involves $<$ or $>$.

- Select a test point that is not on the boundary line and test it in the original inequality. If the statement is true, shade the region containing the point. If the statement is not true, shade the region that does not contain the point.

Examples:
$y > x + 1$
The boundary is a *dashed* line.
The test point $(0, 0)$ is not within the solution region because $0 > 0 + 1$ is not a true statement. Therefore, the region *above* the line is shaded.

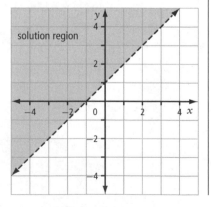

$y < x + 1$
The boundary is a *dashed* line.
The test point (0, 0) is within the solution region because
$0 < 0 + 1$ is a true statement. Therefore, the region *below*
the line is shaded.

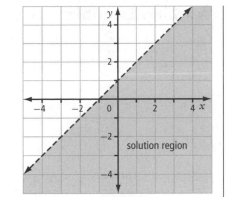

$y \geq x + 1$
The boundary is a *solid* line.
The test point (0, 0) is not within the solution region because
$0 \geq 0 + 1$ is not a true statement. Therefore, the region *above*
the line is shaded.

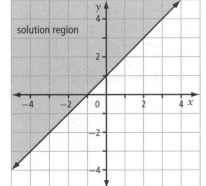

$y \leq x + 1$
The boundary is a *solid* line.
The test point (0, 0) is within the solution region because
$0 \leq 0 + 1$ is a true statement. Therefore, the region *below*
the line is shaded.

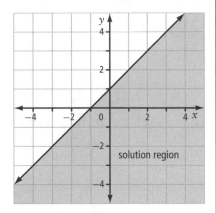

- There are an infinite number of solutions to a linear inequality. Solving a linear inequality means determining the *solution region* in the Cartesian plane, rather than determining a point (or points) on a line.

Working Example 1: Graph a Linear Inequality of the Form *Ax* + *By* < *C*

Graph and label the linear inequality $4x - 3y < -12$ for the set of real numbers.

Solution

Isolate y on the left side of the inequality symbol.

> Remember that if you multiply or divide both sides of an inequality by a negative number, you must reverse the symbol.

Replace the inequality symbol with an equal sign.

The y-intercept is _____. The slope is _____.

Plot the y-intercept on the grid. Then, using the slope, locate a second point on the boundary line.

From the y-intercept, move _____ a distance
                               (*up* or *down*)
of _____ units.

Then, move _____ units to the _____.
                                     (*right* or *left*)

The coordinates of the second point are _____.

Draw a _____ line passing through the points.
      (*solid* or *dashed*)

Select a test point from each region to determine which region contains the solution.

Test point above the boundary: _____

Test point below the boundary: _____

Substitute each point into the inequality.

For the point _____: For the point _____:

The test point _____ satisfies the inequality.

Shade the area _____ the boundary to indicate the solution region.
      (*above* or *below*)

See page 466 of *Pre-Calculus 11* for a similar example.

Working Example 2: Graph a Linear Inequality of the Form $Ax + By \geq C$

Graph and label the linear inequality $2x - 3y \geq 15$ for the set of real numbers.

Solution

Isolate y on the left side of the inequality sign.

> Remember that if you multiply or divide both sides of an inequality by a negative number, you must reverse the symbol.

Replace the inequality sign with an equal sign.

The y-intercept is _____.

Determine the x-intercept.

> Remember that to determine the x-intercept, let $y = 0$ and solve for x.

Plot the x-intercept and y-intercept on the graph.

Draw a _____ line through the intercepts
      (*solid* or *dashed*)
to indicate the boundary.

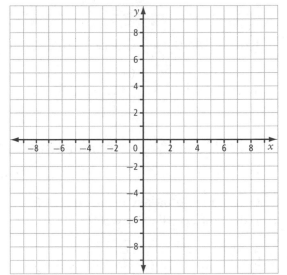

Select a test point from each region to determine which region contains the solution.

Test point above the boundary: _____

Test point below the boundary: _____

Substitute each point into the inequality.

For the point _____:

For the point _____:

The test point _____ satisfies the inequality.

Shade the area _____ the boundary to indicate the solution region.
      (*above* or *below*)

Working Example 3: Write and Solve a Linear Inequality

A sports equipment manufacturer makes footballs and soccer balls. One football requires 4 min on the cutting machine, while one soccer ball requires only 3 min on the machine. Determine an inequality that would represent this situation. Draw a graph of the inequality to show the number of each type of ball that could be made in 30 min or less.

Solution

Let x represent the number of _____, requiring _____ min per ball.

Let y represent the number of _____, requiring _____ min per ball.

Write the inequality. (Hint: The time it takes to make each type of ball must be included in the inequality, and the total time cannot exceed 30 min.)

_____ + _____ ≤ _____

Isolate y on the left side of the inequality.

State the equation that is related to the boundary, expressed in slope-intercept form.

Graph the boundary using either the slope and y-intercept or the x-intercept and y-intercept.

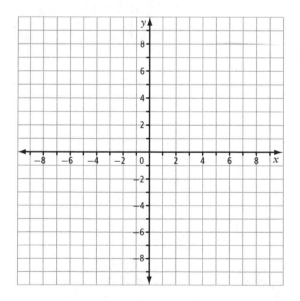

Select a test point from each region to determine which region contains the solution.

Test point above the boundary: _____

Test point below the boundary: _____

Substitute each point into the inequality.

For the point _____:

For the point _____:

The test point _____ satisfies the inequality.

Shade the area _____ the boundary to indicate the solution region.
(*above* or *below*)

Select one point in the solution region to answer the question.

For example, select _____.

You could make _____ footballs and _____ soccer balls.

Check Your Understanding

Practise

1. Which of the ordered pairs are solutions to the given inequality?

a) $4x - 2y \leq -2$

$\{(-1, 4), (0, 0), (4, -3), (3, 7)\}$

b) $-2x + 5y - 8 > 0$

$\{(0, 7), (-2, 5), (3, -1), (-6, 1)\}$

c) $3x < -y - 3$

$\{(0, -3), (-3, -4), (2, -10), (-2, 5)\}$

d) $-2y \geq -2x - 2$

$\{(0, 0), (-2, 5), (-4, -3), (3, 1)\}$

2. Graph each inequality.

a) $y \leq 3x - 2$

Equation of the boundary: _____.

y-intercept: _____.

Slope: _____.

Plot the y-intercept on the grid. Then, using the slope, locate a second point on the boundary.

From the y-intercept, move _____ a distance of _____ units.
(*up* or *down*)

Then, move _____ units to the _____.
(*right* or *left*)

The coordinates of the second point are _____.

Draw a _____ line passing through the points.
(*solid* or *dashed*)

Select a test point from each region to determine which region contains the solution.

Test point above the boundary: _____

Test point below the boundary: _____

Substitute each point into the inequality.

For the point _____:

For the point _____:

The test point _____ satisfies the inequality.

Shade the area _____ the boundary to indicate the solution region.
(*above* or *below*)

b) $4x + y \geq 5$

Isolate y on the left side of the inequality sign.

Replace the inequality sign with an equal sign.

The y-intercept is _____.

Determine the x-intercept.

Plot the x-intercept and y-intercept on the graph.

Draw a _____ line through the intercepts to indicate the boundary.
      (*solid* or *dashed*)

Select a test point from each region to determine which region contains the solution.

Test point above the boundary: _____

Test point below the boundary: _____

Substitute each point into the inequality.

For the point _____:

For the point _____:

The test point _____ satisfies the inequality.

Shade the area _____ the boundary to indicate the solution region.
      (*above* or *below*)

c) $3y - 12x < 12$

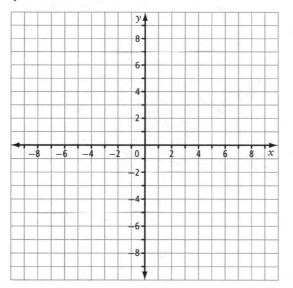

d) $y > 8 - 2x$

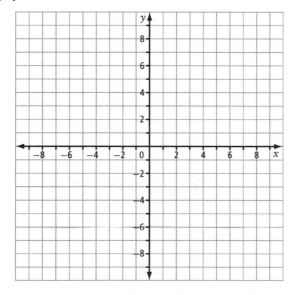

3. Graph each inequality.

a) $4x - 5y > 20$

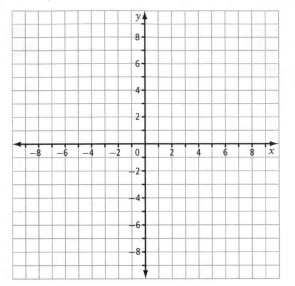

b) $2x + y < 8$

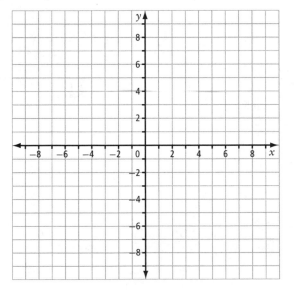

c) $4y - 3x \geq 5$

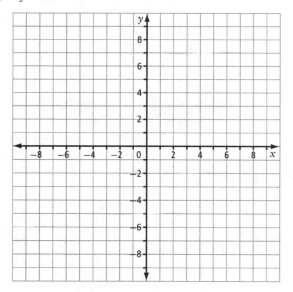

d) $\frac{3}{4}x - \frac{1}{2}y \geq -\frac{3}{2}$

(Hint: Multiply all terms by the lowest common multiple of 2 and 4 to remove the denominator.)

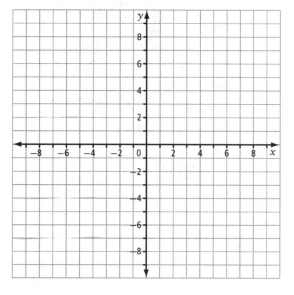

4. Determine the inequality that best describes each of the following graphs.

a)

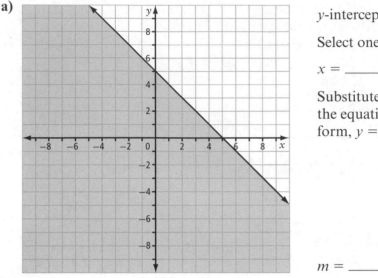

y-intercept: *b* = _____

Select one other point on the line.

x = _____; *y* = _____

Substitute the values for *x*, *y*, and *b* into the equation of the line in slope-intercept form, $y = mx + b$, and solve for *m*.

m = _____

Write the equation of the boundary in slope-intercept form: _____

Is the boundary line solid or dashed? _____

Is the graph shaded above ($>$ or $\geq$) or below ($<$ or $\leq$) the boundary line? _____

Write the equation of the boundary as an inequality: _____

b)

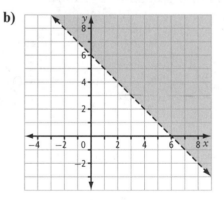

c)

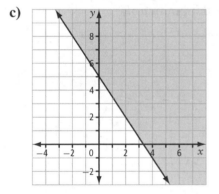

Apply

5. You want to earn at least $300 in interest annually. You want to do this by investing some of your money in a bond that pays interest at a rate of 4% per annum, and the rest in a guaranteed investment certificate (GIC) that pays interest of 5% per annum. Determine the inequality that represents this scenario. Sketch the graph of the inequality to show the amount you could invest at each rate. Select one possible investment combination and check it in the original inequality.

Let x = amount invested in a bond
Let y = amount invested in a GIC

Write the inequality. (Hint: The total interest earned per annum must be greater than or equal to $300.)

_____ + _____ $\geq$ _____

Isolate y on the left side of the inequality.

State the equation that is related to the boundary line. _____

Graph the boundary using either the slope and y-intercept or the intercepts.
Select a test point from each region to determine which region contains the solution.

Test point above the boundary: _____

Test point below the boundary: _____

Substitute each point into the inequality.

For the point _____:

For the point _____:

The test point _____ satisfies the inequality.

Shade the area _____ the boundary to indicate the solution region.
               (*above* or *below*)

Select one point in the solution region to answer the question.

For example, select _____.

You could invest $ _____ in a bond paying 4% annual interest and $ _____ in a GIC paying 5% annual interest to earn at least $300.

6. A vehicle manufacturer produces cars and trucks. In a given week, the company can make up to 100 vehicles. Sketch a graph to show the number of cars and trucks that could be made in one week. Select one possible solution and check it in the original inequality.

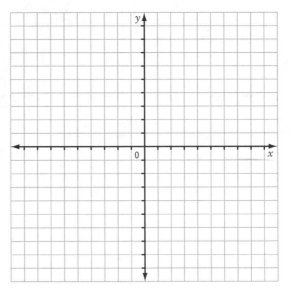

7. Barb has started a new fitness program. She knows she can burn 500 calories per hour jogging and 300 calories per hour walking her dog. Barb wants to do a combination of the two activities and burn at least 3000 calories a week. Draw a graph to show the possible workout combinations she could do in a week. Select one possible combination and check it in the original inequality.

📖 See #15 on page 474 of *Pre-Calculus 11* for a similar question.

8. An airplane can hold up to 1500 kg of luggage. Economy class passengers are allowed to bring 15 kg of luggage. First class passengers are allowed to bring 45 kg of luggage. Assuming that each passenger brings luggage at the maximum allowable weight, draw a graph showing the possible combinations of allowable luggage weight. Select one possible solution and check it in the original inequality.

Connect

9. Use what you learned in Chapter 8 about solving a system of equations graphically to hypothesize what solving a system of inequalities might involve. Include a sketch as part of your explanation.

10. Based on your hypothesis in #9, solve the following system of linear inequalities. Pick one possible solution point to check in each of the original inequalities. Compare your solution with that of a classmate.

$y \geq 2x + 6$

$y \leq -3x + 2$

KEY IDEAS

- Solving quadratic equations by graphing can also be used to solve quadratic inequalities in one variable. Instead of stating the x-intercepts as the solution, the graph is used to identify the intervals of x-values where the y-values of the graph are above or below the x-axis.

- A quadratic inequality in one variable can be written in one of four forms. Therefore, there are four possible scenarios when solving quadratic inequalities graphically.

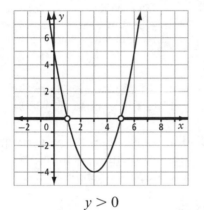

$$y > 0$$

The solution set is the values of x for which the graph of $f(x)$ lies on or above the x-axis. The solution set does not include the x-intercepts.

Solution set: $\{x \mid x < 1 \text{ or } x > 5, x \in \mathbb{R}\}$

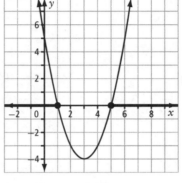

$$y \geq 0$$

The solution set is the values of x for which the graph of $f(x)$ lies on or above the x-axis. The solution set include the x-intercepts.

Solution set: $\{x \mid x \leq 1 \text{ or } x \geq 5, x \in \mathbb{R}\}$

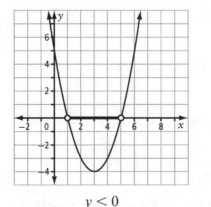

$$y < 0$$

The solution set is the values of x for which the graph of $f(x)$ lies on or above the x-axis. The solution set does not include the x-intercepts.

Solution set: $\{x \mid 1 < x < 5, x \in \mathbb{R}\}$

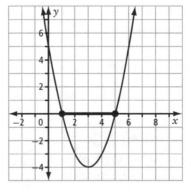

$$y \leq 0$$

The solution set is the values of x for which the graph of $f(x)$ lies on or above the x-axis. The solution set includes the x-intercepts.

Solution set: $\{x \mid 1 \leq x \leq 5, x \in \mathbb{R}\}$

Working Example 1: Solve a Quadratic Inequality of the Form $ax^2 + bx + c > 0$, $a > 0$

Solve $x^2 + x > 6$ graphically.

Solution

Rewrite the inequality so that the quadratic expression is on the left side and a zero is on the right side.

_____

Sketch the graph of the quadratic, labelling all intercepts and the vertex.

| What strategies can you use to sketch the graph of a quadratic function in standard form? |

Highlight the section(s) of the x-axis where the y-values of $f(x)$ are above the x-axis ($f(x) > 0$).

Determine if the solution includes the x-intercepts (closed point) or does not include them (open point). Mark the points appropriately on the graph.

Based on the highlighted portion of the graph, state the solution.

_____

Recall that to solve a quadratic equation algebraically means to factor the quadratic, set each factor equal to zero, and solve.

Quadratics that cannot be factored can be solved by completing the square or by using the quadratic formula.

The method of solving quadratic equations by factoring can be applied to solving quadratic inequalities:

- Factor to determine all possible roots and place them on a number line to form intervals (the number of intervals is one more than the number of roots).

- For each interval, select a point that falls within the interval and test it in the original inequality to see if it is true or false.

- If it is true, the solution falls within that interval.

See page 479 of *Pre-Calculus 11* to review the case analysis method for solving quadratic inequalities.

Working Example 2: Solve a Quadratic Inequality of the Form
$ax^2 + bx + c \leq 0, a > 0$

Solve $2x^2 + 5x \leq 3$ algebraically using roots and test points.

Solution

Rewrite the inequality so that the quadratic expression is on the left side and a zero is on the right side.

Factor the quadratic to determine all possible roots.

Place each root on a number line to form intervals. Label each interval.

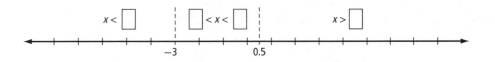

For each interval, choose a point that falls within the interval and test it in the *original* inequality to see if it is true or false.

Does the solution include the roots? Explain.

State the solution.

Working Example 3: Solve a Quadratic Inequality in One Variable

A golfer hits a ball down a fairway. She would like to know the length of time, in seconds, that the ball was at a height of at least 25 m. Solving the inequality $-8x^2 + 40x \geq 25$ will help determine this.

Solution

Rewrite the inequality so that the quadratic expression is on the left side and a zero is on the right side.

Which do you think is the better approach for solving this inequality, solving graphically or solving algebraically? Why?

Solve using your preferred method. If you solve the inequality graphically, include a labelled sketch. If you solve algebraically, include a number line with the test intervals marked.

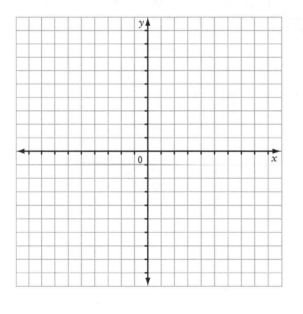

State the solution.

Check Your Understanding

Practise

1. Based on the graph of $f(x) = x^2 + x - 2$, determine the solution to each inequality.

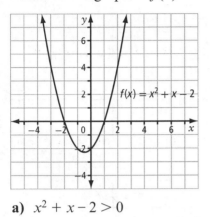

$f(x) = x^2 + x - 2$

a) $x^2 + x - 2 > 0$

b) $x^2 + x - 2 \leq 0$

c) $x^2 + x - 2 < 0$

d) $x^2 + x - 2 \geq 0$

2. Solve each inequality graphically.

a) $x^2 + 2x - 3 \geq 0$

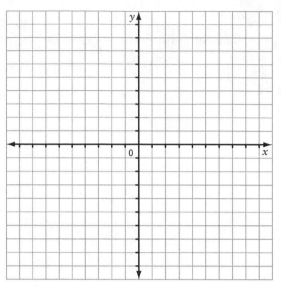

b) $-x^2 + 4x < -5$

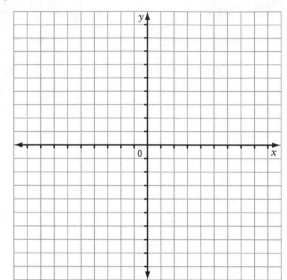

c) $2x^2 + 10x + 12 \leq 0$

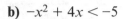

d) $x^2 - 6x < -9$

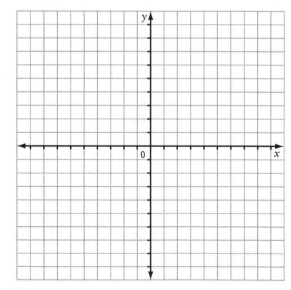

3. Solve the following inequalities algebraically. (Hint: Use a number line.)

a) $x^2 < -3x - 2$

b) $4x^2 < 7x - 3$

c) $6x^2 - 1 \geq x$

d) $2x^2 \geq 7x + 4$

Apply

4. In a right triangle, one leg is 10 cm shorter than twice the length of the other leg. If the length of the hypotenuse is at least 8 cm, solving the inequality $x^2 + (2x - 10)^2 \geq 8^2$ will help you determine the possible lengths of the legs. (Hint: The value of x cannot be a number that would result in a side length less than or equal to 0.)

5. A theatre seats 2000 people and charges $10 per ticket. At this price, all the tickets can be sold. A recent survey indicates that for every $1 increase in price, the number of tickets sold will decrease by 100. Determine the ticket prices that would result in revenue of at least $15 000 by using the inequality $x^2 - 10x \leq 50$, where x is the number of $1 increments in the price of a ticket.

6. A farmer wants to build a rectangular pen that can be divided into four equal compartments by fences that are parallel to the width. If the farmer has only 1000 m of fencing, what dimensions will make the area of the pen at most 15 000 m²? Solve the inequality $x^2 - 200x \le -6000$, where x is the width of the pen, in metres, to help you determine the possible measures of x.

7. Determine two numbers whose sum is 30 and whose product is at least 200. (Hint: Use only one variable.)

8. Create an inequality for each of the following solutions.

    a) $-\frac{1}{2} < x < 4$

    b) $x \le -\frac{3}{2}$ and $x \ge \frac{1}{4}$

    c) $0 \le x \le \frac{4}{3}$

Connect

9. Explain how solving inequalities graphically and algebraically are the same, and how they are different. Which method do you prefer? Why?

KEY IDEAS

- To solve a quadratic inequality in two variables means to determine the solution region. The solution region may be above the parabola related to the inequality, or it may be below it. In addition, the solution region may or may not include the points on the related quadratic function. Therefore, there are eight possible scenarios when solving quadratic inequalities in two variables. In each scenario, the parabola may open upward or downward.

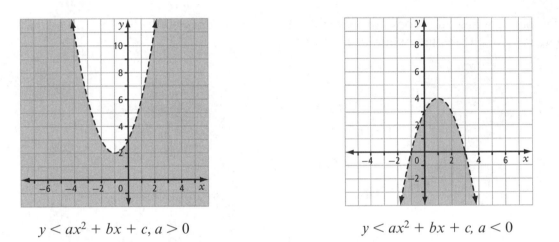

$$y < ax^2 + bx + c, a > 0 \qquad\qquad y < ax^2 + bx + c, a < 0$$

The solution region is below the parabola. The solution does not include the points on the parabola of the related quadratic function.

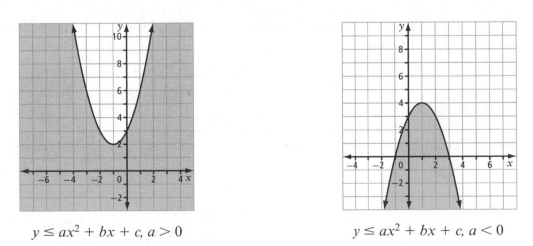

$$y \leq ax^2 + bx + c, a > 0 \qquad\qquad y \leq ax^2 + bx + c, a < 0$$

The solution region is below the parabola. The solution includes the points on the parabola of the related quadratic function.

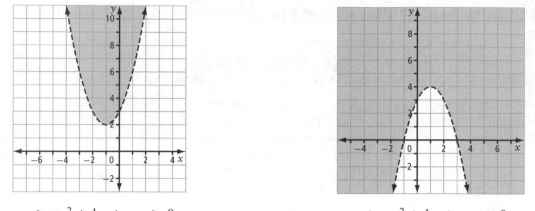

$y > ax^2 + bx + c, a > 0$

$y > ax^2 + bx + c, a < 0$

The solution region is above the parabola. The solution does not include the points on the parabola of the related quadratic function.

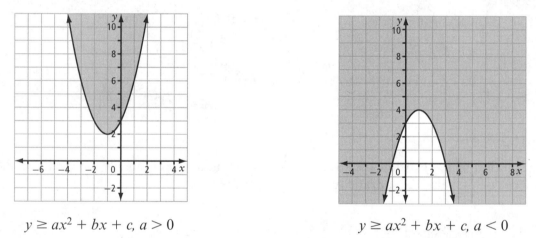

$y \geq ax^2 + bx + c, a > 0$

$y \geq ax^2 + bx + c, a < 0$

The solution region is above the parabola. The solution includes the points on the parabola of the related quadratic function.

- Once you have determined the solution region and shaded it, select a test point in the region area and substitute it into the original inequality to see if it satisfies the inequality. Do not select a point that lies on the boundary.

Working Example 1: Graph a Quadratic Inequality in Two Variables With $a > 0$

Graph $y < 2x^2 + 5x - 3$. Choose a point in the solution region to check in the original inequality.

Solution

Write the related quadratic function in the standard form $y = ax^2 + bx + c$.

_____

Graph the parabola using a graphing calculator to determine the x-intercepts, y-intercept, and vertex.

The x-intercepts are _____ and _____.

The y-intercept is _____.

The vertex is _____.

Sketch the graph of the related quadratic function, labelling all intercepts and the vertex.

Do you draw the parabola using a solid line or a dashed line? Explain.

Select a test point: _____

Substitute the point into the original inequality to see if it satisfies the inequality.

Is the graph to be shaded above the parabola or below it? Explain.

Shade the solution region.

Working Example 2: Graph a Quadratic Inequality in Two Variables With $a < 0$

Graph $y \le -x^2 - 6x + 9$. Choose a test point in the solution region to check in the original inequality.

Solution

Write the equation in the standard form $y = ax^2 + bx + c$.

_____

Enter the equation into a graphing calculator to determine the x-intercepts, y-intercept, and vertex.

The x-intercepts are _____ and _____.

The y-intercept is _____.

The vertex is _____.

Sketch the graph of the related quadratic function, labelling all intercepts and the vertex.

Do you draw the parabola using a solid line or a dashed line? Explain.

Select a test point: _____

Substitute the point into the original inequality to see if it satisfies the inequality.

Is the graph to be shaded above the parabola or below it? Explain.

Shade the solution region.

Working Example 3: Determine the Quadratic Inequality That Defines a Solution Region

Write an inequality to describe the following graph.

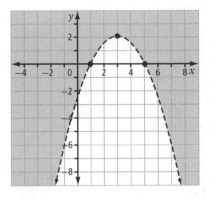

Solution

Identify the vertex: _____

Identify the x-intercepts in the form $(x, 0)$: _____ and _____

Write the equation of the parabola in vertex form, $y = a(x - p)^2 + q$.

Substitute the coordinates of the vertex (p, q) and one of the x-intercepts $(x, 0)$ into the equation to determine the value of a.

Use the values of the parameters a, p, and q to write the equation.

Is the graph shaded above ($>$ or $\geq$) or below ($<$ or $\leq$) the graph of the function?

Is the line solid ($\geq$ or $\leq$) or dashed ($>$ or $<$)?

Write the equation as an inequality using the appropriate sign.

📖 See a similar example on page 493 of *Pre-Calculus 11*.

Check Your Understanding

Practise

1. Circle the ordered pairs that are solutions to the given inequality.

   a) $y < 2x^2 + 4x + 3$

   $\{(0, 0), (0, 3), (-1, 10), (2, 1)\}$

   b) $y \geq 2x^2 + 16x - 34$

   $\{(-4, -5), (-2, 10), (6, 5), (8, -6)\}$

   c) $y \leq 2x^2 + 16x + 36$

   $\{(-2, -10), (-4, 10), (0, 36), (2, -7)\}$

   d) $y > x^2 - 2x + 3$

   $\{(-1, 17), (0, 3), (1, 9), (-4, -5)\}$

2. Name one point that is a solution to the given inequality and one point that is *not* a solution.

   a) $y < 5x^2 + 2x + 1$

   b) $y \geq -4x^2 + 6x - 7$

   c) $y \leq 3x^2 + 7x + 12$

   d) $y > -2x^2 - 3x + 5$

3. Graph each quadratic inequality.

a) $y > x^2 + x - 6$

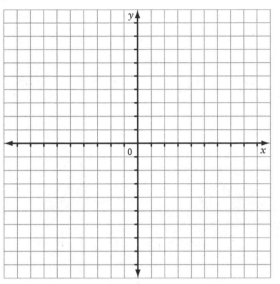

b) $y \leq x^2 - x - 2$

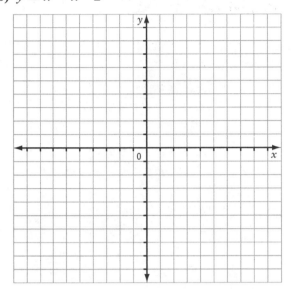

c) $y \geq 2x^2 + 9x + 10$

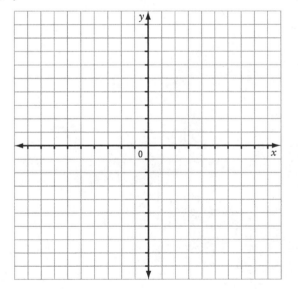

d) $y < 6x^2 - x - 1$

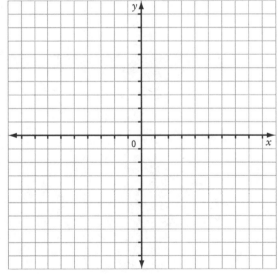

4. Graph each quadratic inequality.

a) $y > (x - 1)^2 + 1$

b) $y \leq (x + 2)^2 - 9$

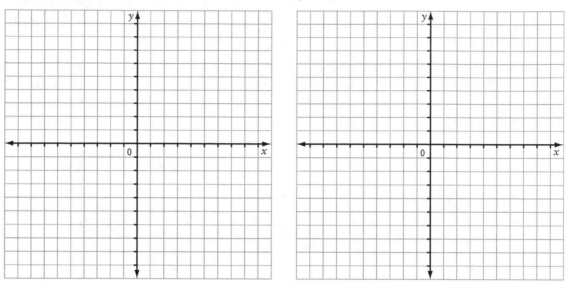

c) $y \geq 2(x - 3)^2 + 8$

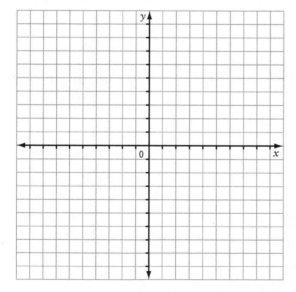

d) $y < (x - 1)^2 + 2$

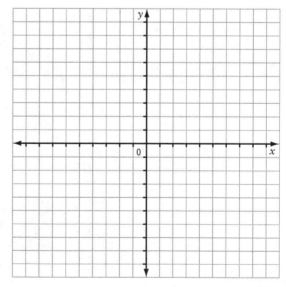

5. Write an inequality to describe each graph given the function that defines the boundary parabola.

a)

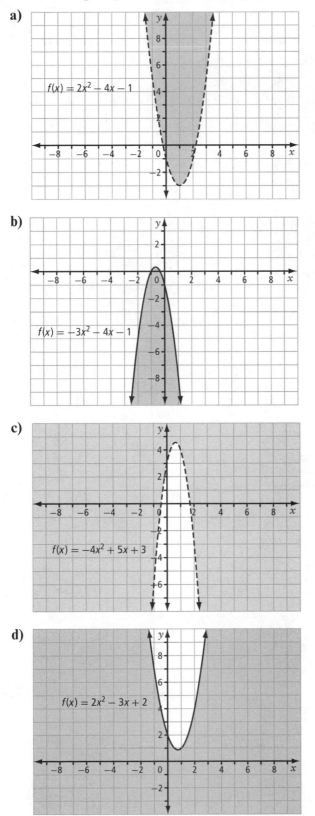

$f(x) = 2x^2 - 4x - 1$

b)

$f(x) = -3x^2 - 4x - 1$

c)

$f(x) = -4x^2 + 5x + 3$

d)

$f(x) = 2x^2 - 3x + 2$

6. Write an inequality for each graph.

a)

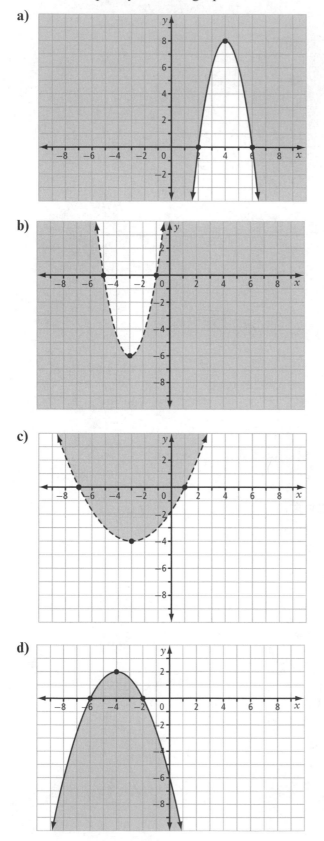

b)

c)

d)

Apply

7. In order to get the most revenue from registrations for a camping trip, an adventure company needs to have as many campers as possible at a price per camper that is reasonable. If 15 people sign up, the price per person is $50. The registration fee is reduced by $2 for each additional camper beyond 15. The relationship between the number of registrations and revenue is given by $y \leq (50 - 2x)(15 + x)$, where x represents the number of campers beyond 15 and y is the total revenue, in dollars.

   a) Graph the quadratic inequality.

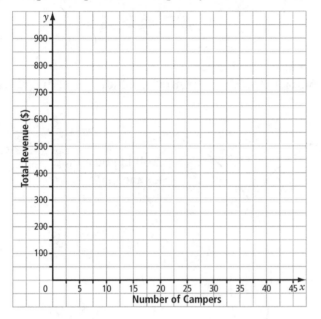

   b) What is the total number of registrations that will generate revenue of at least $500?

Connect

8. Use what you learned in Chapter 8 about solving a system of equations graphically to hypothesize what solving a system of quadratic inequalities might involve. Include a sketch as part of your explanation.

9. Based on your hypothesis in #8, solve the following system of quadratic inequalities. Choose one possible solution point to check in each of the original inequalities. Compare your solution with that of a classmate.

$$y \geq x^2 - 4x - 4$$
$$y \leq -x^2 - 4x + 4$$

10. Based on your work in Chapter 9, complete the Venn diagram. Include notes, diagrams, and examples.

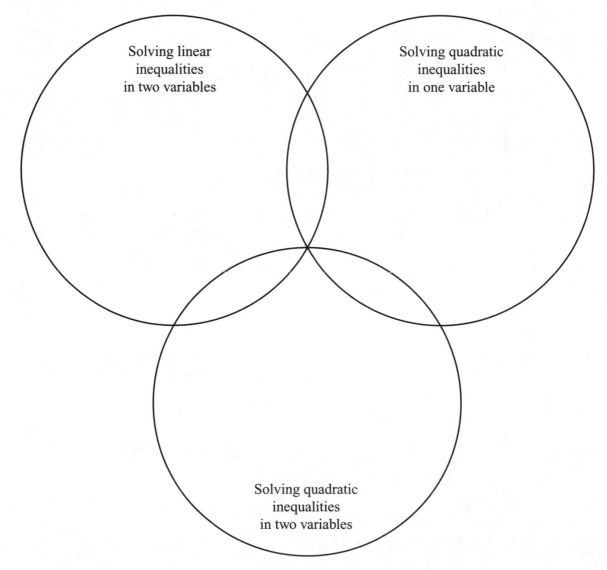

Solving linear
inequalities
in two variables

Solving quadratic
inequalities
in one variable

Solving quadratic
inequalities
in two variables

Chapter 9 Review

9.1 Linear Inequalities in Two Variables, pages 362–378

1. Circle the solutions for each inequality.

   a) $3x + 2y > 5$

   $\{(1, -2), (0, 7), (-3, 4), (5, -3)\}$

   b) $-4x + 5y \le 25$

   $\{(7, 0), (-4, 3), (-3, -4), (5, -1)\}$

2. Graph each inequality.

   a) $2x - 3y \ge 12$

   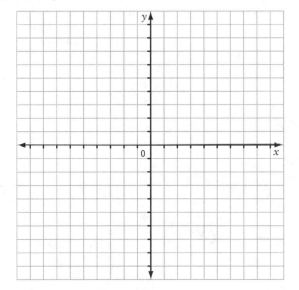

   b) $-5x - y < 0$

   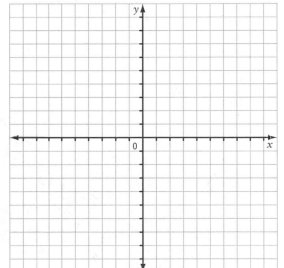

3. Determine the inequality that best describes each graph.

a)

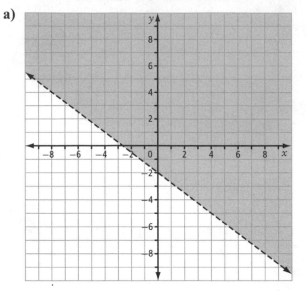

b)

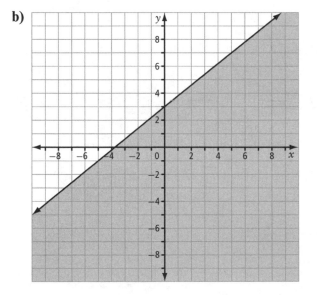

4. Amber is working to earn money for a down payment on a car. She wants to save at least $1000. Amber makes $15 per hour at a part-time job and $10 per hour babysitting. Draw a graph to show some of the possible ways she can work to earn money. Choose one possible solution and check it in the original inequality.

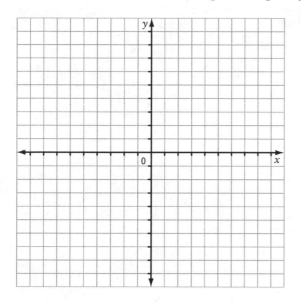

9.2 Quadratic Inequalities in One Variable, pages 379–388

5. Solve $-2x^2 + 3x > -7$ graphically.

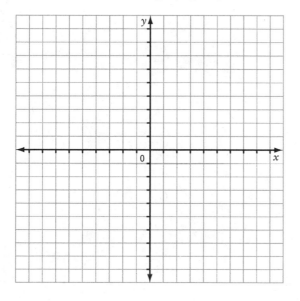

6. Based on the graph below, what is the solution to each inequality?

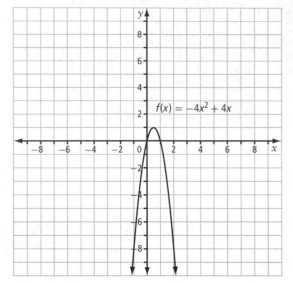

$f(x) = -4x^2 + 4x$

a) $-4x^2 + 4x > 0$

b) $-4x^2 + 4x < 0$

c) $-4x^2 + 4x \leq 0$

d) $-4x^2 + 4x \geq 0$

7. Solve $x^2 - x - 12 \leq 0$ algebraically.

9.3 Quadratic Inequalities in Two Variables, pages 389–400

8. Circle the ordered pairs that are solutions to the given inequality.

a) $y \geq -3x^2 + 2x + 7$

$\{(1, 6), (0, 0), (1, -10), (6, 12)\}$

b) $y < 5x^2 - 10x + 2$

$\{(-1, -2), (3, 4), (2, 5), (0, 3)\}$

9. Graph each quadratic inequality

a) $y > -3x^2 - 3x + 1$

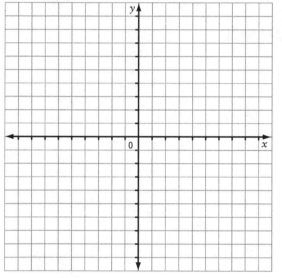

b) $y \leq 0.5x^2 + 4x - 3$

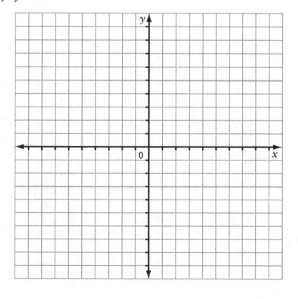

10. Write an inequality to describe each graph.

a)

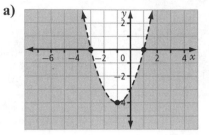

b)

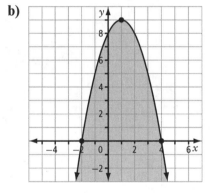

Chapter 9 Skills Organizer

Complete the table for solving a linear inequality in two variables.

Form of Expression of Inequality	Boundary (Dashed *or* Solid)	How to Solve Graphically or Algebraically

Complete the table for solving a quadratic inequality in one variable.

| Form of Expression of Inequality | Solution Set | | How to Solve Graphically or Algebraically | | |
	Position Relative to *x*-axis	*x*-intercept(s) Included?			

Complete the table for solving a quadratic inequality in two variables.

| Form of Expression of Inequality | Boundary (Dashed *or* Solid) | Direction of Parabola | | How to Solve Graphically or Algebraically | |
		a > 0	*a* < 0		

Answers

Chapter 1

1.1 Arithmetic Sequences, pages 1–13

1. **a)** arithmetic; $d = 5$; 29, 34, 39 **b)** not arithmetic
   c) arithmetic; $d = -4$; $-5, -9, -13$
   d) not arithmetic
   e) arithmetic; $d = 3$; 7, 10, 13
   f) arithmetic; $d = -13$; $-30, -43, -56$

2. **a)** 5, 11, 17, 23; $t_n = -1 + 6n$
   b) 50, 41, 32, 23; $t_n = 59 - 9n$
   c) 4.5, 3, 1.5, 0; $t_n = 6 - 1.5n$
   d) $\frac{1}{5}, \frac{3}{5}, 1, \frac{7}{5}$; $t_n = -\frac{1}{5} + \frac{2}{5}d$

3. **a)** $t_1 = 4$ **b)** $t_8 = -11$
   c) $t_{15} = 80.5$ **d)** $t_{20} = -\frac{18}{7}$

4. **a)** $d = 12$; $t_1 = -9$; $-9, 3$, and 15
   b) $d = -8$; $t_1 = 22$; 22, 14, and -10
   c) $d = 3.2$; $t_1 = 16.2$; 16.2, and 22.6, 25.8
   d) $d = 1$; $t_1 = -\frac{3}{2}$; $-\frac{3}{2}$, and $\frac{1}{2}, \frac{3}{2}$

5. **a)** $n = 12$ **b)** $n = 24$ **c)** $n = 16$ **d)** $n = 38$

6. **a)** yes; n is a whole number: $n = 17$
   b) no; n is not a whole number, so 89 is not a term in the sequence
   c) yes; n is a whole number: $n = 6$
   d) yes; n is a whole number: $n = 11$

7. **a)** $d = 4$, $t_1 = 5$; $t_n = 4n + 1$
   b) $d = 6$, $t_1 = -4$; $t_n = 6n - 10$
   c) $d = -3$, $t_1 = -8$; $t_n = -3n - 5$
   d) $d = 4.5x$, $t_1 = 3 - 22x$; $t_n = 4.5xn + 3 - 26.5x$

8. 822 members

9. 7 m

10. $x = 5$; 5, 9.5, 14

11. after 16 years

12. 4, 11, 18, 25

13. **a)** an arithmetic sequence; because the common difference between consecutive terms is 1; $t_n = n$
   b) an arithmetic sequence; because the common difference between consecutive terms is 7; $t_n = -4 + 7n$
   c) yes; they have a common difference, 8; $t_n = -6 + 8n$

14. **a)** Yes. The points (x, y) represent a sequence where the x-values represent n and the y-values represent the terms of the sequence. The sequence is arithmetic because the points form a straight line, which means that the difference between points is constant. The points in the sequence are 7, 5, 3, 1, $-1, -3, -5, -7$.

b) by substituting into the formula for the general term, $t_n = t_1 + (n-1)d$; $t_n = 9 - 2n$

c) $t_{60} = 9 - 2(60) = -111$; $t_{300} = 9 - 2(300) = -591$

d) The slope is -2, which is the coefficient of n in the formula $t_n = 9 - 2n$.

e) The y-intercept is 9, which is the constant term in the formula $t_n = 9 - 2n$.

1.2 Arithmetic Series, pages 14–21

1. **a)** $S_6 = 153$ **b)** $S_7 = 385$
   c) $S_9 = 441$ **d)** $S_{10} = -110$

2. **a)** $S_{30} = 280.5$ **b)** $S_{30} = 1762.5$
   c) $S_{30} = \frac{445}{3}$

3. **a)** $S_{18} = -9$ **b)** $S_{23} = 1715.8$

4. **a)** $t_1 = -101$ **b)** $t_1 = 10$ **c)** $t_1 = 15$ **d)** $t_1 = 5$

5. **a)** $n = 20$ **b)** $n = 20$ **c)** $n = 16$ **d)** $n = 9$

6. 204 cans

7. $2 + 6 + 10 + 14 + 18$

8. $2 + 5 + 8 + 11 + 14$

9. $S_n = \frac{n}{2}(3n - 1)$

10. **a)** First determine t_1, which is the first multiple of 5 greater than one: $t_1 = 5$. Then determine t_n, the last multiple of 5 less than 999: $t_n = 995$. Finally, determine n, the total multiples of 5: $n = \frac{995}{5} = 199$. Substitute into the formula, $S_n = \frac{n}{2}(t_1 + t_n)$; $S_{199} = 99\ 500$.

11. Job A pays a total of \$4350 and Job B pays a total of \$4650. The student should select Job B because it pays \$300 more.

1.3 Geometric Sequences, pages 22–31

1. **a)** not geometric
   b) geometric; $r = 3$; 81, 243, 729
   c) geometric; $r = 0.1$; 0.0003, 0.000 03, 0.000 003
   d) not geometric
   e) geometric; $r = \frac{1}{5}$; $\frac{1}{25}, \frac{1}{125}, \frac{1}{625}$
   f) geometric; $r = -0.5$; $-0.5, 0.25, -0.125$

2. **a)** $t_n = 3(4)^{n-1}$ **b)** $t_n = 36\left(-\frac{1}{3}\right)^{n-1}$
   c) $t_n = 4.5(-1.5)^{n-1}$ **d)** $t_n = \frac{1}{5}\left(-\frac{2}{5}\right)^{n-1}$

3. **a)** $t_{10} = -1024$ **b)** $t_9 = 32\ 768$
   c) $t_{11} = -0.000\ 000\ 1$ **d)** $t_{200} = 1$

4. **a)** E **b)** D **c)** A
   d) B **e)** F **f)** C

5. **a)** $t_n = -3(-2)^{n-1}$
   b) $t_n = (4)^{n-1}$ or $t_n = -1(-4)^{n-1}$
   c) $t_n = 512(0.5)^{n-1}$

6. $8, 8\sqrt{3}, 16$

7. a) $n = 7$ **b)** $n = 10$ **c)** $n = 8$ **d)** $n = 7$

8. a) two; There are two sequences.

   b) 2, 6, 18, 54, 162, ... and 2, −6, 18, −54, 162, ...

9. 24 576, 12 288, 6144, 3072

10. a) ± 8 and ± 32 **b)** 12 and 72 **c)** ± 6 and ± 24

11. approximately 352 514 people

12. $x = 10$

13. a) $1000 **b)** $1562.50

14. a) The x-values of the points on the graph correspond to n, and the y-values are the terms of the sequence for each value of x. The first five terms of the sequence are the y-values that correspond to the x-values 1, 2, 3, 4, 5: 48, 24, 12, 6, 3. There is a common ratio of 0.5 between these y-values, so the points represent a geometric sequence.

   b) yes; $t_n = 48(0.5)^{n-1}$

15. a) The sequence is 20 000, 2000, 200, 20, 2. This is a geometric sequence with common ratio $r = 0.1$.

   b) Use the general term of the sequence or write the terms until the seventh term is found (by multiplying the previous term by 0.1). The volume on the seventh day is 0.02 cm^3.

1.4 Geometric Series, pages 32–40

1. a) yes; a common ratio of 3; $S_7 = 6558$

   b) yes; a common ratio of −3; $S_7 = 4376$

   c) no; no common ratio

   d) yes: a common ration of $\frac{1}{2}$; $S_7 = \frac{127}{192}$

2. a) $t_1 = 2, r = 3, n = 8; S_8 = 6560$

   b) $t_1 = 2.1, r = -2, n = 9; S_9 = 359\frac{1}{10}$

   c) $t_1 = 30, r = -\frac{1}{6}, n = 7; S_7 = 25\frac{5555}{7776}$

   d) $t_1 = 24, r = -\frac{3}{4}, n = 6; S_6 = 11\frac{35}{128}$

3. a) $S_{12} - 2730$ **b)** $S_8 = 29\,999\,999\,700$

4. a) $S_n = 335\,923$ **b)** $S_n = \frac{3\,333\,333}{2500}$

   c) $S_n = 78\,642$ **d)** $S_n = \frac{6315}{6571}$

5. a) $S_n = 3^n - 1$ **b)** $S_n = 5(2^n - 1)$

   c) $S_n = 4^n - 1$ **d)** $S_n = 4(2^n - 1)$

6. a) $n = 11; S_{11} = 6141$ **b)** $n = 6; S_6 = -92.969$

7. $S_7 = 5465$ employees

8. 13 terms

9. 664.78 cm

10. 397 mg

11. $S_{10} = 2046$

12. approximately 89.5 turns per second

13. approximately 183 m

14. Example: The sum of the first three terms can be written as $t_1 + t_1 r + t_1 r^2 = 93$. From the given term, $t_2 = 15$, or $t_1 r = 15$, write an expression for t_1. Substitute this expression into the quadratic equation and solve: $r = 5$ or $r = \frac{1}{5}$;

   $3 + 15 + 75 + \ldots$ or $75 + 15 + 3 + \ldots$

15. a) a geometric series; terms have common ratio 0.7

   b) use $S_n = \frac{t_1(r^n - 1)}{r - 1}$ and substitute $t_1 = 50, r = 0.7$; $S_7 \approx 153$ m

1.5 Infinite Geometric Series, pages 41–49

1. a) convergent; $S_\infty = -\frac{243}{4}$

   b) convergent; $S_\infty = 32$

   c) divergent; sum does not exist

   d) convergent; $S_\infty = 0.2$

   e) divergent; sum does not exist

   f) divergent; sum does not exist

2. a) $S_\infty = -4$ **b)** sum does not exist

   c) $S_\infty = -108$ **d)** $S_\infty = \frac{1728}{19}$

   e) $S_\infty \approx 3.31$ **f)** sum does not exist

3. a) $\frac{1}{3}$ **b)** $\frac{25}{99}$ **c)** $\frac{447}{99}$ **d)** $\frac{556}{495}$

4. yes; $S_\infty = 3 + \dfrac{\frac{9}{10}}{\frac{9}{10}} = 4$

5. a) $S_\infty = 5$ **b)** $S_\infty = \frac{21}{11}$

6. a) $-1 < x < 1$ **b)** $-2 < x < 2$

7. 260 cm

8. 80 m

9. a) To solve for t_1, substitute the known values $S_\infty = 105$, and $r = -\frac{2}{3}$ into the formula $S_\infty = \frac{t_1}{1 - r}$: $t_1 = 175$.

   b) $175 - \frac{350}{3} + \frac{700}{9} - \ldots$

10. a) Solve for r by substituting the known values $S_\infty = -45$ and $t_1 = -18$ into the formula $S_\infty = \frac{t_1}{1 - r}$: $r = \frac{3}{5}$.

   b) $-18 - \frac{54}{5} - \frac{162}{25} - \frac{486}{125} - \ldots$

Chapter 1 Review, pages 50–54

1. a) not arithmetic

   b) arithmetic; $d = \frac{1}{2}, t_n = 1\frac{1}{2} + \frac{1}{2}n$

   c) not arithmetic

   d) arithmetic; $d = -3x^2, t_n = x^2 - 3nx^2$

2. a) 1, –3, –7, –11, –15

  b) –6, 0, 6, 12, 18

  c) $5m, 5m + 3, 5m + 6, 5m + 9, 5m + 12$

  d) $c + 1, 2c - 1, 3c - 3, 4c - 5, 5c - 7$

3. a) $t_1 = 4, d = 3$ **b)** $t_1 = 42, d = 2$

  c) $t_1 = -19, d = 7$ **d)** $t_1 = 67, d = -5$

4. a) 64   **b)** 56   **c)** 32   **d)** 28

5. $30 000

6. a) 290   **b)** 600   **c)** 180   **d)** 375

7. a) 893   **b)** 3604   **c)** –400   **d)** 0

8. $3 + 7 + 11 + 15 + 19$

9. $n = 21$

10. a) 1 and 25 or –1 and –25   **b)** 15 and 75

11. a) $n = 10$ **b)** $n = 8$ **c)** $n = 11$ **d)** $n = 8$

12. $r = \pm 3; \pm 6, 18, \pm 54$

13. a) $t_n = 4(3)^{n-1}$ **b)** $t_n = 891\left(\pm\frac{1}{3}\right)^{n-1}$

14. 6 reductions

15. a) $t_1 = 24, r = -\frac{1}{2}; S_{10} = \frac{1023}{64}$

  b) $t_1 = 0.3, r = \frac{1}{100}; S_{15} = \frac{10}{33}$

  c) $t_1 = 8, r = -1; S_{40} = 0$

  d) $t_1 = 1, r = -\frac{1}{3}; S_{12} = \frac{132\,860}{177\,147}$

16. a) $S_n = 3066$ **b)** $S_n = 10\,922.5$

17. a) $S_n = 1905$ **b)** $S_n = -250\,954$

18. a) 12 terms   **b)** 6 terms

19. 11 weeks

20. a) convergent; $S_\infty = -\frac{256}{5}$

  b) divergent; sum does not exist

  c) convergent; $S_\infty = \frac{61}{8}$

  d) divergent; sum does not exist

21. $t_1 = 168; 168 - \frac{336}{5} + \frac{672}{25} - \cdots$

22. 300 cm

Chapter 2

2.1 Angles in Standard Position, pages 60–67

1. a)

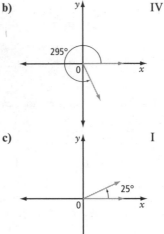

b)

c)

d)

2. a) $\theta_R = 5°$

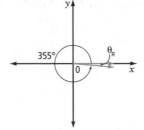

  b) $\theta_R = 45°$

  c) $\theta_R = 80°$

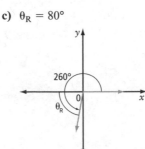

d) $\theta_R = 70°$

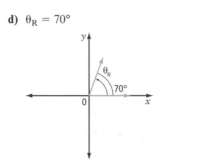

3. a) 110°, 250°, 290° **b)** 140°, 220°, 320°
  c) 130°, 230°, 310° **d)** 91°, 269°, 271°
  e) 153°, 207°, 333°

4. a) 140° **b)** 323° **c)** 260°
  d) 45° **e)** 170° **f)** 275°

5.

	$\theta = 30°$	$\theta = 45°$	$\theta = 60°$
$\sin \theta$	$\dfrac{1}{2}$	$\dfrac{1}{\sqrt{2}}$	$\dfrac{\sqrt{3}}{2}$
$\cos \theta$	$\dfrac{\sqrt{3}}{2}$	$\dfrac{1}{\sqrt{2}}$	$\dfrac{1}{2}$
$\tan \theta$	$\dfrac{1}{\sqrt{3}}$	1	$\sqrt{3}$

6. $x = 6\sqrt{3}$, $y = 6$

7. $128 + 128\sqrt{3}$

8. $\dfrac{81}{\sqrt{3}}$

9. 1.40 m by 1.40 m

10. $(4\sqrt{3} - 4)$ m

11. Completed table has the following information:
  I, $0° < \theta < 90°$, $\theta_R = \theta$,

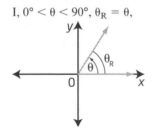

  II, $90° < \theta < 180°$, $\theta_R = 180° - \theta$,

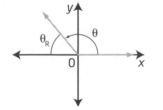

  III, $180° < \theta < 270°$, $\theta_R = \theta - 180°$,

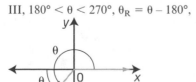

IV, $270° < \theta < 360°$, $\theta_R = 360° - \theta$,

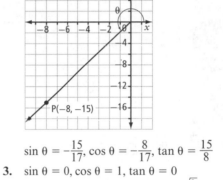

2.2 Trigonometric Ratios of Any Angle, pages 73–79

1. a) $x = 6$, $y = -8$, $r = 10$
  b) $\sin \theta = -\dfrac{4}{5}$, $\cos \theta = \dfrac{3}{5}$, $\tan \theta = -\dfrac{4}{3}$

2.

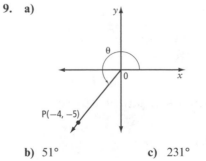

  $\sin \theta = -\dfrac{15}{17}$, $\cos \theta = -\dfrac{8}{17}$, $\tan \theta = \dfrac{15}{8}$

3. $\sin \theta = 0$, $\cos \theta = 1$, $\tan \theta = 0$

4. a) $\sin 210° = -\dfrac{1}{2}$, $\cos 210° = -\dfrac{\sqrt{3}}{2}$,
    $\tan 210° = \dfrac{1}{\sqrt{3}}$
  b) $\sin 315° = -\dfrac{1}{\sqrt{2}}$, $\cos 315° = \dfrac{1}{\sqrt{2}}$,
    $\tan 315° = -1$
  c) $\sin 270° = -1$, $\cos 270° = 0$,
    $\tan 270° = $ undefined

5. $\sin \theta = -\dfrac{6}{\sqrt{61}}$, $\cos \theta = -\dfrac{5}{\sqrt{61}}$

6. $\sin \theta = \dfrac{\sqrt{95}}{12}$, $\tan \theta = -\dfrac{\sqrt{95}}{7}$

7. $\sin \theta = -\dfrac{9}{41}$, $\tan \theta = -\dfrac{9}{40}$

8. a) $\theta = 28°, 332°$ **b)** $\theta = 117°, 297°$

9. a)

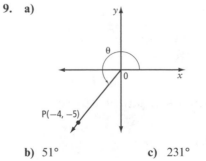

  b) 51° **c)** 231°

10. a)

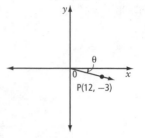

P(12, −3)

b) 14°   **c)** 346°

11.

Trigonometric Ratio	$\sin \theta = \dfrac{y}{r}$	$\cos \theta = \dfrac{x}{r}$	$\tan \theta = \dfrac{y}{x}$
0°	0	1	0
Quadrant I	+	+	+
90°	1	0	undefined
Quadrant II	+	−	−
180°	0	−1	0
Quadrant III	−	−	+
270°	−1	0	undefined
Quadrant IV	−	+	−
360°	0	1	0

2.3 The Sine Law, pages 86–93

1. a) 15.4   **b)** 24.6

c) 26°   **d)** 11°

2. a) 15.3 m   **b)** 11.7 km

3. a) 38°   **b)** 15°   **c)** 112°

4. a) 68.40   **b)** 9.64 m

c) 2.20   **d)** 43.30

5. a) right angle, 1 triangle   **b)** 0 triangles

c) $a = b$, 0 triangles   **d)** $h < a < b$, 2 triangles

e) $b \leq a$, 1 triangle

6. 1.7754 Å

7. $\angle A = 35°$, $\angle B = 29°$, $\angle C = 116°$, $a = 120$, $b = 100$, $c = 188$

8. acute $\triangle ABC$: $\angle A = 41°$, $\angle B = 56°$, $\angle C = 83°$, $a = 12.3$ cm, $b = 15.6$ cm, $c = 18.61$ cm
obtuse $\triangle ABC$: $\angle A = 41°$, $\angle B = 124°$, $\angle C = 15°$, $a = 12.3$ cm, $b = 15.6$ cm, $c = 4.85$ cm

9. Answers may vary.

2.4 The Cosine Law, pages 98–102

1. a) $a^2 = b^2 + c^2 - 2bc \cos A$

b) $c^2 = a^2 + b^2 - 2ab \cos C$

c) $l^2 = j^2 + k^2 - 2jk \cos L$

d) $y^2 = x^2 + z^2 - 2xz \cos Y$

2. 246

3. 44 mm or 4.4 cm

4. 145 mm or 14.5 cm

5. a) 39°   **b)** 121°   **c)** 36°

6. 8.1 cm

7. $\angle A = 22°$, $\angle B = 142°$, $\angle C = 16°$, $a = 21$, $b = 35$, $c = 16$

8. 28.7 ft

9.

Given Information	Solve For	Formula
m, $\angle L$, n (SAS)	l	$l^2 = m^2 + n^2 - 2mn \cos L$
l, $\angle M$, n (SAS)	m	$m^2 = l^2 + n^2 - 2ln \cos M$
l, $\angle N$, m (SAS)	n	$n^2 = l^2 + m^2 - 2lm \cos N$
l, m, n (SSS)	$\angle L$	$\cos L = \dfrac{l^2 - m^2 - n^2}{-2mn}$
l, m, n (SSS)	$\angle M$	$\cos M = \dfrac{m^2 - l^2 - n^2}{-2ln}$
l, m, n (SSS)	$\angle N$	$\cos N = \dfrac{n^2 - l^2 - m^2}{-2lm}$

Chapter 2 Review, pages 103–105

1. a)

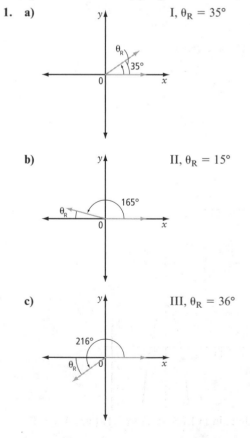

I, $\theta_R = 35°$

b) II, $\theta_R = 15°$

c) III, $\theta_R = 36°$

2. a) -1　　**b)** $\frac{1}{\sqrt{3}}$　　**c)** $-\frac{1}{\sqrt{2}}$

3. $\sin\theta = \frac{5}{\sqrt{41}}$, $\cos\theta = -\frac{4}{\sqrt{41}}$, $\tan\theta = -\frac{5}{4}$

4. $\cos\theta = -\frac{8}{17}$, $\tan\theta = -\frac{15}{8}$

5. a) $54°, 306°$　　**b)** $300°, 240°$

6. a) $19°$　　**b)** 205

7. a) 0 triangles　　**b)** 2 triangles

8. a) 13.4　　**b)** $27°$

Chapter 3

3.1 Investigating Quadratic Functions in Vertex Form, pages 110–119

1. a) $(3, 5)$; no x-intercepts

b) $(0, 1)$; two x-intercepts

c) $(11, 0)$; one x-intercept

d) $\left(-\frac{1}{2}, \frac{7}{3}\right)$; two x-intercepts

2. a) opens upward, $x = 5$; minimum value is -8

b) opens downward, $x = -3$; maximum is -5

3. a) $a = 1$, $p = -4$, $q = -2$; opens upward, minimum value -2; translated 4 units to the left and 2 units down; domain $\{x \mid x \in \mathbb{R}\}$, range $\{y \mid y \geq -2, y \in \mathbb{R}\}$

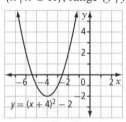

b) $a = -4$, $p = -7$, $q = 2$; opens downward, maximum value 2; translated 7 units to the left and 2 units up; domain $\{x \mid x \in \mathbb{R}\}$, range $\{y \mid y \leq 2, y \in \mathbb{R}\}$

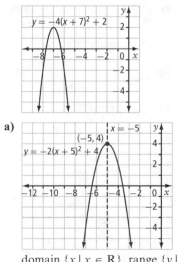

4. a)

domain $\{x \mid x \in \mathbb{R}\}$, range $\{y \mid y \leq 4, y \in \mathbb{R}\}$

b)

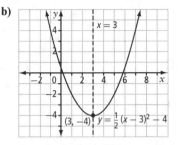

domain $\{x \mid x \in \mathbb{R}\}$, range $\{y \mid y \geq -4, y \in \mathbb{R}\}$

5. a) $y = -(x + 5)^2 + 2$　　**b)** $y = \frac{1}{2}(x + 6)^2$

6. a) $y = 5x^2 + 4$　　**b)** $y = -2(x - 3)^2$

c) $y = 4(x - 1)^2 - 1$

7. a) $(-6, 0)$　　**b)** $(1, -1)$　　**c)** $(-2, 4.5)$

8. a) $y = \frac{1}{9}x^2$　　**b)** $y = \frac{1}{9}(x - 3)^2 - 1$

c) Example: The vertical stretch and domain remain the same while the vertex, axis of symmetry, and range are different.

9. a) There are infinitely many parabolas. For example, any parabola with vertex on the line $x = 4$.

b) Example: maximum at $(4, 16)$ gives $y = -(x - 4)^2 + 16$

c) Example: maximum at $(4, 8)$ gives $y = -\frac{1}{2}(x - 4)^2 + 8$

d) One or more of p and q change when the vertex of a parabola changes, depending on how the vertex is moved. The value of a may change when the location of the vertex changes.

10. a) Example: If $\theta = 30°$, then $d = -0.088v^2$. This graph has its vertex at the origin and is vertically stretched compared to the graph of $y = x^2$, but opens downward.

b) Answers may vary.

c) Example: All the parabolas will have vertices at the origin. The vertical stretch factor will change depending on the angles. The domain and range will be the same for all graphs.

11. a) $\$3700$

b)

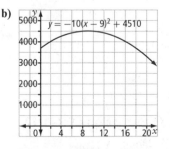

c) Example: As prices initially rise more revenue will result, but with each price increase fewer people will buy a shirt. So, eventually prices can be so high that total revenue will decrease.

d) The vertex (9, 4510) is the maximum point on the graph. So, when $x = 9$ the price of each T-shirt is $21 and the maximum revenue is $4510.

3.2 Investigating Quadratic Functions in Standard From, pages 123–132

1. a) quadratic: $f(x) = -5x^2 - 20x - 12$

b) not quadratic

c) quadratic: $f(x) = 8x^2 - 29x - 55$

d) not quadratic

2. a) vertex (1, 4), axis of symmetry $x = 1$, y-intercept 3, x-intercepts −1 and 3, maximum value 4, domain $\{x \mid x \in \mathbb{R}\}$, range $\{y \mid y \le 4, y \in \mathbb{R}\}$

b) vertex (−3, 0), axis of symmetry $x = -3$, y-intercept 9, x-intercept −3, minimum value 0, domain $\{x \mid x \in \mathbb{R}\}$, range $\{y \mid y \ge 0, y \in \mathbb{R}\}$

c) vertex (−2, 2), axis of symmetry $x = -2$, y-intercept −6, x-intercepts −3 and −1, maximum value 2, domain $\{x \mid x \in \mathbb{R}\}$, range $\{y \mid y \le 2, y \in \mathbb{R}\}$

3. a) vertex (2.5, −7.3), axis of symmetry $x = 2.5$, minimum value −7.3, domain $\{x \mid x \in \mathbb{R}\}$, range $\{y \mid y \ge -7.25, y \in \mathbb{R}\}$, x-intercepts −0.2 and 5.2, y-intercept −1

b) vertex (0.3, 3.1), axis of symmetry $x = 0.3$, maximum value 3.1, domain $\{x \mid x \in \mathbb{R}\}$, range is $\{y \mid y \le 3.1, y \in \mathbb{R}\}$, x-intercepts 1.5 and −1, y-intercept 3

c) vertex (11, −3), axis of symmetry $x = 11$, minimum value −3, domain $\{x \mid x \in \mathbb{R}\}$, range $\{y \mid y \ge -3, y \in \mathbb{R}\}$, x-intercepts 7.5 and 14.5, y-intercept 27.3

4. a) (2, −16) **b)** (−1, −4)

c) (4, 41) **d)** $\left(\frac{3}{2}, -\frac{19}{2}\right)$

5. a) two x-intercepts **b)** two x-intercepts
c) one x-intercept **d)** two x-intercepts
e) no x-intercepts **f)** no x-intercepts

6. a) 0 m **b)** 5 m after 1 s **c)** 2 s

d) domain $\{t \mid 0 \le t \le 2, t \in \mathbb{R}\}$, range $\{h \mid 0 \le h \le 5, h \in \mathbb{R}\}$

7. a) $a = \dfrac{v^2}{25}$

b) vertex (0, 0), axis of symmetry $x = 0$, x- and y-intercept of 0

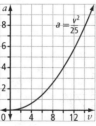

c) domain $\{v \mid v \ge 0, v \in \mathbb{R}\}$; since speed is positive

d) range $\{a \mid a \ge 0, a \in \mathbb{R}\}$; since the graph opens up

e) The curve does not fit the criteria. Example: When $v = 14$, $a = 7.84$ m/s² which is not 6 m/s².

8. a) Yes, it is possible to have more than one correct answer. Example:

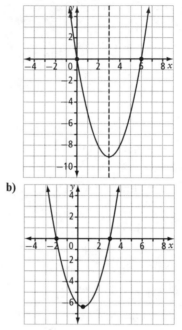

b)

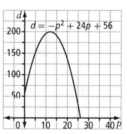

9. a) (12, 200)

b)

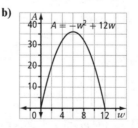

c) The vertex indicates that maximum demand is 200 at a price of $12.

d) Demand initially increases as price increases, but when price exceeds $12 demand decreases.

10. a) $A = w(12 - w)$; polynomial of degree 2

b)

c) (6, 36); represents the maximum area of the dog enclosure

d) 6 m by 6 m; maximum area of 36 m²

11. a) Knowing the location of the vertex and direction of opening allows you to visualize the parabola and its number of x-intercepts.

b) Knowing the axis of symmetry and direction of opening is not enough to know the number of x-intercepts because the vertex may be above, on, or below the x-axis and so may have two, one, or no x-intercepts. Examples may vary.

12. $y = \dfrac{4ac - b^2}{4a}$. Explanations may vary.

3.3 Completing the Square, pages 137–141

1. a) $y = (x + 1)^2 + 2$; vertex $(-1, 2)$

b) $y = (x + 6)^2 - 16$; vertex $(-6, -16)$

c) $y = -(x - 4)^2 + 9$; vertex $(4, 9)$

d) $y = -(x + 5)^2 - 6$; vertex $(-5, -6)$

2. a) $y = 2(x + 2)^2 - 7$; vertex $(-2, -7)$

b) $y = 5(x - 6)^2 - 14$; vertex $(6, -14)$

c) $y = -4(x - 3)^2 + 15$; vertex $(3, 15)$

d) $y = -7(x + 3)^2 + 66$; vertex $(-3, 66)$

3. a) $y = (x - 5)^2 - 7$

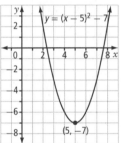

b) $y = -2(x - 2)^2 + 11$

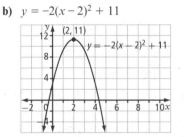

4. a) not quadratic

b) quadratic; $y = -2x^2 + 4x + 28$ with vertex $(1, 30)$

c) quadratic; $y = 2x^2 - 19x + 41$ with vertex $\left(\dfrac{19}{4}, -\dfrac{33}{8}\right)$

d) not quadratic

5. a) Expanding $y = (x + 1)^2 - 36$ leads to the function $y = x^2 + 2x - 35$. Completing the square on $y = x^2 + 2x - 35$ results in $y = (x + 1)^2 - 36$. Also, the graphs of the two functions appear identical.

b) Expanding $y = -2(x - 4)^2 + 3$ leads to the function $y = -2x^2 + 16x - 29$. Completing the square on $y = -2x^2 + 16x - 29$ results in $y = -2(x - 4)^2 + 3$. Also, the graphs of the two functions appear identical.

c) Expanding $y = \dfrac{1}{2}(x - 5)^2 - 4$ leads to the function $y = \dfrac{1}{2}x^2 - 5x + \dfrac{17}{2}$. Completing the square on $y = \dfrac{1}{2}x^2 - 5x + \dfrac{17}{2}$ results in $y = \dfrac{1}{2}(x - 5)^2 - 4$. Also, the graphs of the two functions appear identical.

6. a) minimum of -6.33 at $x = 0.67$

b) minimum of -2 at $x = 6$

c) maximum of 7 at $x = 4$

d) minimum of 0.99 at $x = 0.06$

7. 80 components

8. a) The maximum height is 22 m after 2 s.

b) Answers may vary.

c) The maximum height is 22.39 m. Answers may vary.

9. a) $r = (12 + x)(500 - 25x)$, where x is the number of \$1 price increases and r is the sales revenue

b) $r = -25(x - 4)^2 + 6400$

c) The vertex represents the number of \$1 price increases that yields the maximum revenue.

d) There should be 4 increases of \$1, so the price of the product should be \$16 to obtain a maximum revenue of \$6400.

10. a) $2l + 10w = 100$

b) Answers may vary. Example: $l = -5w + 50$

c) $A = w(-5w + 50)$ **d)** $(5, 125)$

e) The length should be 25 m and each width should be 5 m.

Chapter 3 Review, pages 142–144

1. a) two x-intercepts, $x = -5$, domain $\{x \mid x \in \mathbb{R}\}$, range $\{y \mid y \le 6, y \in \mathbb{R}\}$

b) one x-intercept, $x = 8$, domain $\{x \mid x \in \mathbb{R}\}$, range $\{y \mid y \ge 0, y \in \mathbb{R}\}$

2. a) $(3, -7)$; maximum value is -7

b) $(-11, 8)$; minimum value is 8

3. a)

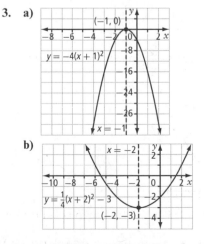

b)

4. a) $y = -\dfrac{5}{16}x^2$ **b)** $y = -\dfrac{5}{16}(x-4)^2 + 5$

    c) Answers may vary. Example: The value of a is the same but the values of p and q change.

5. a) x-intercepts -4 and 2, y-intercept -8

    b) x-intercepts -9 and -1, y-intercept 9

6. a) $-\dfrac{3}{2}$ **b)** $-\dfrac{5}{6}$

7. a) $x = -5$, opens downward

    b) $x \approx 0.67$, opens upward

8. a) $y = (x + 3)^2 + 6$, domain $\{x \mid x \in R\}$,
range $\{y \mid y \geq 6, y \in R\}$

    b) $y = -3(x + 6)^2 + 8$, domain $\{x \mid x \in R\}$,
range $\{y \mid y \leq 8, y \in R\}$

    c) $y = 2(x - 4)^2 - 10$, domain $\{x \mid x \in R\}$,
range $\{y \mid y \geq -10, y \in R\}$

    d) $y = \dfrac{1}{2}(x - 1)^2 + \dfrac{5}{2}$, domain $\{x \mid x \in R\}$,
range $\left\{y \mid y \geq \dfrac{5}{2}, y \in R\right\}$

9. a) $(10, 105)$

    b) The maximum profit of $105 occurs on the 10th day of sales.

10. a) $r = (10 + v)(120 - 5v)$

    b) The maximum revenue of $1445 occurs at a price of $17.

Chapter 4

4.1 Graphical Solutions of Quadratic Equations, pages 151–155

1. a) 2, because there are two x-intercepts; $x = -2, 2$

    b) 0, because there are no x-intercepts; no root

    c) 2, because there are two x-intercepts; $x = 0, 3$

    d) 1, because there is one x-intercept; $x = -5$

2. a) $x = 1, 8$

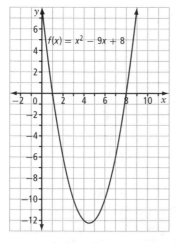

b) $x = -9, -5$

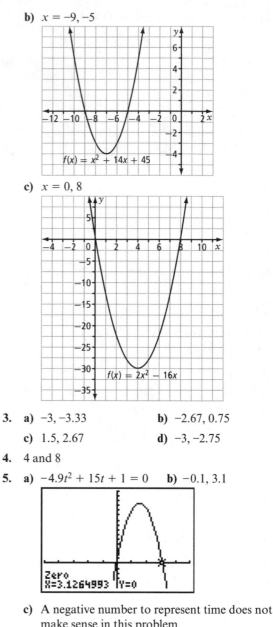

c) $x = 0, 8$

3. a) $-3, -3.33$ **b)** $-2.67, 0.75$

   c) $1.5, 2.67$ **d)** $-3, -2.75$

4. 4 and 8

5. a) $-4.9t^2 + 15t + 1 = 0$ **b)** $-0.1, 3.1$

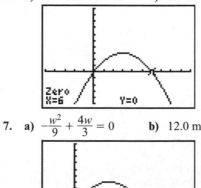

   c) A negative number to represent time does not make sense in this problem.

6. a) $d = 0$ and $d = 6$ **b)** $6.0\,\text{m}$

7. a) $-\dfrac{w^2}{9} + \dfrac{4w}{3} = 0$ **b)** $12.0\,\text{m}$

8. a) $-4.5t^2 + 8.3t + 2.1 = 0$ **b)** 2.1 s

9. Examples:

a) The value of a is the same in both cases.

b) The form $y = a(x - p)^2 + q$ is more useful for finding the vertex.

10. Examples:

a) $y = (x - 7)^2$

b) The vertex is on the x-axis, so $x = 7$ is the only root.

4.2 Factoring Quadratic Equations, pages 160–164

1. a) $(x - 6)(x - 3)$ **b)** $5(b - 3)(b + 2)$

2. a) $(n - 4)(3n + 1)$ **b)** $(x + 2)(4x + 3)$

c) $(t - 6)(2t - 5)$ **d)** $(3x + 2)(4x - 3)$

3. a) $\frac{1}{2}(x - 6)(x + 2)$ **b)** $\frac{1}{4}(x - 4)(x + 6)$

c) $0.1(a - 6)(a + 5)$ **d)** $0.1(z - 10)(5z - 4)$

4. a) $(0.9x + 0.5y)(0.9x - 0.5y)$

b) $(1.1k - 0.1x)(1.1k + 0.1x)$

c) $\left(\frac{1}{5}d - \frac{1}{7}f\right)\left(\frac{1}{5}d + \frac{1}{7}f\right)$

d) $2(2a - 3b)(2a + 3b)$

5. a) $(x + 6)(x - 2)$ **b)** $4(x + 4)(x + 3)$

c) $(x + 6)(2x - 1)$ **d)** $(10x - 7)(10x - 3)$

6. a) $-9, 5$ **b)** $-\frac{9}{2}, 4$

c) $-\frac{3}{4}, \frac{11}{2}$ **d)** $0, \frac{14}{3}$

7. a) $4, 5$ **b)** -6 **c)** $-6, \frac{7}{3}$

d) $\frac{3}{4}, \frac{3}{2}$ **e)** $0, -6$ **f)** $-9, -6$

8. a) $w(w + 3) = 154$ **b)** 11 in. by 14 in.

9. a) $x + 1$ **b)** $x(x + 1) = 156$

c) 12 and 13, or -13 and -12

10. a) $-0.1d^2 + 4.8d = 0$ **b)** 48 m

11. a) 140 m^2

b) $(2x + 8)(2x + 12) = 140; 1 \text{ m}$

12. If $c = 0$, then one of the factors equals zero. Example: $x^2 - 3x = 0$ factors to $x(x - 3)$, and the factors are 0 and 3.

13. Example: Graph the corresponding function and determine the x-intercepts.

4.3 Solving Quadratic Equations by Completing the Square, pages 168–171

1. a) 36 **b)** $\frac{9}{4}$ **c)** $\frac{1}{64}$ **d)** 0.16

2. a) $-1, 9$ **b)** $-9, 3$ **c)** $-2\sqrt{5} - 5, 2\sqrt{5} - 5$

d) $-2\sqrt{10} + 1, 2\sqrt{10} + 1$ **e)** $-\sqrt{6} - \frac{3}{2}, \sqrt{6} - \frac{3}{2}$

3. a) $-1, 5$ **b)** $-12, 2$ **c)** $-\frac{5}{3}, \frac{1}{3}$ **d)** $\frac{1}{5}, \frac{13}{5}$

4. a) $-5, 11$ **b)** $-\sqrt{10} + 2, \sqrt{10} + 2$

c) $-2\sqrt{2} + 5, 2\sqrt{2} + 5$ **d)** $-3\sqrt{2} - 2, 3\sqrt{2} - 2$

5. a) $A = \pi(x + 5)^2$ **b)** 1.9 m

6. a) The room is a rectangle with sides $8 + x$ and $6 + x$.

b) $(6 + x)(8 + x) = 144$ **c)** 11.0 ft by 13.0 ft

7. line 2 should be $x^2 - x + \frac{1}{4} = 5 + \frac{1}{4}; \frac{-\sqrt{21} + 1}{2}, \frac{\sqrt{21} + 1}{2}$

8. 8, 15, 17

9. 100 yd

10. Example: $x^2 + 4x = -10$; Any equation that requires the square root of a negative number cannot be solved.

11. Example: It depends on whether the zeros of the quadratic function or the vertex of the graph are required.

4.4 The Quadratic Formula, pages 177–180

1. a) 1 root **b)** 2 roots

c) 0 roots **d)** 1 root

2. a) $\frac{3 - \sqrt{3}}{3}, \frac{\sqrt{3} + 3}{3}$ **b)** $-\frac{2}{3}, \frac{1}{2}$

c) $\frac{2 + \sqrt{2}}{3}, \frac{2 - \sqrt{2}}{3}$ **d)** $\frac{5 + \sqrt{57}}{8}, \frac{5 - \sqrt{57}}{8}$

3 a) $-0.6, 1.6$ **b)** $0.2, 2.2$

c) $-1.5, 10$ **d)** $-1.5, 3.5$

4. 0 or 6

5. 3, 12

6. 5 cm

7. a) 4.34 s **b)** 4.30 s

c) In both cases, one root is negative, which does not make sense in this context.

8. 69.28 m

9. a) row 1: 125; 5   row 2: 100; 2

row 3: $(100)(125)$; $(125 + 5n)(100 - 2n)$

b) $(125 + 5n)$ represents the cost of a calculator for any number of price increases of $5.

$(100 - 2n)$ represents the fact that for each price increase, the store sells two fewer calculators.

The revenue is the price multiplied by the number sold, so $r(n) = (125 + 5n)(100 - 2n)$.

c) Set the revenue equation equal to 14 000 and solve for n. Since $n = 10$ and $n = 15$, there can be 10 to 15 price increases, resulting in a price range of $175 to $200.

Chapter 4 Review, pages 181–186

1. a) $-1, 5$ **b)** 3

2. a) Example: The location of the vertex and the direction of opening determine the number of zeros for the quadratic function. In this case, the graph would intersect the x-axis in two places.

b) Example: The location of the vertex is on the x-axis.

c) Example: The minimum is above the x-axis, or the maximum is below the x-axis, meaning that the graph does not intersect the x-axis.

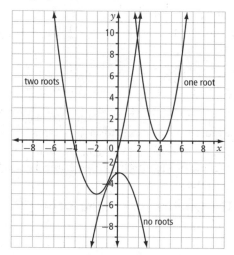

3. a) $2.8, 7.2$

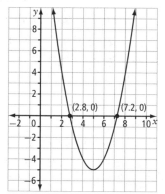

b) $8.6, 13.4$

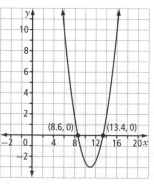

c) $0.1, 3.1$

4. a) $(a - 7b + 68)(a + 7b - 58)$

b) $(x + 3)(x - 5)$ **c)** $\left(\dfrac{3m}{4} + \dfrac{10n}{9}\right)\left(\dfrac{3m}{4} - \dfrac{10n}{9}\right)$

5. a) $-4, -2$ **b)** $\dfrac{2}{3}, 1$

c) $\dfrac{3}{2}, \dfrac{9}{2}$ **d)** $-\dfrac{3}{2}, \dfrac{3}{2}$

6. 9 in. by 12 in.

7. a) ± 13 **b)** $-18, 4$

c) $-4\sqrt{5} + 12, 4\sqrt{5} + 12$ **d)** $-5, 3$

8. a) $-\sqrt{23} - 4, \sqrt{23} - 4; -8.8, 0.8$

b) $-3\sqrt{2} + 5, 3\sqrt{2} + 5; 0.8, 9.2$

9. 30th day

10. a) 2 roots   **b)** 2 roots

c) 1 root   **d)** 0 roots

11. a) $5 - \sqrt{15}, 5 + \sqrt{15}; 1.1, 8.9$

b) $\dfrac{-1 + \sqrt{41}}{5}, \dfrac{-1 - \sqrt{41}}{5}; -1.5, 1.1$

12. a) $7, 3$ **b)** $-\dfrac{2}{5}, 3$

c) $\dfrac{-9 + \sqrt{57}}{4}, \dfrac{-9 - \sqrt{57}}{4}$

Chapter 5

5.1 Working With Radicals, pages 193–198

1.

Mixed Radical	$5\sqrt{5}$		$3\sqrt{7}$		$-2\sqrt[3]{7}$	
Entire Radical		$\sqrt{252}$		$-\sqrt{375}$		$\sqrt[4]{486}$

2. a) $b\sqrt[3]{by}$ **b)** $\sqrt{4a}, a \geq 0$

c) $-2x\sqrt[3]{6y}$ **d)** $2a\sqrt[4]{2a}, a \geq 0$

e) $\sqrt{98y^2z}, y \geq 0, z \geq 0$ **f)** $-\sqrt{45m^5}, m \geq 0$

3. $\sqrt{63} = 3\sqrt{7}$, so $\sqrt{63}$ and $\sqrt{7}$, are like radicals; $-\sqrt{27} = -3\sqrt{3}$ and $3\sqrt{75} = 15\sqrt{3}$, so $-\sqrt{27}$ and $3\sqrt{75}$ are like radicals; $\sqrt[3]{250} = 5\sqrt[3]{2}$ and $4\sqrt[3]{16} = 8\sqrt[3]{2}$, so $\sqrt[3]{250}$ and $4\sqrt[3]{16}$ are like radicals

4. a) Example: $-5\sqrt{7}$ b) Example: $5\sqrt[3]{2}$
   c) Example: $10\sqrt{2m}$ d) Example: $8a\sqrt[4]{2a}$
   e) Example: $5x\sqrt{2}$ f) Example: $-4y\sqrt{5xy}$

5. a) $-\sqrt{60}, -8, -2\sqrt{17}, -5\sqrt{3}$
   b) $18, \frac{3}{10}\sqrt{3500}, 9\sqrt{\frac{15}{4}}, \sqrt{300}$
   c) $3\sqrt[4]{8}, 5, \sqrt[4]{615}, 4\sqrt[4]{\frac{9}{4}}$

6. a) $8\sqrt{7}$ b) $15\sqrt{7} - 17\sqrt{2}$
   c) $\sqrt[3]{9} + 2$ d) 0

7. a) $13\sqrt{m}, m \geq 0$ b) $-x\sqrt{3x}, x \geq 0$
   c) $-3ab\sqrt{2b}, a \geq 0, b \geq 0$ d) $2y\sqrt{y}, y \geq 0$

8. 3 in.

9. 5 s

10. $8\sqrt{2}$ ft

11. $4\sqrt{2}$ ft

12. $20\sqrt{42}$ ft

13. The error made was that the unlike radicals were added. You must simplify and then add. The answer should be $6\sqrt{b}$.

14. $25\sqrt{5} - 3\sqrt{3}$

15. The two legs of the triangle are $\frac{s}{\sqrt{2}}$.
$$A = \frac{1}{2}ab$$
$$= \frac{1}{2}\left(\frac{s}{\sqrt{2}}\right)\left(\frac{s}{\sqrt{2}}\right)$$
$$= \frac{s^2}{4}$$

5.2 Multiplying and Dividing Radical Expressions, pages 203–209

1. a) $30\sqrt{6}$ b) $12a^2\sqrt{6}$
   c) $-70x^2$ d) $(3y^2)\sqrt[3]{y}$

2. a) $2\sqrt{30} + 4\sqrt{5}$ b) $-5\sqrt{30} + 3\sqrt{2}$
   c) $6\sqrt{35x} - 2x\sqrt{7}$ d) $5\sqrt{21a} - 7a\sqrt{3} + 6\sqrt{7a}$

3. a) $-22 + 13\sqrt{3}$ b) $58 + 12\sqrt{6}$
   c) 4 d) $3\sqrt{21} - 2\sqrt{7} - 12\sqrt{3} - 1$

4. a) $-9k + 19\sqrt{3k} - 20, k \geq 0$
   b) $2 - 6\sqrt{10m} + 45m, m \geq 0$
   c) $-40x + 5x\sqrt{10} - 4\sqrt{10x} + 5\sqrt{x}, x \geq 0$
   d) $16y + 40y\sqrt[3]{4y^2} - y\sqrt[3]{2y} - 5y^2$, any real number

5. a) 3 b) -20 c) $\frac{3\sqrt{7}}{4}$
   d) $\frac{-3\sqrt{6}}{16}$ e) $\frac{\sqrt{6}}{2y}$ f) $\frac{3\sqrt{2a} - 3a\sqrt{6}}{16a}$

6. row 1: $4 - \sqrt{5}$, 11; row 2: $-5 + 3\sqrt{3}$, -2; row 3: $7\sqrt{5} - 4\sqrt{2}$, 213; row 4: $2\sqrt{z} + \sqrt{3}, 4z - 3$

7. a) $\frac{-(4\sqrt{2} + 28)}{47}$ b) $\frac{-(3\sqrt{30} - 12\sqrt{5})}{10}$
   c) $-\frac{4\sqrt{5} + 8\sqrt{2} + 10\sqrt{10} + 25}{109}$ d) $\frac{36 + 9\sqrt{x}}{16 - x}$

8. $60\sqrt{10}$

9. $32\pi\sqrt{13}$

10. a) $10\sqrt{2}$ cm^2 b) 242 cm^2 c) $12\sqrt{6}$ cm^2

11. Tineka did not apply the distributive rule properly when expanding the squared binomial. The proper solution is $23 - 6\sqrt{10}$.

12. $(2 - \sqrt{7})^2, (\sqrt{7} + 2)(\sqrt{7} - 2), \sqrt{7}(\sqrt{7} + 2), (\sqrt{7} + 2)^2$

13. 2.26 m

14. Anthony made an error when multiplying the numerator. The product should be $4\sqrt{m} + m - 12$. Also, the denominator should be $36 - m$. The correct solution is $\frac{4\sqrt{m} + m - 12}{36 - m}, m > 0, m \neq 36$.

15. i) All possible factors have been removed from each radical.
    ii) The radical contains no fractions.
    iii) The denominator is a rational number.

16. False. The radicand of a radical with an even index must be positive. Therefore, $\sqrt{-8}$ and $\sqrt{-2}$ are not real numbers.

5.3 Radical Equations, pages 216–222

1. a) $16x^2 - 40x + 25$ b) $7y$ c) $2x - 3$
   d) $324m$ e) $9n - 48\sqrt{n} + 64$

2. $x = 2$ is correct, $x = 6$ is extraneous

3. a) $x = 83, x \geq 2$ b) $m = 10\,000, m \geq 0$
   c) $a = 6, a \geq 1$
   d) $p = 1, p \leq 2$; $p = -2$ is an extraneous root
   e) $n = 5$; $n \geq \frac{-19}{6}$; $n = -3$ is an extraneous root
   f) $c = 10$ and $c = 9, c \geq \frac{54}{7}$

4. a) $x = 0$ b) $x = -3 + 3\sqrt{3}$; $x \leq \frac{-3\sqrt{2}}{2}$ or $x \geq \frac{3\sqrt{2}}{2}$
   c) $x = 16, x \geq 7$

5. a) $n = 1$ b) $x = 20$ c) $y = 3, -1$ d) $c = 2$

6. The term $(m - 4)$ was squared incorrectly. The correct squaring is $m^2 - 8m + 16$. You can factor this equation, resulting in roots of $m = 3$ and $m = 2$, both of which are extraneous.

7. a) 19.44 m/s b) 70 km/h

8. 39.06 ft

9. 1.528 m

10. 8 cm

11. a) $(a - b)^2 = (a - b)(a - b)$
    $= a^2 - 2ab + b^2$
    Therefore, $(a - b)^2 \neq a^2 - b^2$.
    b) Example: Let $a = 10$ and $b = 6$
    Left side = 16; Right side = 64
    The left side is not equal to the right side.
    c) If $a = b$, then $(a - b)^2 = a^2 - b^2$.

12. $\sqrt{4n + 8} - 3 = n$

$\quad\sqrt{4n + 8} = n + 3$ Isolate the radical.

$\quad(\sqrt{4n + 8})^2 = (n + 3)^2$ Square both sides.

$\quad 4n + 8 = n^2 + 6n + 9$

$\quad 0 = n^2 + 2n + 1$

$\quad 0 = (n + 1)(n + 1)$ Factor.

$\quad n + 1 = 0$ Use the zero property.

$\quad n = -1$

Verify by substitution.

Left Side	Right Side
$\sqrt{4(-1) + 8} - 3$	-1
$= \sqrt{4} - 3$	
$= 2 - 3$	
$= -1$	

The left side equals the right side, therefore $n = -1$ is the solution.

13. a) $\sqrt{2a + 9} - \sqrt{a - 4} = 0$

$\quad\quad \sqrt{2a + 9} = \sqrt{a - 4}$

$\quad\quad (\sqrt{2a + 9})^2 = (\sqrt{a - 4})^2$

$\quad\quad 2a + 9 = a - 4$

$\quad\quad\quad a = -13$

Substituting into the original yields $\sqrt{-17}$, which is non-real.

b) Example: $\sqrt{x - 7} - \sqrt{5x + 1} = 0$

Chapter 5 Review, pages 223–227

1. a) $12\sqrt{2}$ **b)** $8c\sqrt{2}$

c) $2a^2b\sqrt{6b}, b \geq 0$ **d)** $5xy\sqrt[3]{2y^2}$

2. a) $\sqrt{96}$ **b)** $-\sqrt{175m^2}$

c) $\sqrt[3]{54y^5}$ **d)** $-\sqrt[4]{96x^5y^3}, x \geq 0, y \geq 0$

3. a) $-\sqrt{6}$ **b)** $-3\sqrt{5}$

c) $-9\sqrt{2} + 6\sqrt{2x} - 4x\sqrt{2x}, x \geq 0$

d) 0, x is any real number, y is any real number

4. $4\sqrt{15}, \sqrt{250}, 16, 3\sqrt{30}$

5. $4\sqrt{197}$ ft

6. a) $2\sqrt{21}$ **b)** $6x^3, x \geq 0$

c) $-200y\sqrt{10}$ **d)** $-21 + 3\sqrt{3}$

e) $2 - 6\sqrt{10r} + 45r, r \geq 0$ **f)** $9 - 2x, x \geq 0$

7. a) $\dfrac{4\sqrt{5}}{5}$ **b)** $\dfrac{-\sqrt{6}}{24}$ **c)** $-\dfrac{(3\sqrt{5} - 12)}{11}$

d) $\dfrac{-(3\sqrt{2} - 6\sqrt{5} + 4\sqrt{6} - 8\sqrt{15})}{18}$

e) $\dfrac{\sqrt{6}}{2y}, x > 0, y > 0$

f) $\dfrac{3n^2\sqrt{10n} + 2n\sqrt{5n}}{10n}, n > 0$

8. a) $\sqrt{3k} + 5$ **b)** $-3\sqrt{2} + 4\sqrt{7}$

9. a) $16\sqrt{3} + 4\sqrt{30}$ cm   **b)** 72 cm^2

10. a) $6, a \geq 0$ **b)** $48, n \geq 44$

c) $6, b \leq 6$ **d)** $5, x \geq 4$

11. 9 cm and 18 cm

12. 144 squares

Chapter 6

6.1 Rational Expressions, pages 234–240

1. a) $x \neq -4$ **b)** $x \neq \dfrac{1}{2}$ **c)** $x \neq 0, 1$

d) $x \neq -2, \dfrac{2}{3}$ **e)** $x \neq -3, 0$ **f)** $x \neq -7, 3$

g) $x \neq 0, \dfrac{1}{2}$ **h)** $x \neq \pm 10$

2. a) $2x, x \neq -1$ **b)** $3x, x \neq 0, \dfrac{3}{2}$

c) $\dfrac{x - 7}{x + 7}, x \neq -7, -4$ **d)** $\dfrac{2x + 7}{x}, x \neq -6, 0$

3. a) $\dfrac{2x^2y}{3}, y \neq 0$ **b)** $\dfrac{r}{2h}, r \neq 0, h \neq 0$

c) $\dfrac{2x + 14}{x + 1}, x \neq -1, 0$

d) $\dfrac{a - b^2}{5 + 25a}, a \neq 0, -\dfrac{1}{5}; b \neq 0$

4. a) $\dfrac{x + 5}{x + 10}, x \neq -10, 5$ **b)** $\dfrac{x - 1}{x}, x \neq -6, 0$

c) $\dfrac{x + 5}{2}, x \neq 7$ **d)** $2x + 4, x \neq -1$

e) $\dfrac{a + 1}{a + 7}, a \neq -7, 2$ **f)** $\dfrac{z + 6}{z - 6}, z \neq -3, 6$

g) $\dfrac{2x + 1}{x + 1}, x \neq -1, 6$ **h)** $\dfrac{3x + 1}{3x - 6}, x \neq 2, 3$

5. a) $1 - x; -1$ **b)** $x - 2; -1$

c) $b - 2a; -1$ **d)** $5x + 2; -1$

6. a) $\dfrac{-3a}{7 + a}, a \neq \pm 7$ **b)** $\dfrac{-x - 9}{2x}, x \neq 0, 9$

c) $\dfrac{4x}{x - 3}, x \neq 3$ **d)** $\dfrac{-a}{2b + a}, a \neq \pm 2b$

7. a) $\dfrac{6x^2 - 24x + 16}{x^3 - 6x^2 + 8x}, x \neq 0, 2, 4$

b) $x > 4$; all sides have positive lengths

8. $\dfrac{2r + 2h}{rh}, r, h \neq 0$

9. a) No; the numerator is not a polynomial

b) $a \neq 0$; otherwise $y = ax^2 + bx + c$ becomes $y = bx + c$, which is a linear relation, not a quadratic relation

10. a) $x \neq 1, 3$

b) Example: any answer in which the denominator is $x^2 - 5x + 6$

c) $x - 8, x \neq -3$ **d)** Example: $\dfrac{x^2 - 7x - 8}{x + 1}$

11. no; cannot cancel terms

6.2 Multiplying and Dividing Rational Expressions, pages 245–251

1. a) $x \neq 2, 4$ **b)** $r \neq -h, 0$

c) $x \neq \pm 1, -\dfrac{2}{3}$ **d)** $y \neq -1, -6, -10$

2. a) $\dfrac{7x}{3}$　　　　**b)** $\dfrac{x+4}{2x-7}$

c) $\dfrac{6x-3}{x^2+2x+1}$　　**d)** $\dfrac{1}{49-x^2}$

3. a) $l \neq 0, w \neq 0, 2$　　**b)** $x \neq \pm 2, \dfrac{3}{2}, -5$

4. a) $\dfrac{x^2 y}{2}, x, y \neq 0$　　**b)** $\dfrac{x}{2}; x \neq 0, 3$

c) $\dfrac{x+6}{x+2}, x \neq -2, 6$　**d)** $\dfrac{x^2+4x+3}{x-4}, x \neq 2, 4$

e) $2x+2, x \neq -3, 4$　**f)** $-\dfrac{x}{x+5}, x \neq \pm 10, -5, 4$

5. a) $\dfrac{1}{2}, x \neq \dfrac{5}{4}, -2$　**b)** $ab^2, a, b \neq 0, c \neq 1$

c) $\dfrac{x+6}{3x-24}, x \neq -2, 7, 8$

d) $\dfrac{x^2-x-30}{x^2+3x+2}, x \neq -5, -3, -2, -1$

6. a) $\dfrac{x+8}{x}, x \neq -8, 0, 4$　**b)** $\dfrac{-x+8}{x-1}, x \neq \pm 3, 1, 9$

c) $\dfrac{x+4}{22-2x}, x \neq -4, 0, \pm 11$

d) $\dfrac{x^2-18x+80}{5x-60}, x \neq -5, 8, 12$

7. a) $\dfrac{2}{x-5}, x \neq -6, \pm 5, 4$

b) $\dfrac{x^2+11x+10}{x^2}, x \neq -10, -1, -\dfrac{1}{2}, 0, 3$

c) $\dfrac{-3x^2-8x+3}{50x+450}, x \neq -9, 0, \dfrac{1}{3}, 1, 3, 8$

8. did not cancel a factor of the first numerator (step 1); did not use the distributive law correctly (step 3); $\dfrac{x+2}{4}, x \neq -1, -2$

9. multiplied instead of divided (step 2) *or* did not take the reciprocal of the second rational expression (missed a step); missing the non-permissible values from the numerator of the second expression (step 3); $\dfrac{x^2-8x+16}{x^2+9x+18}, x \neq -6, -3, 4$

10. approximately 0.52 or 52%

11. $\dfrac{2x^2-13x+21}{x-5}; x \neq -6, 5$; Heather's solution is more efficient; explanations will vary.

6.3 Adding and Subtracting Rational Expressions, pages 256–262

1. a) $\dfrac{10x-3}{4x}, x \neq 0$　**b)** $\dfrac{x^2+2x+2}{x-8}, x \neq 8$

2. a) $\dfrac{3x-9}{x^2}, x \neq 0$　**b)** $\dfrac{x^2+2x+1}{x^2-25}, x \neq \pm 5$

c) $x-1, x \neq -9$　**d)** $-x-6, x \neq 6$

3. a) $5xy$　　　　　**b)** $3x^2$

c) $x(x+1)$　　　**d)** $(x-7)(x+5)$

e) $(x+2)(x+6)(x-2)$

f) $-1(x-5)(x-5)$

4. a) $\dfrac{y+6}{6xy}, x, y \neq 0$　**b)** $\dfrac{x-7}{7x^2}, x \neq 0$

c) $\dfrac{x+1}{x(x-3)}, x \neq 0, 3$

d) $\dfrac{x-9}{(x+7)(x-8)}, x \neq -7, 8$

e) $\dfrac{2x-1}{(x+2)(x+4)(x-3)}, x \neq -4, -2, 3$

f) $\dfrac{x-3}{-1(x-4)(x-4)}, x \neq 4$

5. a) $\dfrac{a^2+7a+14}{(a+7)(a+5)}, a \neq -7, -5$

b) $\dfrac{x+6}{x+1}, x \neq -1, 4$

6. a) $\dfrac{x^2-18x}{(x-9)(x-12)}, x \neq 9, 12$

b) $\dfrac{x+1}{(x+6)(x+2)}, x \neq -6, \pm 2$

7. a) $\dfrac{5}{n}, n > 0$　　**b)** $\dfrac{5}{n-1}, n > 1$

c) $\dfrac{10n-5}{n^2-n}, n > 1$

8. a) $\dfrac{480}{y}, y > 0$　　**b)** $\dfrac{120}{y-5}, y > 5$

c) $\dfrac{600y-2400}{y^2-5y}, y > 5$

9. a) $\dfrac{x^2+3x-14}{x-2}, x \neq -7, 1, 2$

b) $\dfrac{x^2+4x+9}{2x^2+3x}, x \neq -10, -\dfrac{3}{2}, 0, 6, 7$

10. Answers will vary.

6.4 Solving Rational Equations, pages 268–273

1. a) $7+3 = 4x(5x-3), x \neq 0$

b) $(x+2)(x+1) + (x-8)(2x+1) = -7, x \neq -2, 8$

c) $2x(21-5x) = 2(x) - (x-3)(x-2), x \neq 0, 3$

2. a) $x = 3; x \neq 0$　　**b)** $x = 3, x = 4; x \neq \pm 1$

3. a) $x = 9; x \neq 0, 8$　　**b)** $x = 3; x \neq 0, 5$

4. 6 min

5. approximately 41 min

6. 107 km/h

7. 7.3 km/h; 1 h 42 min

8. −22, −21

9. 28, 30

10. Answers will vary.

Chapter 6 Review, pages 274–276

1. a) $\dfrac{x-5}{x-6}, x \neq 5, 6$　**b)** $\dfrac{x+1}{x}, x \neq -4, 0$

2. Yes; by factoring out (−1) from both terms of the numerator, you can then cancel out $(x-7)$ in the numerator and denominator.

3. $\dfrac{-2x+1}{3x+18}, x \neq -6, 0, 4, 7$

4. $\dfrac{x^2+7x+12}{5x-10}, x \neq -3, 2$

5. $4x(x-6)(x+6)$

6. a) $\dfrac{x^2-5x-10}{x^2-100}, x \neq \pm 10$

b) $\dfrac{x^2-14x+3}{x(x+5)(x-1)}, x \neq -5, 0, 1$

7. 15.4 min

Chapter 7

7.1 Absolute Value, pages 280–284

1. **a)** $\frac{5}{6}$ **b)** $1\frac{1}{4}$ **c)** 0.8

   d) 12   **e)** 1.2   **f)** 0

2. $2\frac{3}{5}$, $|-2.5|$, $\left|\frac{-15}{7}\right|$, $|-2.09|$, -2, $-2\frac{6}{9}$

3. **a)**

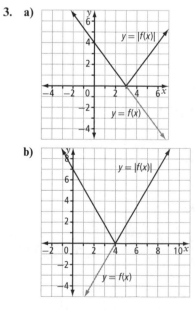

   b)

   c)

4. **a)** 0.3   **b)** -8 **c)** 8

   d) -1 **e)** 0.09   **f)** 4

5. **a)** $|156 - (-458)|$ or $|-458 - 156|$ **b)** 614 m

6. **a)** $|-39 - 357|$ or $|357 - (-39)|$ **b)** 396

7. **a)** $|-23 - (-27)|$ or $|-27 - (-23)|$

   b) $|15 - 35|$ or $|35 - 15|$

8. **a)** $|25.98 - 26.83|$ or $|26.83 - 25.98|$

   b) rise of $0.85

9. Differences: use of absolute value symbols; Similarities: both expressions will produce the same result, that is: $(x_1 - x_2)^2 = |x_1 - x_2|^2$

10. Answers will vary.

7.2 Absolute Value Functions, pages 290–296

1. **a)** 0, 6, 12, 14   **b)** 7, 4, 1, 2, 5

2. $(-1, 10)$, $(0, 6)$, $(1, 2)$, $(2, 2)$

3. **a)**

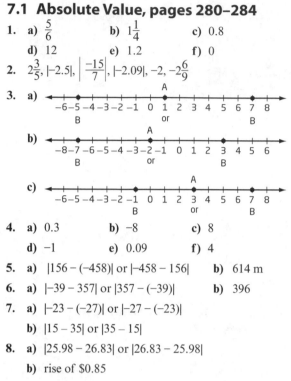

   b)

4. **a)**

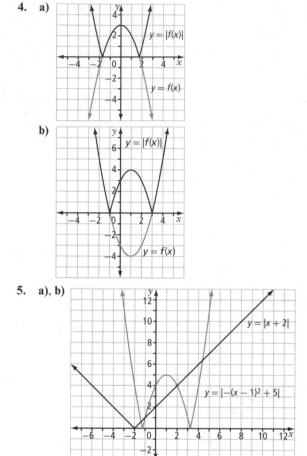

   b)

5. **a), b)**

   For $y = |x + 2|$: x-intercept -2, y-intercept 2, domain $\{x \mid x \in \mathbb{R}\}$, range $\{y \mid y \geq 0, y \in \mathbb{R}\}$
   For $y = |-(x - 1)^2 + 5|$: x-intercepts $1 \pm \sqrt{5}$, y-intercept 4, domain $\{x \mid x \in \mathbb{R}\}$, range $\{y \mid y \geq 0, y \in \mathbb{R}\}$

6. **a)** $y = \begin{cases} x - 5, & \text{if } x \geq 5 \\ -(x - 5), & \text{if } x < 5 \end{cases}$

   b) $y = \begin{cases} \frac{1}{3}x + 2, & \text{if } x \geq -6 \\ -\left(\frac{1}{3}x + 2\right), & \text{if } x < -6 \end{cases}$

7. **a)** $y = \begin{cases} -x^2 + 2, & \text{if } -\sqrt{2} \leq x \leq \sqrt{2} \\ -(-x^2 + 2), & \text{if } x < -\sqrt{2} \text{ or } x > \sqrt{2} \end{cases}$

   b) Example: $y = \begin{cases} 2(x - 1)^2 - 2, & \text{if } x \leq 0 \text{ or } x \geq 2 \\ -[2(x - 1)^2 - 2], & \text{if } 0 < x < 2 \end{cases}$

8. **a)**

x	$y = \left\|\frac{1}{2}x - 6\right\|$
0	6
12	0
2	5
4	4
18 or 6	3
-2	7
-6	9

b)

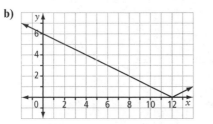

c) Domain: $\{x \mid x \in R\}$; Range: $\{y \mid y \geq 0, y \in R\}$

d) $y = \begin{cases} \frac{1}{2}x - 6, \text{ if } x \geq 12 \\ -\left(\frac{1}{2}x - 6\right), \text{ if } x < 12 \end{cases}$

9. a) $y = |(x + 2)^2 - 7|$

b) $(-2, 7), (-2 - \sqrt{7}, 0), (-2 + \sqrt{7}, 0), (0, 3)$

c)

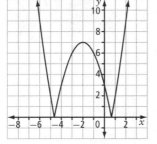

d) Domain: $\{x \mid x \in R\}$;

Range: $\{y \mid y \geq 0, y \in R\}$

e) $y = \begin{cases} x^2 + 4x - 3, \text{ if } x \leq -2 - \sqrt{7} \text{ or } x \geq -2 + \sqrt{7} \\ -(x^2 + 4x - 3), \text{ if } -2 - \sqrt{7} < x < -2 + \sqrt{7} \end{cases}$

10. a) none; none; none

b) The graphs are the same.

c)

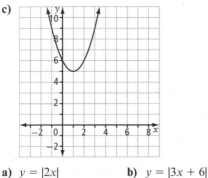

11. a) $y = |2x|$ **b)** $y = |3x + 6|$

12. a) Yes, by definition, $2 - x = 2 - x$ and $2 - x = -2 + x$, both equations have $x = 2$ as the solution.

b) Yes, $|x^2| = x^2$, by definition, $x^2 = x^2$ for all real values of x, and $x^2 = -(x^2)$, only if $x = 0$.

13. a)

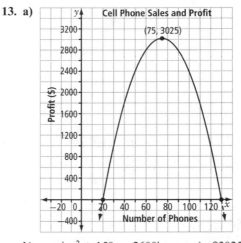

b) $y = |-x^2 + 150x - 2600|$ **c)** $3025

d) No, sales can go to infinity according to the function from part b); so, profit can go to infinity.

7.3 Absolute Value Equations, pages 303–308

1. a) 11, −11   **b)** 6, −6   **c)** 2, −2   **d)** 9.5, −9.5

2. a) 7, −3   **b)** 6, −12   **c)** 13, −3

3. a) 10, $\frac{-76}{7}$ **b)** No solution   **c)** No solution

4. a) 6, −14   **b)** $\pm\sqrt{5}$, −1

5. a) Example: $0.5 = |x - 32|$ **b)** 31.5 oz and 32.5 oz

6. a) Example: $0{:}15 = |x - 08{:}00|$ **b)** 8:15 to 7:45

7. a) Example: $0.01 = |x - 2.5|$ **b)** 2.49 mm to 2.51 mm

8. a) Example: $0.002 = |i - 0.036|$

b) 0.038 A to 0.034 A

9. Example: $0.35 = |x - 9.6|$; 9.25 lb to 9.95 lb

10. 24 screens, \$64 000

11. No; 4 incorrectly grouped with −9 in step 1.

$$4 - 9|-6 - x| = -15$$
$$-9|-6 - x| = -19$$
$$|-6 - x| = \frac{19}{9}$$
$$-6 - x = \frac{19}{9}$$
$$x = \frac{-73}{9}$$
$$-6 - x = \frac{-19}{9}$$
$$x = \frac{-35}{9}$$

12. a) No; $d = |a| + |b| + |c|$.

b) Example: let $a = 7, b = -5, c = -1$
$$d = |7| + |-5| + |-1|$$
$$d = 7 + 5 + 1$$
$$d = 13$$
$$d = |7 + (-5) + (-1)|$$
$$d = |1|$$
$$d = 1$$
$$|a + b + c| \neq |a| + |b| + |c|$$

13. a) Example: $d = |m_1 - m_2|$

b)–c) Answers may vary.

14. a) $|4x + 7| + 8 = 2$ Isolate the absolute value
$|4x + 7| = -6$; This is not possible according to the definition of absolute value.

b) Example: $|2x - 8| = -10$; This is not possible according to the definition of absolute value.

7.4 Reciprocal Functions, pages 318–323

1.

$y = f(x)$	$y = \dfrac{1}{f(x)}$
$y = -x$	$y = \dfrac{1}{-x}$
$y = 3x - 1$	$y = \dfrac{1}{3x - 1}$
$y = x^2 - 4x + 4$	$y = \dfrac{1}{x^2 - 4x + 4}$
$y = x^2$	$y = \dfrac{1}{x^2}$
$y = \dfrac{x}{2}$	$y = \dfrac{2}{x}$

2. a) $x = 0$ **b)** $x = -5$ **c)** $x = \frac{2}{7}$
d) $x = 4$ and $x = -4$ **e)** $x = -3$ and $x = 2$

3.

$y = f(x)$	$y = \dfrac{1}{f(x)}$	Invariant Point(s)
$y = x - 8$	$y = \dfrac{1}{x - 8}$	$(9, 1), (7, -1)$
$y = 3x - 4$	$y = \dfrac{1}{3x - 4}$	$\left(\dfrac{5}{3}, 1\right), (1, -1)$
$y = x^2 - 25$	$y = \dfrac{1}{x^2 - 25}$	$(\sqrt{26}, 1),$ $(-\sqrt{26}, 1),$ $(\sqrt{24}, -1),$ $(-\sqrt{24}, -1)$
$y = x^2 - x - 29$	$y = \dfrac{1}{x^2 - x - 29}$	$(6, 1), (-5, 1),$ $\left(\dfrac{1 - \sqrt{113}}{2}, -1\right),$ $\left(\dfrac{1 + \sqrt{113}}{2}, -1\right)$

4. a) $\{x \mid x \neq 0, x \in \mathrm{R}\}$; $\{y \mid y \neq 0, y \in \mathrm{R}\}$; $x = 0$
b) $\{x \mid x \neq 1, x \in \mathrm{R}\}$; $\{y \mid y > 0, y \in \mathrm{R}\}$; $x = 1$

5. a)

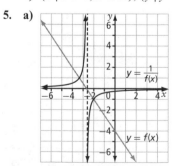

b)

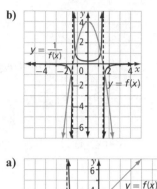

6. a)

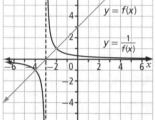

$x = -3, y = 0; (-2, 1), (-4, -1);$
$f(x)$: $(-3, 0), (0, 3);$ $\dfrac{1}{f(x)}$: $\left(0, \dfrac{1}{3}\right)$

b)

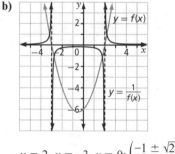

$x = 2, x = -3, y = 0; \left(\dfrac{-1 \pm \sqrt{29}}{2}, 1\right),$
$\left(\dfrac{-1 \pm \sqrt{21}}{2}, -1\right);$ $f(x)$: $(2, 0), (-3, 0), (0, -6);$
$\dfrac{1}{f(x)}$: $\left(0, \dfrac{-1}{6}\right)$

7. a)

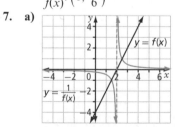

Example: Use the vertical asymptote to find the zero of the function. Then, use the given point to find the equation. $y = 2x - 4$

b)

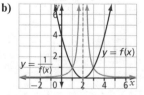

Example: Use the vertical asymptote to find the zero of the function. Then, use an invariant point to find the equation. $y = (x - 2)^2$

8. a) $\frac{s}{\sqrt{d}} = 365$ **b)** $d = \left(\frac{s}{365}\right)^2$
c) i) 4.80 km **ii)** 2.53 km **iii)** 0.27 km

9.

Characteristic	$y = 2x + 5$	$y = \dfrac{1}{2x + 5}$
x-intercept	$\dfrac{-5}{2}$	none
y-intercept	5	$\dfrac{1}{5}$
Invariant points	$(-2, 1)$ $(-3, -1)$	

10. a)

Height, h (m)	Distance, d (km)
2	5.0
11.3	12
40	22.6
100	35.7
125.4	40

b)

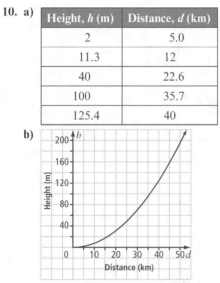

c) approximately 16 km **d)** approximately 5 m

11.

	$f(x)$	$g(x)$	$h(x)$
x-intercept(s)	$\sqrt{3}, -\sqrt{3}$	$\sqrt{3}, -\sqrt{3}$	none
y-intercept(s)	-3	3	$-\dfrac{1}{3}$
Domain	$\{x \mid x \in \mathbb{R}\}$	$\{x \mid x \in \mathbb{R}\}$	$\{x \mid x \neq \pm\sqrt{3}, x \in \mathbb{R}\}$
Range	$\{y \mid y \geq -3, y \in \mathbb{R}\}$	$\{y \mid y \geq 0, y \in \mathbb{R}\}$	$\{y \mid y \neq 0, y \in \mathbb{R}\}$
Piecewise function		$g(x) = x^2 - 3$, for $x \leq -\sqrt{3}$ or $x \geq \sqrt{3}$ $g(x) = -(x^2 - 3)$ for $-\sqrt{3} < x < \sqrt{3}$	
Invariant points	For $f(x)$ and $h(x)$: $(\pm 2, 1)$, $(\pm\sqrt{2}, -1)$		
Asymptote(s)	none	none	$x = \sqrt{3}$, $x = -\sqrt{3}$ $y = 0$

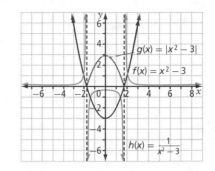

Chapter 7 Review, pages 324–331

1. a) 17 **b)** $-1\frac{1}{2}$ **c)** 1.02

2. $\left|\frac{41}{2}\right|$, $|-20.1|$, $\left|-19\frac{3}{4}\right|$, -19.65, $-|20|$, -20.2

3. a) 18 **b)** 6 **c)** 8

4. a) $|9 - 12| + (-2)(4) = -5$

b) $|(1.3 - 3.3)|^3 = 8$ or $|(1.3 - 3.3)^3| = 8$

c) $8 - 11|12 - 15| = -25$

5. a) Example: $|-732 - 600|$ **b)** 1332 ft

6. a)

x	$f(x)$	$g(x)$
-1	-3	3
0	-1	1
1	1	1
2	3	3
3	5	5
4	7	7

b)

c)

	$f(x)$	$g(x)$
Domain	$\{x \mid x \in \mathbb{R}\}$	$\{x \mid x \in \mathbb{R}\}$
Range	$\{y \mid y \in \mathbb{R}\}$	$\{y \mid y \geq 0, y \in \mathbb{R}\}$
x-intercepts	0.5	0.5
y-intercepts	-1	1
Piecewise function	N/A	$y = \begin{cases} 2x - 1, \text{ if } x \geq 0.5 \\ -2x + 1, \text{ if } x < 0.5 \end{cases}$

7. a)

x	$f(x)$	$g(x)$
−3	−5	5
−2	0	0
−1	3	3
0	4	4
1	3	3
2	0	0
3	−5	5

b)

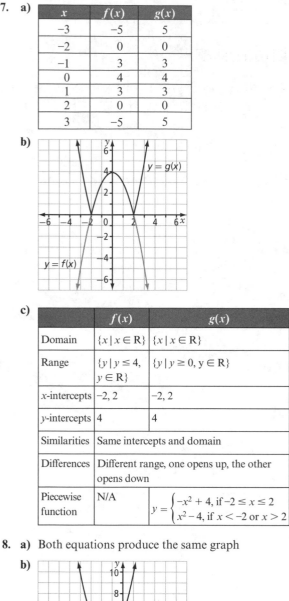

c)

	$f(x)$	$g(x)$
Domain	$\{x \mid x \in \mathbb{R}\}$	$\{x \mid x \in \mathbb{R}\}$
Range	$\{y \mid y \le 4,\ y \in \mathbb{R}\}$	$\{y \mid y \ge 0,\ y \in \mathbb{R}\}$
x-intercepts	−2, 2	−2, 2
y-intercepts	4	4
Similarities	Same intercepts and domain	
Differences	Different range, one opens up, the other opens down	
Piecewise function	N/A	$y = \begin{cases} -x^2 + 4, & \text{if } -2 \le x \le 2 \\ x^2 - 4, & \text{if } x < -2 \text{ or } x > 2 \end{cases}$

8. a) Both equations produce the same graph

b)

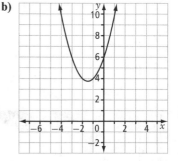

9. $y = \left| \dfrac{1}{2}x + 3 \right|$

10. a) $x = 1$ and $x = -1$

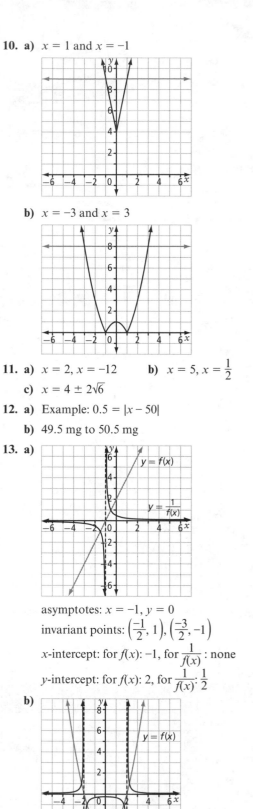

b) $x = -3$ and $x = 3$

11. a) $x = 2,\ x = -12$ **b)** $x = 5,\ x = \dfrac{1}{2}$

c) $x = 4 \pm 2\sqrt{6}$

12. a) Example: $0.5 = |x - 50|$

b) 49.5 mg to 50.5 mg

13. a)

asymptotes: $x = -1$, $y = 0$

invariant points: $\left(\dfrac{-1}{2}, 1\right), \left(\dfrac{-3}{2}, -1\right)$

x-intercept: for $f(x)$: −1, for $\dfrac{1}{f(x)}$: none

y-intercept: for $f(x)$: 2, for $\dfrac{1}{f(x)}$: $\dfrac{1}{2}$

b)

asymptotes: $x = 2$, $x = -2$, $y = 0$
invariant points: $(\sqrt{5}, 1), (-\sqrt{5}, 1), (\sqrt{3}, -1),$
$(\sqrt{3}, -1)$

x-intercepts: for $f(x)$: 2, –2; for $\dfrac{1}{f(x)}$: none

y-intercept: for $f(x)$: –4, for $\dfrac{1}{f(x)}$: $\dfrac{-1}{4}$

14. a)

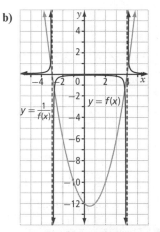

	$f(x)$	$\dfrac{1}{f(x)}$
Asymptotes	N/A	$x = \dfrac{-4}{3}, y = 0$
x-intercept	$\dfrac{-4}{3}$	None
y-intercept	4	$\dfrac{1}{4}$
Invariant points	$(-1, 1), \left(\dfrac{-5}{3}, -1\right)$	
Domain	$\{x \mid x \in R\}$	$\left\{x \mid x \neq \dfrac{-4}{3}, x \neq 0, x \in R\right\}$
Range	$\{y \mid y \in R\}$	$\{y \mid y \neq 0, y \in R\}$

b)

(graph)

	$f(x)$	$\dfrac{1}{f(x)}$
Asymptotes	None	$x = 4, x = -3,$ $y = 0$
x-intercepts	4, –3	None
y-intercept	–12	$\dfrac{-1}{12}$
Invariant points	$\left(\dfrac{1 \pm \sqrt{53}}{2}, 1\right), \left(\dfrac{1 \pm 3\sqrt{5}}{2}, -1\right)$	
Domain	$\{x \mid x \in R\}$	$\{x \mid x \neq 0, x \neq 4,$ $x \neq -3, x \in R\}$
Range	$\{y \mid y \geq -12.25,$ $y \in R\}$	$\{y \mid y \neq 0, y \in R\}$

15. a) $R = \dfrac{P}{I^2}$ **b)** 125 ohms

c) 5 amperes   **d)** 150 watts

Chapter 8

8.1 Solving Systems of Equations Graphically, pages 338–344

1. a) $(0, -3)$ **b)** $(-1, 5)$ **c)** $(-2, 11)$

2. a) quadratic-quadratic; $(-2, -2)$ and $(2, -2)$

b) linear-quadratic; $(0, -4)$

c) quadratic-quadratic; no solution

3. a) $(-4, -3)$ and $(2, 3)$

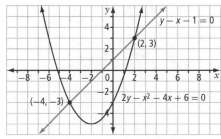

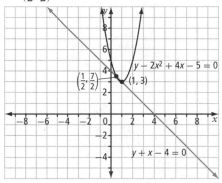

b) $\left(\dfrac{1}{2}, \dfrac{7}{2}\right)$ and $(1, 3)$

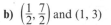

c) no solution

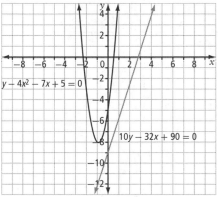

4. a) $(-1, 7)$ and $(2, -2)$

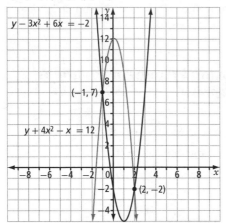

b) no solution

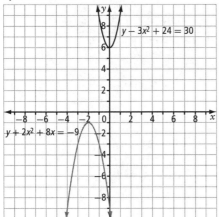

c) $(3, 4)$

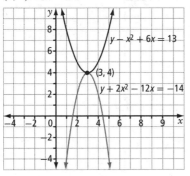

5. Example:

a)

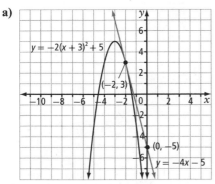

b) $(-2, 3)$ and $(0, -5)$; $y = -4x - 5$ **c)** $(-2, 3)$

6. Example:

a)

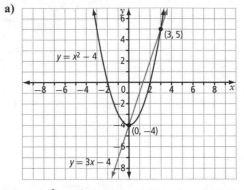

b) $y = x^2 - 4$ **c)** $(0, -4)$ and $(3, 5)$

7. a) $(-2, 15)$ and $(2, 19)$

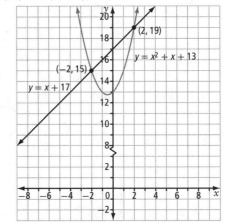

b) $(-2, 15)$ cannot be used because the question states that both numbers are positive.

8. They intersect at $(5, 75)$. After 5 s, they are both 75 m above the ground.

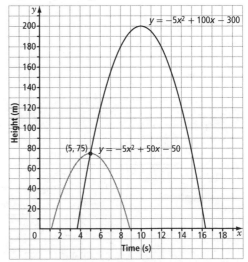

9. **a)** No solution. The parabola opens upward. The y-intercept of the line is below the vertex.

b) An infinite number of solutions. When the first equation is expanded, it is exactly the same as the second equation.

c) One solution. The parabolas share the same vertex at $(-2, 4)$. One parabola opens upward, the other downward.

d) Two solutions. The vertex of one parabola is directly above the other. One parabola has a smaller vertical stretch factor.

8.2 Solving Systems of Equations Algebraically, pages 350–355

1. **a)** $(2, 2)$ **b)** $(0, 1)$ and $(1, 2)$

c) $(-2, -1)$ and $(3, 14)$ **d)** $\left(-\frac{1}{2}, 2\right)$ and $(1, 5)$

2. **a)** $(-1, 3)$ and $(3, -37)$

b) $\left(-\frac{1}{4}, \frac{1}{4}\right)$

c) $(-1, 7)$ and $\left(-\frac{10}{3}, -\frac{7}{9}\right)$

d) no solution

3. $m = 4, n = 16$

4. **a)** $x + y = 11$

b) $x^2 - 5x + 6 = 5y$

c) $x = 7, y = 4$

d) base $= 8$ cm, height $= 5$ cm, and width $= 6$ cm

5. 11 and 8

6. $(1.45, 3.80)$ and $(3.22, -0.91)$

Chapter 8 Review, pages 356–360

1. **a)**   no solution   1 solution

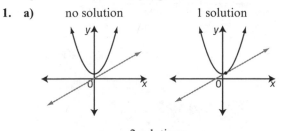

2 solutions

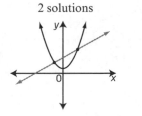

b)   no solution   1 solution

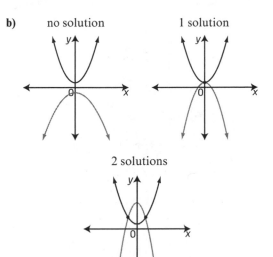

2 solutions

2. **a)** $(0, 4)$

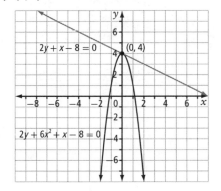

b) $(4, 4)$ and $(1, -5)$

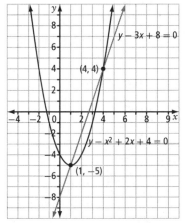

c) $(-3, -3)$ and $(-1, -3)$

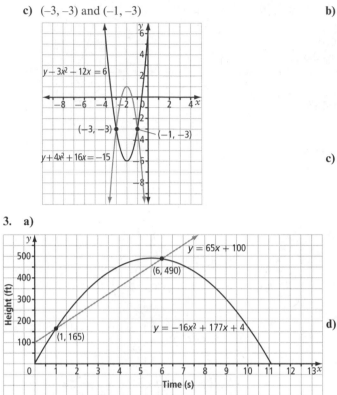

3. a)

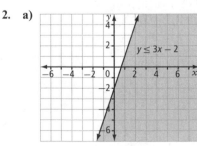

b) $(1, 165)$ and $(6, 490)$; The boy sees the rocket as it goes up (1 s after release, at a height of 165 ft) and as it is coming down (6 s after release, at a height of 490 ft).

4. a) $(1, 9)$ and $(-2, 27)$ **b)** $(-4, -3)$

c) $(-0.57, 6.23)$ and $(1.77, 5.29)$

5. 3 and 7

6. $(3.75, 2.94)$; The balls will hit each other at approximately 2.94 m in the air. The point where the balls collide is a distance of 3.75 m from the first player and 5.25 m from the second player.

Chapter 9

9.1 Linear Inequalities in Two Variables, pages 368–378

1. a) $(-1, 4), (3, 7)$ **b)** $(0, 7), (-2, 5), (-6, 1)$

c) $(-3, -4), (2, -10)$ **d)** $(0, 0), (-4, -3), (3, 1)$

2. a)

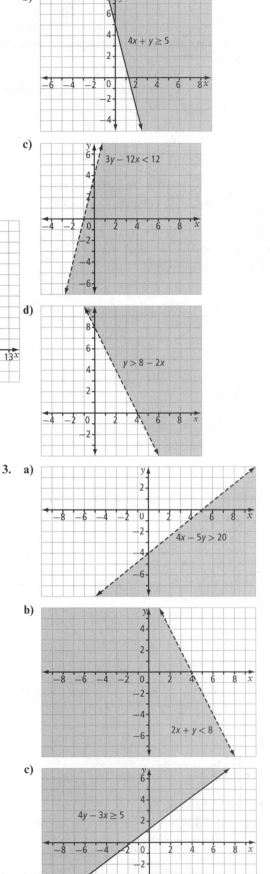

d)

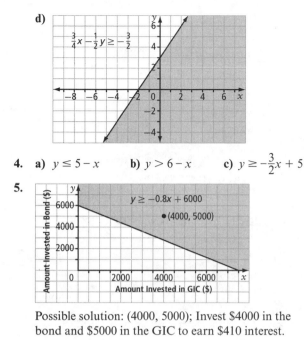

$\frac{3}{4}x - \frac{1}{2}y \geq -\frac{3}{2}$

4. a) $y \leq 5 - x$ **b)** $y > 6 - x$ **c)** $y \geq -\frac{3}{2}x + 5$

5.

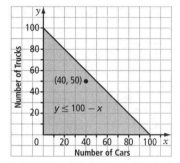

$y \geq -0.8x + 6000$
• (4000, 5000)

Possible solution: (4000, 5000); Invest $4000 in the bond and $5000 in the GIC to earn $410 interest.

6.

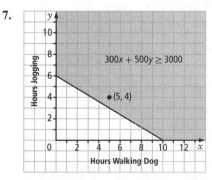

(40, 50) •

$y \leq 100 - x$

Possible solution: (40, 50); Make 40 cars and 50 trucks.

7.

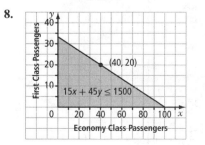

$300x + 500y \geq 3000$

• (5, 4)

Possible solution: (5, 4); Barb could walk her dog for 5 hr and jog for 4 hr.

8.

$15x + 45y \leq 1500$
• (40, 20)

Possible solution: (40, 20); If each passenger brings luggage at their maximum allowable weight, the airplane can carry a maximum of 40 economy class passengers and 20 first class passengers.

9. Example: To solve a system of equations graphically, graph each equation and find the point(s) of intersection. This system would have two solutions as there are two points at which the graphs intersect.

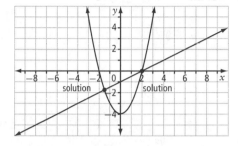

solution   solution

Solving a system of inequalities means finding the intersection; it will be an area of intersection not a point of intersection. Using the same functions but changing them to inequalities, the solution might look like this:

solution region

10.

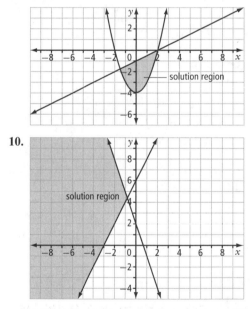

solution region

9.2 Quadratic Inequalities in One Variable, pages 383–388

1. a) $\{x \mid x < -2 \text{ or } x > 1, x \in R\}$

b) $\{x \mid -2 \leq x \leq 1, x \in R\}$

c) $\{x \mid -2 < x < 1, x \in R\}$

d) $\{x \mid x \leq -2 \text{ or } x \geq 1, x \in R\}$

2. a)

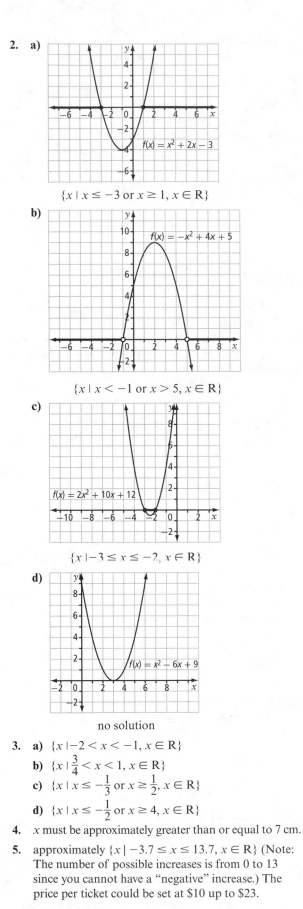

$\{x \mid x \le -3 \text{ or } x \ge 1, x \in \mathbb{R}\}$

b)

$f(x) = -x^2 + 4x + 5$

$\{x \mid x < -1 \text{ or } x > 5, x \in \mathbb{R}\}$

c)

$f(x) = 2x^2 + 10x + 12$

$\{x \mid -3 \le x \le -2, x \in \mathbb{R}\}$

d)

$f(x) = x^2 - 6x + 9$

no solution

3. a) $\{x \mid -2 < x < -1, x \in \mathbb{R}\}$

   b) $\{x \mid \frac{3}{4} < x < 1, x \in \mathbb{R}\}$

   c) $\{x \mid x \le -\frac{1}{3} \text{ or } x \ge \frac{1}{2}, x \in \mathbb{R}\}$

   d) $\{x \mid x \le -\frac{1}{2} \text{ or } x \ge 4, x \in \mathbb{R}\}$

4. x must be approximately greater than or equal to 7 cm.

5. approximately $\{x \mid -3.7 \le x \le 13.7, x \in \mathbb{R}\}$ (Note: The number of possible increases is from 0 to 13 since you cannot have a "negative" increase.) The price per ticket could be set at $10 up to $23.

6. approximately $\{x \mid 36.8 \le x \le 163.2, x \in \mathbb{R}\}$; possible measures for x are from 36.8 m up to 163.2 m.

7. $\{x \mid 10 \le x \le 20, x \in \mathbb{R}\}$

8. a) Example: $2x^2 - 7x - 4 < 0$
      or $(2x + 1)(x - 4) < 0$

   b) Example: $8x^2 + 10x - 3 \ge 0$
      or $(2x + 3)(4x - 1) \ge 0$

   c) Example: $3x^2 - 4x \le 0$
      or $(x)(3x - 4) \le 0$

9. Answers may vary.

9.3 Quadratic Inequalities in Two Variables, pages 394–400

1. a) $(0, 0)$ and $(2, 1)$
   b) $(-4, -5)$ and $(-2, 10)$
   c) $(-2, -10)$, $(2, -7)$, and $(0, 36)$
   d) $(1, 9)$ and $(-1, 17)$

2. a) Example: $(-5, -5)$ is a solution; $(0, 5)$ is not a solution
   b) Example: $(5, -5)$ is a solution; $(1, -15)$ is not a solution
   c) Example: $(4, -7)$ is a solution; $(-1, 20)$ is not a solution
   d) Example: $(-10, -3)$ is a solution; $(0, 0)$ is not a solution

3. a)

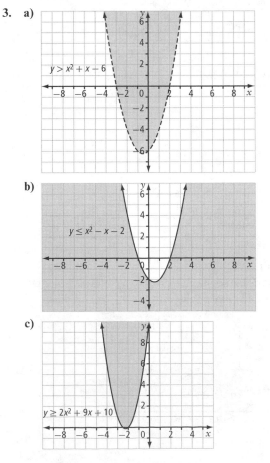

$y > x^2 + x - 6$

b)

$y \le x^2 - x - 2$

c)

$y \ge 2x^2 + 9x + 10$

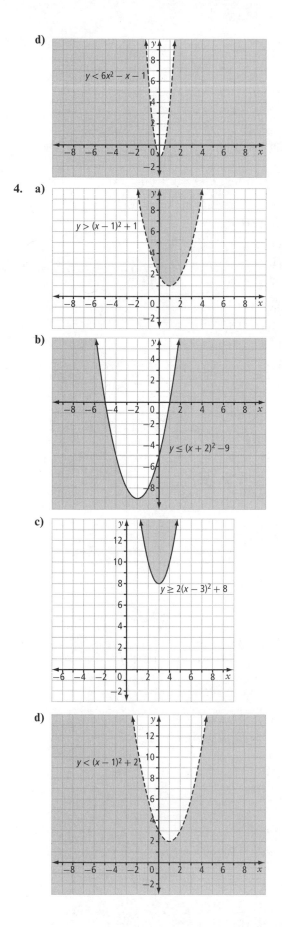

d)

$y < 6x^2 - x - 1$

4. a)

$y > (x - 1)^2 + 1$

b)

$y \leq (x + 2)^2 - 9$

c)

$y \geq 2(x - 3)^2 + 8$

d)

$y < (x - 1)^2 + 2$

5. a) $y > 2x^2 - 4x - 1$ **b)** $y \leq -3x^2 - 4x - 1$

   c) $y > -4x^2 + 5x + 3$ **d)** $y \leq 2x^2 - 3x + 2$

6. a) $y \geq -2(x - 4)^2 + 8$ **b)** $y < 1.5(x + 3)^2 - 6$

   c) $y > 0.25(x + 3)^2 - 4$ **d)** $y \leq -0.5(x + 4)^2 + 2$

7. a)

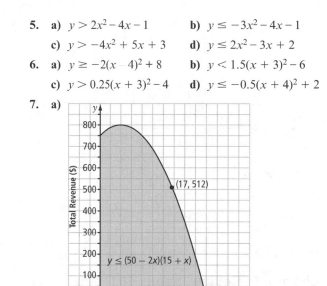

b) from 0 to 17 additional campers; 15 to 32 campers in total

8. Example: To solve a system of quadratic *equations* graphically, graph each equation and determine the point(s) of intersection. This system would have two solutions, as there are two points where the graphs intersect.

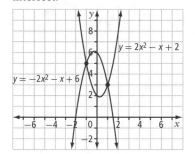

Solving a system of quadratic *inequalities* means determining the intersection; the solution will be an area of intersection, not a point (or points) of intersection. Using the same functions, but changing them to inequalities, the solution might look like this:

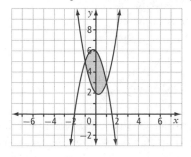

9.

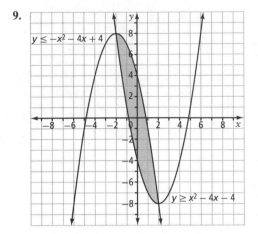

$y \le -x^2 - 4x + 4$

$y \ge x^2 - 4x - 4$

10. Answers may vary.

Chapter 9 Review, pages 401–406

1. a) $(0, 7), (5, -3)$ **b)** $(7, 0) (-3, -4) (5, -1)$

2. a)

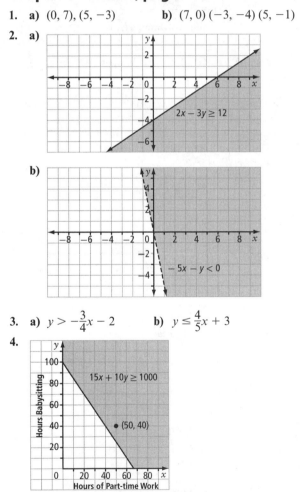

$2x - 3y \ge 12$

b)

$-5x - y < 0$

3. a) $y > -\frac{3}{4}x - 2$ **b)** $y \le \frac{4}{5}x + 3$

4.

```
y
100
        15x + 10y ≥ 1000
 80
 60
 40         • (50, 40)
 20

  0   20  40  60  80   x
      Hours of Part-time Work
```
Hours Babysitting

Possible solution: (50, 40); Amber could work
50 h at her part-time job and babysit for a total of
40 h. This would help her save $1150.

5.

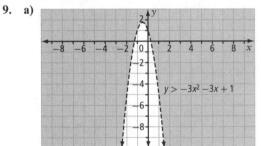

$y = -2x^2 + 3x + 7$

approximately $\{x \mid -1.3 < x < 2.8, x \in R\}$

6. a) $\{x \mid 0 < x < 1, x \in R\}$

b) $\{x \mid x < 0 \text{ or } x > 1, x \in R\}$

c) $\{x \mid x \le 0 \text{ or } x \ge 1, x \in R\}$

d) $\{x \mid 0 \le x \le 1, x \in R\}$

7. $\{x \mid -3 \le x \le 4, x \in R\}$

8. a) $(1, 6), (6, 12)$

b) $(-1, -2), (3, 4)$

9. a)

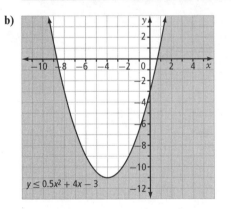

$y > -3x^2 - 3x + 1$

b)

$y \le 0.5x^2 + 4x - 3$

10. a) $y < (x + 1)^2 - 4$

b) $y \le -(x - 1)^2 + 9$